STANDARD PLANT OPERATOR'S QUESTIONS & ANSWERS

STANDARD PLANT OPERATOR'S QUESTIONS & ANSWERS
Second Edition

VOLUME II

Stephen Michael Elonka

Contributing Editor, Power *magazine; Licensed Chief Marine Steam Engineer, Oceans, Unlimited Horsepower; Licensed as Regular Instructor of Vocational High School, New York State; Member, National Association of Power Engineers (life, honorary); National Institute for the Uniform Licensing of Power Engineers, Inc., Honorary Chief Engineer*

Joseph Frederick Robinson

Retired Borough Supervisor of Custodian Engineers, Bureau of Plant Operation and Maintenance, Board of Education, City of New York; Licensed Chief Marine Steam Engineer, Oceans, Unlimited Horsepower; Stationary Engineer, New York City; Commissioned Inspector of Boiler and Pressure Vessels, National Board (New York, Pennsylvania, Maryland, and Washington, D.C.); Lieutenant Commander (Engineering Duties), U.S. Naval Reserve, Retired

McGraw-Hill Book Company

New York   St. Louis   San Francisco   Auckland
Bogotá   Hamburg   Johannesburg   London   Madrid
Mexico   Montreal   New Delhi   Panama   Paris
São Paulo   Singapore   Sydney   Tokyo   Toronto

Library of Congress Cataloging in Publication Data

Elonka, Stephen Michael.
  Standard plant operator's questions & answers.

  Includes index.
  1. Power-plants. I. Robinson, Joseph Frederick,
joint author. II. Title.
TJ164.E42   1981   621.4   80–29066

2 3 4 5 6 7 8 9 10 11   BKP BKP   8 9 8 7 6 5 4 3

ISBN 0-07-019316-9 {V.2}

The editors for this book were Robert L. Davidson, Frank J. Cerra,
and Olive Collen, the designer was Mark E. Safran, and the production supervisor was Teresa F. Leaden. It was set in Baskerville
by The Kingsport Press.

Printed and bound by The Book Press, Inc.

Dedicated to the plant operator of today,
who is so vital in conserving
our precious lifeline of finite fuels

CONTENTS

PREFACE

This second, revised edition has the latest on EPA pollution and OSHA safety information, solar heating, examination questions and answers, firing information for efficient combustion, and today's license requirements in the United States and Canada.

Few occupations offer such an opportunity for youngsters to rise rapidly as does that of an operator of energy systems. Anyone who can read and write and absorb the technical study material written in simple, clear English in these two volumes may, while gaining experience on the job, advance from boiler operator all the way up to chief engineer, on land or sea.

Today, over a quarter of a million of the books in the *Standard* series are in use around the world in various languages. Since the first edition, in 1956, they have become the "bible" for:

1. Plant and building operators and other practical persons who study to pass examinations and improve their basic knowledge.

2. Industrial and utility firms that have a training program for upgrading employees.

3. License examining boards (stationary engineers; refrigeration, diesel, building operators, etc.), as a source of answers in one reliable, up-to-date work.

4. Schools, especially short-course cram schools, and trade schools and technical institutes that seek a practical textbook. It is also intended

as a text for preliminary courses on the many power services covered.
  5. Executives and personnel managers, to use as a guide when interviewing candidates for employment or upgrading.
  6. Sales and service personnel, to gain a better background on plant equipment.
  7. Professional and consulting engineers, for reference in many practical areas not usually found in handbooks.
  8. Boiler operators, oilers, water tenders, plant operators, and engineers, as a study for upgrading or for obtaining an original license.

The titles in this *Standard* series provide probably the most complete information published today, from calculations to operation and maintenance, on energy equipment.

In acknowledgment, we are deeply grateful, for illustrations, technical data, and even books for reference, to the many manufacturers of energy systems, *Power* magazine, Babcock & Wilcox, Combustion Engineering, and too many others to mention here in detail. Our thanks go, too, to the many license examiners for sample questions and answers. In addition, material from some of the other books in this *Standard* series has been used here where appropriate.

As we mentioned above, the opportunities for operators of energy systems are excellent nowadays. We do not wish to suggest, when we use the pronouns "he" or "his" to refer to the plant operator, that these opportunities exist only for one gender; in fact, women are increasingly entering the field. Our purpose in using these pronouns, and terms such as "fireman," was for ease of communication and to avoid stilted language.

Stephen Michael Elonka, 1980   **Joseph Frederick Robinson, 1980**
Charleston, South Carolina   *Williamsburg, Virginia*

STANDARD PLANT
OPERATOR'S
QUESTIONS & ANSWERS

10

OIL AND GAS ENGINES

Today's oil and gas engines are used for generating continuous electric power, standby power, and peaking power, and for driving (direct-connected) pumps and compressors. As emergency power generators, they can switch on automatically in case of power failure. Many large buildings and hospitals have them.

Engines come in sizes from a few horsepower up to the largest in the world, a mammoth 40,000-hp engine in Belgium. Some engines burn diesel oil, some oil and/or gas (dual fuel), and others Bunker C oil.

Supercharging has made them produce more horsepower per pound of weight. Of the many designs, vertical in-line (cylinders), V type, and opposed pistons are the basic ones. This chapter contains the minimum information the operator must know in order to keep oil and gas engines working efficiently.

BASIC DESIGNS

Q What is a diesel engine?

A A diesel engine is an internal-combustion engine in which fuel is ignited entirely by heat resulting from compressing air that is supplied for combustion. In a typical diesel engine, air is compressed to about 450 psi, which brings its temperature up to about 1000°F. Finely atomized oil, sprayed into this hot air, ignites and burns. The heat causes the gases to expand and push the pistons. Thus, in a diesel engine, the high compression ratio needed for reliable ignition means high efficiency.

Q What is an internal-combustion engine?

A An internal-combustion (ic) engine is an engine in which fuel and air are combined and burned directly in the engine, and not in a separate furnace.

Q What is a diesel engine cycle?

A This is a cycle in which the order of events is as follows: (1) An intake stroke admits air to the cylinders, (2) a compression stroke raises the air in the cylinder to a high pressure, (3) fuel is injected, with consequent burning, and (4) an exhaust stroke eliminates the products of combustion so that air can be drawn in again to repeat the cycle.

Q What is a four-cycle engine?

A See Fig. 10-1. A four-cycle engine completes one cycle in four strokes

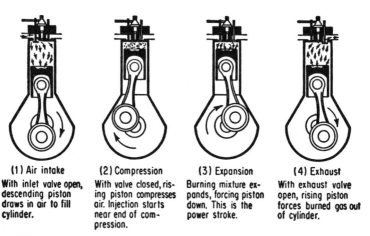

(1) Air intake	(2) Compression	(3) Expansion	(4) Exhaust
With inlet valve open, descending piston draws in air to fill cylinder.	With valve closed, rising piston compresses air. Injection starts near end of compression.	Burning mixture expands, forcing piston down. This is the power stroke.	With exhaust valve open, rising piston forces burned gas out of cylinder.

FIG. 10-1.   A four-stroke cycle has one power stroke to two revolutions.

or two revolutions. Cyclic events are known by the following strokes: (1) air intake, (2) compression, (3) power (expansion), and (4) exhaust.

Q What is meant by a 6 × 3¾ × 5 × 1500 engine?

A It is an engine having six cylinders, a 3¾-in. bore, a 5-in. stroke, and a speed of 1500 r/min.

Q What is a two-cycle engine?

A See Fig. 10-2. A two-cycle engine completes one cycle in two strokes or one revolution. Cyclic events are known by the following strokes: (1) air intake, (2) compression, (3) expansion, and (4) exhaust.

Q Name the essential parts of a four-cycle diesel engine.

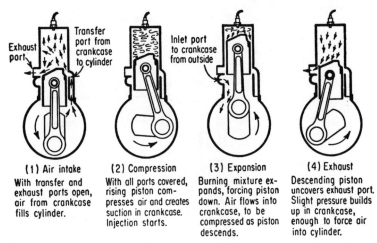

(1) Air intake	(2) Compression	(3) Expansion	(4) Exhaust
With transfer and exhaust ports open, air from crankcase fills cylinder.	With all ports covered, rising piston compresses air and creates suction in crankcase. Injection starts.	Burning mixture expands, forcing piston down. Air flows into crankcase, to be compressed as piston descends.	Descending piston uncovers exhaust port. Slight pressure builds up in crankcase, enough to force air into cylinder.

FIG. 10-2. A two-stroke cycle has one power stroke to each revolution.

A See Fig. 10-3.

Q What is an air-injection engine?

A This is an older-type engine in which fuel is injected into the cylinders with compressed air at around 1200 psi. There are few, if any, air-injection engines built today.

Q What is a solid-injection engine?

A In a solid- or mechanical-injection engine, a fuel charge completely fills the injection system and is forced into the cylinder under pressure built up by the fuel pump.

Q What is a common-rail injection system?

A See Fig. 10-4. In a common-rail injection system, a single pump supplies high-pressure fuel to the header, while a relief valve holds the pressure constant. A control wedge adjusts the lift of a mechanically operated valve to set the time and amount of injection.

Q What is the controlled-pressure system of injection?

A See Fig. 10-5. This is another form of the common-rail injection system. It employs a pump to maintain a set header pressure. Pressure-relief and timing valves regulate the time and amount of injection. A spring-loaded spray valve acts as a check.

Q Describe the in-line, V, and opposed-piston types.

A In the usual form of internal-combustion engine, cylinders are arranged vertically (Fig. 10-6). Up to 16 cylinders can be placed in line, one after

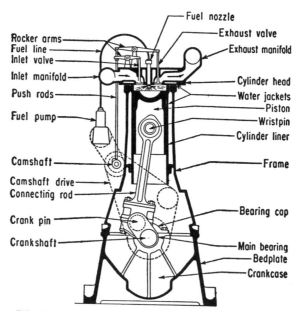

FIG. 10-3.   Essential parts of a four-stroke cycle engine.

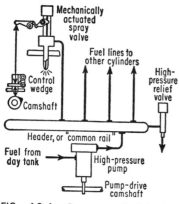

FIG. 10-4.   Common-rail injection system.

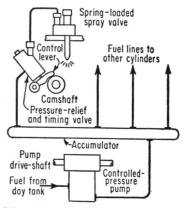

FIG. 10-5.   Controlled-pressure injection system.

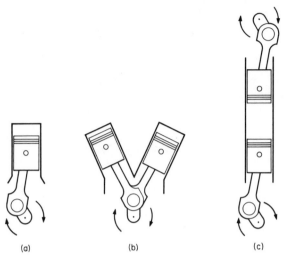

FIG. 10-6.   In-line cylinder may have *(a)* vertical, *(b)* V, or *(c)* opposed pistons.

the other. The V configuration, an increasingly popular type, is built in 8-, 12-, and 16-cylinder combinations. Engine length is reduced by almost one-half.

Lines of cylinders, known as cylinder banks, range from 30 to 75° apart. If the V is increased to 90°, we have the right-angle type. Where a flat engine is desired, the V can be opened to 180°, yielding the opposed-cylinder type, not to be confused with the opposed-piston type (in which two pistons operate in what is essentially a single vertical cylinder with a combustion chamber in the center between the pistons and a crankshaft at each end).

Q   What is an integral engine design?
A   The integral gas-engine compressor (Fig. 10-7*a*) has in-line power cylinders with compressor pistons connected to the engine crankshaft. The V-type integral design (Fig. 10-7*b*) has compressor cylinders on both sides with each tied to the engine crankshaft through a crosshead. Integral designs are widely used on gas transmission lines to move gas along for many miles to the point of distribution.

Q   Describe the horizontal and special designs.
A   The horizontal configuration produces a flat engine of single- or opposed-cylinder design. Single-cylinder units, generally slow-speed with rugged construction and heavy flywheel, are used mostly in Europe.

Today, a larger, low-speed 1100-hp rotary engine of 1000 r/min is manufactured, mostly for packaged applications in a variety of attended and

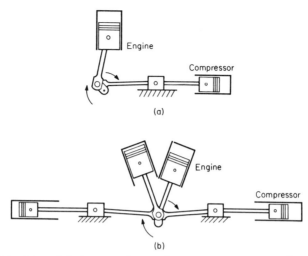

FIG. 10-7. Integral design may feature these two arrangements of engine and compressor pistons: *(a)* integral gas-engine compressor; *(b)* V-type integral design.

unattended services. It is becoming popular as a prime mover greatly simplified by the absence of camshafts, valves, pistons, connecting rods, and cylinder heads. The fuel is natural gas, ignited by spark, producing thermal efficiency up to 32 percent.

Q What is a dual-fuel engine?

A A dual-fuel engine burns either a liquid fuel or gas. Basically, it is the same as a full diesel and can be either two- or four-cycle, supercharged or normally aspirated (aspirated means drawing in air). Since the gases in dual-fuel engines cannot be compression-ignited, they must be ignited from some other source. A spark is used in gas engines, while in dual-fuel engines, a diesel fuel is injected first; when it burns, it ignites the gas. When enough gas is available, the amount of diesel fuel injected may be as low as 8 percent. If there isn't enough gas, the governor increases the amount of fuel oil injected to compensate for the reduced gas flow. Should the gas supply fail, the engine automatically operates as a full diesel.

To avoid loss of gas when both the inlet and exhaust valves are open at the top of the exhaust stroke and at the beginning of the suction stroke, the gas isn't premixed with air in the intake manifold. Instead, the gas enters the cylinders when the exhaust valve closes. The small quantity of fuel oil injected to ignite the gas is termed the "pilot oil."

The most sophisticated horizontal type is the radial engine (Fig. 10-8). The firing order is consecutive around the circle. Balance is achieved

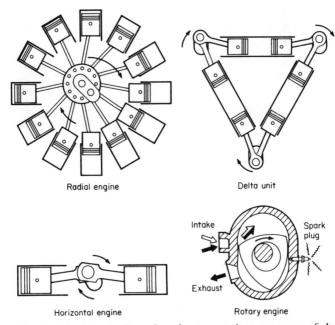

Radial engine   Delta unit

Horizontal engine   Rotary engine

FIG. 10-8. Radial, delta, horizontal, and rotary engines are some of the more recent designs since World War II.

by actual convergence of combustion pressures and inertial forces at one focal point on the crankshaft axis. The inner ends of the connecting rods are secured by knuckle pins equally spaced around a master bearing mounted on the crankpin. Reciprocating motion of each piston converts into rotary motion at the crankshaft through connecting rods.

The delta cylinder (Fig. 10-8) is a compact design, with three sets of cylinder blocks forming the sides, and three crankcases, one at each apex of the triangle.

The rotary engine (Wankel) (Fig. 10-8) is a four-cycle, high-speed (3000 to 8000 r/min), lightweight, spark-ignition gasoline engine. Adding rotors is the equivalent of adding cylinders to reciprocating engines.

SCAVENGING

Q What does the term "scavenging air" mean?
A In a two-cycle engine, usually separate low-pressure air from a blower is supplied or blown into the power cylinder during the exhaust period

to help clean the cylinder of exhaust gas. This displacement furnishes fresh air for the next cycle. Scavenging air is always used for two-cycle engines and sometimes for four-cycle engines.

Q Name four methods of air scavenging.
A Four methods of air scavenging are:
1. *Separate scavenging.* Air is compressed in a compressor or blower that is driven by an independent source.
2. *Integral scavenging* (see Fig. 10-9). Air is compressed in a compressor

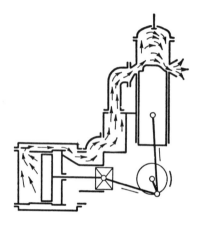

FIG. 10-9.   Integral scavenger.

or blower that is directly connected, geared, or belted to the engine scavenged.
3. *Under-piston scavenging.* Air is compressed on the underside of the power piston in a chamber separate from the crankcase. The upstrokes of the power piston draw air into this chamber from the atmosphere. The downstrokes of the power piston compress the air.
4. *Crankcase scavenging.* Here, the upstrokes of the power piston draw air from the atmosphere into individual crank chambers, one on each cylinder. Then, the air is compressed in the crank chambers by the downstrokes of the power piston.

Q How is scavenging air introduced into the power cylinder?
A There are three ways to introduce scavenging air into the power cylinder.
1. *The port-scavenging* method in which the air enters the cylinder of a two-cycle engine through a series of ports in the cylinder wall, forcing out burned gases through another series of ports into the exhaust line.
2. *The valve-scavenging* method in which air enters the engine cylinder

through a mechanically operated valve or valves, usually in the cylinder head. Burned gases are forced into the exhaust line, usually through a series of ports in the cylinder wall.

3. *The port- and valve-scavenging* scheme in which air enters the engine cylinder through a series of ports in the cylinder wall and forces burned gases through a mechanically operated valve or valves in the cylinder head.

SUPERCHARGING

Q Explain the term "supercharging."

A Supercharging is the process of supplying the intake of an engine with air at a density greater than the density of the surrounding atmosphere. This increased density is retained in the cylinders at the start of the compression stroke.

> RESULT: The same engine can burn more fuel; thus the engine's horsepower is increased.

Q How are engines supercharged?

A There are two general ways to supercharge an engine. (1) Exhaust gases from the engine cylinder are used to drive an exhaust-gas turbine which is directly connected to a blower that supplies air to the engine's intake manifold. There are no mechanical connections between the engine and the turbine. (2) A blower that supplies air to the intake manifold is either driven directly from the engine or separately by an electric motor or other prime mover. When separately driven, the extra power needed to drive the blower is added when calculating the net bhp rating of the engine.

Q Scavenging air is supplied to two-cycle engines at a density greater than that of the atmosphere. Does this mean that the engine is supercharged?

A No, not unless the air of increased density is retained in the power cylinders after the exhaust ports or the valves are closed.

Q What is meant by compression ratio?

A The compression ratio is defined as the volume in the cylinder of an engine before compression divided by the volume in the cylinder after compression. In Fig. 10-10 the compression ratio is 6:1. In practice it isn't efficient to compress more air than is needed to ignite the fuel oil. The pressure and temperature resulting from a given compression ratio depend on engine speed, cylinder size, and other factors. A typical compression pressure in diesel engines ranges from about 450 to 600 psi. Small high-speed engines usually have higher compression pressures than

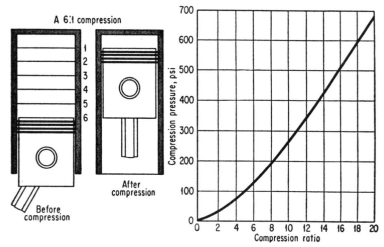

FIG. 10-10.   Compression ratio of this engine is 6:1.

large low-speed engines. High compression ratios give high efficiency on a relatively low-cost nonhazardous fuel, and they need no ignition system.

Q How is power output increased without increasing the revolutions or size of an engine?

A Power output is increased by supercharging; the same engine burns more fuel and increases the mep without increasing cylinder size or turning faster. Instead of the engine drawing in atmospheric air, the air is forced into the cylinders by a blower at about 10 psi above atmospheric pressure. This increases the engine's output by about 40 percent.

Q What is the difference between supercharging and turbocharging?

A See Fig. 10-11. The purpose of supercharging is to cram more air into the cylinder so that more fuel can be burned and, thus, to boost output. In turbocharging, the energy in the hot exhaust gas from the diesel is recovered in a gas turbine. The turbine drives a centrifugal blower that supplies air at supercharging pressure. The turbine and blower rotors are usually mounted on a common shaft in a single case. In the Buchi turbocharging system, valve timing, exhaust manifolding, and turbine design are coordinated to create timed pressure pulsations. Engines of four cylinders and over use a multiple exhaust manifold. This allows the complete scavenging of one cylinder before the exhaust valve opens on another. No controls are needed; speed, air quantity, and charging pressure follow the engine load and speed changes.

Q How are superchargers driven?

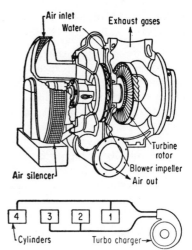

FIG. 10-11. Turbocharger has an exhaust-gas turbine at right, centrifugal compressor at center, and air inlet at left.

A Superchargers are driven by either the engine or a separate power source. Positive-displacement and centrifugal blowers are widely used, positive-displacement units finding favor where torque over a wide speed range is needed.

Q Why are superchargers intercooled?
A Intercooling reduces the manifold temperature of an engine. This increases the air density and, thus, gives greater weight of air per unit volume, increasing the effect of supercharging.

FUEL OIL CHARACTERISTICS

Q What are the characteristics of an ideal diesel-fuel oil?
A (1) The pour point of an ideal diesel-fuel oil is below the lowest temperature encountered by the engine. (2) Viscosity is low enough so that the oil flows freely at the engine's lowest temperatures, high enough to lubricate the injection system and prevent leakage, and correct for the atomization and penetration needs of the combustion chamber. (3) The cetane number is high enough for starting and proper combustion. (4) Gravity is between 22 and 28 for maximum economy. (5) Carbon residue is low for clean combustion. (6) The oil is free from corrosive materials. (7) The flash point of the oil is above the legal requirement for safety. (8) The sediment content should be zero.

Q What are the major properties of a diesel-fuel oil?
A (1) Ignition quality, (2) volatility, (3) carbon residue, (4) viscosity, (5)

sulfur content, (6) ash, (7) water and sediment, (8) flash point, (9) pour point, (10) acidity, and (11) heating value.

Q Explain ignition quality.

A Ignition quality is expressed by an index called the cetane number; it is one of the most important properties of a diesel-fuel oil. High-speed diesel engines need a cetane number of about 50. Its value as a diesel-fuel characteristic is similar to the octane number of gasoline. Ignition quality not only determines the ease of ignition and cold starting but also the kind of combustion obtained from the fuel. A fuel with a better ignition quality (a higher cetane number) gives easier starting, even at low temperatures; quicker warm-up; smoother and quieter operation; lower maximum cylinder pressures; and more efficient combustion, hence lower fuel consumption.

Q What is volatility?

Q The volatility of a diesel-fuel oil is indicated by the 20 percent distillation temperature. At this temperature, 90 percent of a sample of oil has distilled off. The lower this temperature, the higher the volatility of the fuel. In small diesel engines a higher fuel volatility is needed than in larger engines to obtain a low fuel consumption, low exhaust temperatures, and minimum smoke. For high-output diesel engines, a 90 percent distillation temperature is 675°F.

Q What is carbon residue?

A Carbon residue is what is left after burning off all the volatile matter in a sample of diesel-fuel oil under certain conditions. It indicates the tendency of the fuel to form carbon deposits on engine parts. Some specifications allow a maximum carbon residue of 0.10 percent.

Q What is viscosity?

A Viscosity is the measure of the internal friction or resistance to flow of a diesel-fuel oil and is expressed in the number of seconds needed for a certain volume of liquid at some standard temperature to flow through an orifice or hole of a definite diameter. The longer it takes, the higher the viscosity. In the United States, a Saybolt viscosimeter, with a universal orifice, is used to measure viscosity. The data it gives are designated as Seconds Saybolt Universal (SSU).

Q Explain sulfur content.

A The sulfur in a diesel-fuel oil burns along with the fuel oil in an engine cylinder and produces a highly corrosive gas that condenses on the cylinder walls. This is bad when the engine is run at low load and the cylinder temperature drops. Corrosion due to sulfur gas from the fuel oil is often found in the exhaust system of a diesel engine. Some specifications don't permit fuel with a sulfur content of over 1 percent.

Q Explain ash, water, and sediment troubles.
A The ash and sediment in a diesel-fuel oil is the abrasive material that causes excessive engine wear. Sediment may also cause clogging of the fuel system. Engine wear may be increased by corrosion if the fuel contains water, especially salt water. Don't use an oil with an ash content of over 0.01 percent or with a combined water and sediment content of more than 0.05 percent.

Q What is flash point?
A The flash point of a diesel-fuel oil is the minimum temperature to which the oil must be heated in order to give off flammable vapors in a sufficient quantity to flash or ignite momentarily when brought in contact with a flame. A fuel oil having a very low flash point is dangerous to store and handle. A minimum flash point for diesel-fuel oil is 150°F.

Q Explain pour point.
A The pour point of a diesel-fuel oil is the temperature at which the oil solidifies or congeals. It is especially important in connection with cold starting an engine and for handling oil between storage and the engine. The pour point must be lower than the coldest atmospheric temperature at which the oil is to be pumped.

Q What harm is done to an engine that burns acidic diesel fuel oil?
A Diesel-fuel oil must not be corrosive or contain free acids. If it does, it will damage metal surfaces in both the storage tanks and the engine.

Q Why must you check the specifications of fuel delivered to your plant?
A Fuel oil that does not meet specifications may result in (1) difficult cold starting of the engine, (2) reduced maximum power output, (3) high fuel consumption, (4) smoky exhaust, (5) rough and noisy engine operation, (6) piston rings and valves sticking, and (7) deposits of carbon and gummy substances on the pistons and cylinder liners. So, make a careful check of the specifications of fuel delivered to your plant.

TIMING

Q Explain the timing diagram of a typical medium-speed four-stroke-cycle diesel engine.
A See Fig. 10-12. (1) The inlet valve opens at 20° before the top dead center (tdc) and closes at 35° after the bottom dead center (bdc). (2) Compression starts at 35° after bdc and ends at tdc. (3) Fuel injection starts at 10° before tdc and ends at 20° after tdc. (4) Expansion starts at 20° after tdc and ends at 35° before bdc. (5) The exhaust valve opens at 35° before bdc and closes at 20° after tdc.

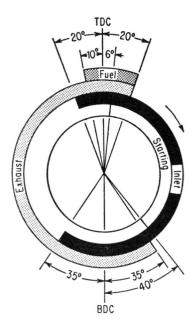

FIG. 10-12. Timing diagram of a
four-stroke-cycle engine.

Q What is meant by the packing effect?

A On the first downward movement of the piston with the inlet valve open, air rushes into the cylinder to fill the partial vacuum caused by the downward-moving piston. When the piston reaches bdc, it seems that the inlet valve should close. This is because an upward movement of the piston tends to force air from the cylinder. But, according to the timing diagram (Fig. 10-12), the inlet valve remains open until it is 35° after bdc. This is because the inertia of the incoming air keeps rushing into the cylinder, even though the piston is on the upstroke. This is called the packing effect. When the piston reaches a point on the upstroke where any further upward movement would back the air out of the inlet valve, the inlet valve closes. By taking advantage of the packing effect, we increase volumetric efficiency. This is the ratio of the volume of fresh charge taken in during the suction stroke to the full piston displacement. We also increase the potential horsepower of the engine, since we have more air to burn more fuel. Because of the greater volume of air at the beginning of compression, our compression ratio can be so much less in arriving at the normal final compression pressure and temperature (Fig. 10-13).

Q What is meant by the ignition lag?

A Fuel is injected into the cylinder before tdc and is heated to its autoigni-

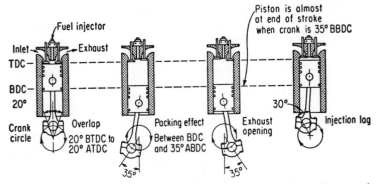

FIG. 10-13. Packing effect is from inertia of the incoming air on the upstroke.

tion temperature. The time that it takes for the fuel to reach this temperature is known as the ignition lag. The amount of this advance of fuel injection varies with the speed of the engine, the quality of the fuel, the compression ratio, the degree of atomization, and other design features.

Q What is meant by the injection lag?
A On the timing diagram (Fig. 10-12) fuel is actually injected into the cylinder 10° before tdc. This is the arc of injection. By noting the position of the fuel cam at the point where the pump plunger starts to pump fuel (with all bypass ports closed), we find that the cam is timed about 30° before tdc. Yet, fuel injection does not occur until 10° before tdc. The 20° difference between these crank angles is known as the injection lag (Fig. 10-14).

Q What causes the injection lag?
A (1) Expansion of the fuel-oil discharge lines under high pressure, resulting in the need for an additional volume of fuel to be displaced. (2) Com-

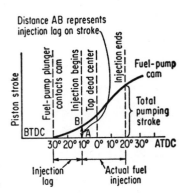

FIG. 10-14. Injection lag effect.

pressibility of the fuel; when fuel is near 3000 psi, it is compressed at about 1 percent by volume. (3) Leakage past the fuel-oil plunger. We should express the injection lag as the percent of the pumping stroke. Figure 10-14 shows how great the injection lag can be in a pumping stroke. It is often as high as 20 percent. This is why you must position your fuel cam correctly on the camshaft.

Q What are the major steps in balancing the load on each cylinder of a diesel engine?

A (1) Record the exhaust temperature of each cylinder. (2) Adjust the fuel-pump metering control rod so that the temperature is the same from all cylinders. (3) Check the cylinder temperatures again after adjusting the fuel. (4) With all exhaust temperatures the same, take indicator cards at full load *only*. These cards show whether or not each cylinder is doing its share of the work. Remember that cylinder temperatures may balance perfectly, yet combustion pressures may be out of balance. This is the most important step in the balancing operation. (5) Study the pressure cards for unbalance by checking them against the engine maker's instruction book. (6) Make adjustments to bring all the cylinder firing pressures to the same level. (7) Depending on the engine design, make the final adjustment. If combustion is low, adjust the fuel cam with the pump's timing marks centered in the pump's window frames. To raise pressures, advance the adjustable cam; to lower pressures, retard the cam. By raising the oil pressures, you get lower temperatures; by retarding the pressures, higher temperatures. (8) Check the cylinder temperatures after making the cam adjustments. (9) Take the indicator cards again and compare them with those taken before making the cam adjustments. (10) Take a set of "pull" cards at full load as a further check on individual cylinder performance. This is also an important check for obtaining the fuel-oil performance of any type of diesel engine.

Q What is a draw or jerk card?

A See Fig. 10-15. A draw or jerk card is made by pulling the indicator cord by hand. If the cord is pulled slowly, the pressures in the cylinder

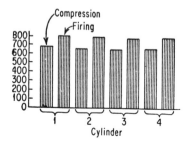

FIG. 10-15. Pull diagrams show the compression and firing pressures.

are recorded as vertical lines, and you can check the compression and firing pressures. In multicylinder engines you can compare these pressures to see if they are the same in all cylinders. Keep a continuous record of cylinder-compression readings to see if there is a falling off of compression caused by wear, sticking piston rings, or leaking valves. Take consecutive records on the same card, first of the compression, then of the firing pressures of each cylinder. To avoid stopping the engine in order to mount the indicator, have a cock on each cylinder.

To make a draw card, press your pencil lightly against the paper for a few strokes. Move the drum about $\frac{1}{32}$ in. after each stroke. For measuring compression, cut off the fuel to the cylinder. You can also test compression by running the engine on starting air.

REMEMBER: Leakage past the piston rings and valve seats is greater at lower speeds; so compression pressures will be lower.

Q How would you take hand-pulled diagrams? What do they tell?

A See Fig. 10-16. Diagrams are taken by hand-pulling the indicator cord

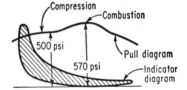

FIG. 10-16. Hand-pulled diagram compared with an indication diagram.

sharply and evenly just before the engine piston reaches its top position on the compression stroke. In the hand-pulled diagram shown, combustion starts at dead center and pressure rise is gradual (only 70 psi above compression). The regular diagram, in the same sketch, tells the same story, but not as clearly.

Q How do you calculate ihp from the indicator cards?

A See the discussion of steam-engine indicators in Chap. 3, in the section Indicator Diagrams, for more complete information on this subject.

Q How do you start a large diesel engine?

A (1) Open the inlet and outlet to the jacket- and cylinder-head cooling water. (2) Hand-pump the lube-oil pressure to about 5 or 10 psi to prevent bearings from scoring. (3) Open the fuel valve and hand-pump the fuel to make sure that the lines are filled; this also clears the lines of air. (4) Open the blowoff valves of each cylinder to avoid damage from water in the cylinder (resulting from a cracked linear). (5) Open the starting-air valve on the air-storage tank. (6) Set the governor to starting speed. (7)

Open the starting-air valve to crank the engine; then close it as soon as the engine is firing and rolling. (8) Test the cylinders for water by holding a dry rag under the blowoff valves of the open cylinder. (9) Bring the speed up slowly. If cold, wait until the lube-oil temperature reaches 100°F. Observe the oil, fuel, and cooling pressures; then throw on the load. (10) Check the exhaust temperatures of all the cylinders with the selector switch. (11) Take the temperature of the bearings and other temperatures every hour. (12) Check the voltage and load. Do this every hour and use a log book to record your findings. Also log all the temperatures and pressures. (13) Enter the time that the engine was started and any other important information.

Q If the camshaft on your four-cycle diesel engine is removed and the timing is completely lost, how would you time the engine in a hurry?

A The intake valve on a four-cycle diesel engine opens from 10 to 20° before the piston reaches the tdc, and the exhaust valve closes from 10 to 20° past tdc. For quick timing, jack the piston of any cylinder to tdc, with the camshaft gear out of mesh. Then, turn the camshaft until the inlet valve starts to open and the exhaust valve starts to close. Mesh the gears while the camshaft is in this position. Timing will usually be correct to one gear tooth.

Q What are the four basic types of ignition systems used in gas engines to provide the high voltages needed for spark formation?

A (1) The high-tension magneto (Fig. 10-17) supplies high-voltage cur-

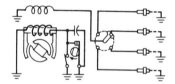

FIG. 10-17. High-tension magneto supplies high voltage to distributor, which then delivers high-tenstion current to spark plugs.

rent to the distributor, which then delivers high-tension current to the spark plugs. (2) The low-tension battery distributor has a four-lobe cam to interrupt current for all cylinders; then four separate cams distribute current to the coils. (3) The pulse generator system does not depend on interrupters for normal operation. Here, a revolving magnetic rotor replaces the conventional cam. (4) Electronic ignition systems (see Fig. 8-38) use a 110-V supply to actuate transistors by normal breaker points, which trigger the primary circuit.

NOTE: Electronic ignition systems are rapidly coming into use. Breaker points will continue to be used for many years, but most gas-engine manufacturers are going electronic.

ATOMIZING FUEL OIL

Q Why must fuel injectors be kept in perfect working condition?

A Unless oil sprayed into the cylinder is finely atomized, the oil cloud does not burn properly and some fuel is wasted in smoke.

Some diesels have a coarse spray and still burn oil efficiently, but they depend on precombustion or turbulence chambers to mix the oil with the air before it enters the cylinder. A cloud of tiny oil drops, sprayed directly into the cylinder, will ignite when heated to the right temperature. The smallest drops heat up faster and burn first; the larger particles ignite later and need more time to burn. If the particles are too large, they will exhaust before burning completely.

Q What are the requirements for good combustion?

A (1) Fine atomization, (2) a high temperature for prompt ignition, and (3) high relative velocity between the fuel and the air particles.

Atomization penetration and dispersion of fuel depend a lot on the injection system. Compression ratio, cylinder dimensions, and cooling arrangements determine the temperature conditions. Mixing depends on the proper relation to the injection pattern, air-intake system, and the shape of the combustion space formed by the cylinder head, walls, and piston crown.

Q What is an open combustion chamber?

A See Fig. 10-18. In an open-combustion-chamber scheme, the shape

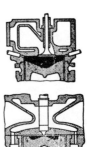

FIG. 10-18.   Open combustion chambers.

and layout of the piston crown, the inlet port, and the valve produce the turbulent effect of fuel mixture. Open combustion chambers are used mostly in medium- and large-bore engines operating at low and medium speeds.

Q What is a turbulence chamber?

A See Fig. 10-19. In a turbulence-chamber arrangement, fuel is injected into an auxiliary chamber that is separated from the cylinder by an orifice or throat. This space is shaped to create highly turbulent conditions. It holds most of the cylinder charge at the end of compression.

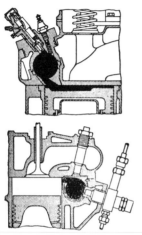

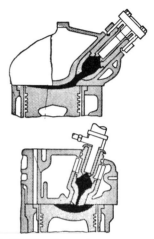

FIG. 10-19. Turbulence combustion chambers.

FIG. 10-20. Precombustion combustion chambers.

Q What is the difference between a turbulence chamber and a precombustion chamber?

A See Fig. 10-20. Although these two chambers look very similar, the basic principles differ. In a precombustion-chamber system, the auxiliary chamber contains only a part of the air charge; the remainder is in the cylinder space. A precombustion chamber provides a quiet space in which the fuel starts to burn with insufficient air. This very rich mixture tends to explode, throwing unburned fuel into the main chamber and mixing it thoroughly. A precombustion chamber is usually cylindrical.

Q What is an air cell?

A See Fig. 10-21. The nozzle injects fuel directly into the main combustion space, where burning starts. The space in the piston or cylinder head (air cell) is for air that is trapped during the compression stroke. The air is close to maximum pressure when the piston starts its downward stroke and when pressure in the main space starts to drop. The pressure difference between the air cell and the cylinder causes the air in the cell to expand and flow out into the main combustion space, where it creates additional turbulence and ensures complete burning.

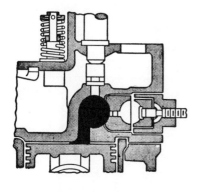

FIG. 10-21. Air cells ensure better burning of fuel.

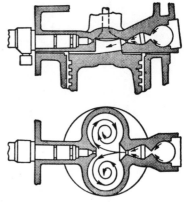

FIG. 10-22. Energy cells create higher pressure, better combustion.

Q What is the difference between an air cell and an energy cell?

A See Fig. 10-22. Whereas an air cell simply stores and gives up an air charge, fuel is blown into the energy cell and burns there, using the air that is already in the cell. The products of combustion blow back into the main chamber to create turbulence. The major advantage of an energy cell is that combustion in the cell creates a higher pressure and, thus, greater turbulence, leaving no idle air in the cell.

Q Explain how a unit injector works.

A See Fig. 10-23. A unit injector combines a pump, fuel valve, and nozzle in a single housing, thus eliminating discharge tubing. This permits very high injection pressures, up to 20,000 psi. A plunger has a helical groove in its side that connects to a space under the plunger. Two ports are on one side and the inlet port and bypass port are above the plunger. With the plunger in its highest position, the fuel enters the inlet port until the lower edge of the plunger closes it and the pressure rise begins. When the pressure reaches its proper level, oil discharges through a valve on the nozzle. As the downstroke begins, the lower edge of the helix passes

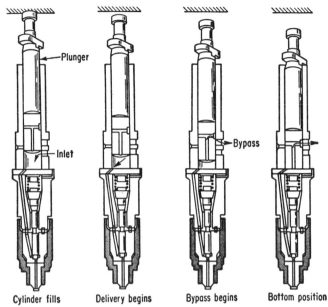

Cylinder fills   Delivery begins   Bypass begins   Bottom position

FIG. 10-23. Unit injectors perform as a pump, fuel valve, and nozzle in single housing.

the bypass port, releasing pressure. Then a spring closes the nozzle valve. The bypass continues to the end of the stroke. By turning the plunger you can change the effective stroke.

Q What is a constant-stroke port-controlled fuel pump?
A See Fig. 10-24. When the plunger in this type of fuel pump goes all the way down, the pump chamber is filled with fuel oil. As the plunger rises, it closes the ports and puts the oil under pressure until the delivery valve opens. As the stroke continues, a helix opens the bypass port, the

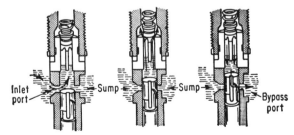

FIG. 10-24. Constant-stroke port-controlled fuel pump at work.

pressure drops, and the delivery valve is snapped shut. The turning plunger changes the time that the helix uncovers the bypass.

Q What are the features of a pump-injection system?

A This system is also known as the jerk-pump system. It has two essential parts to each cylinder—the injection pump and the fuel nozzle. On a high-speed diesel engine, the injection pump must measure and deliver a very small quantity of fuel under high pressure and at exactly the right time. The volume of the fuel injected is extremely small compared with the piston displacement; at full load, it is about 1/20,000 of piston displacement. When the engine is idling, the volume of fuel needed is only about one-fifth of the full-load needs. This gives a volume ratio of about 1/100,000.

Q Explain the basic fuel nozzle used in diesel engines.

A Fuel nozzles used in diesel engines are either the open or closed type. The open type is usually a simple spray nozzle with a check valve. The check prevents high-pressure gas in the engine cylinder from passing to the pump. While it is simple and commonly used, it does not give proper atomization. The closed nozzle (Fig. 10-25) is the most popular type today.

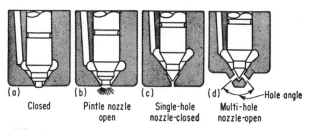

(a) Closed   (b) Pintle nozzle open   (c) Single-hole nozzle-closed   (d) Multi-hole nozzle-open — Hole angle

FIG. 10-25. Basic fuel nozzle of the closed type is popular.

Basically, it is a hydraulically operated spring-loaded needle valve. Most closed nozzles open inward under pressure, acting on the differential area of the needle valve, and are seated by a spring when the pressure is cut off. There are two main types of closed nozzles—the pintle and the hole.

Q What is a pump-injection system?

A See Fig. 10-26. An individual pump or a pump's cylinder connects directly to each fuel nozzle. Meters on the pump charge and control the injection timing. The nozzle contains a delivery valve that is actuated by fuel-oil pressure.

Q What are two types of distributor-injection systems?

A See Fig. 10-27. The cam-operated poppet-valve type of distributor-

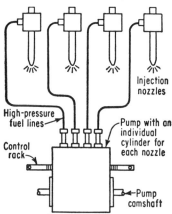

FIG. 10-26. Pump-injection system.

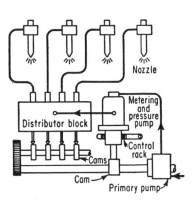

FIG. 10-27. Cam-operated poppet-valve type of distributor injection.

injection system has a single pump to meter the fuel charge. Distribution of the fuel to the cylinders in the right firing order is controlled by cam-operated poppet valves that open before injection. The nozzles are spring-loaded.

A second system is shown in Fig. 10-28. Here, gear pumps deliver fuel to the distributor at low pressure. The distributor directs the flow to a pump which meters the fuel to the desired cylinder. A mechanically actuated fuel nozzle raises the fuel to the injection pressure and controls the injection timing.

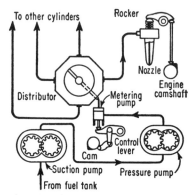

FIG. 10-28. Rotary distributor-type fuel-injection system uses two gear pumps.

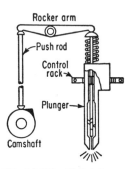

FIG. 10-29. Unit injector.

Q What is a unit injector?

A See Fig. 10-29. A unit injector is a mechanically actuated pump plunger that raises fuel to a high pressure, meters the quantity, and controls the injection timing. The nozzles contain a spring-loaded delivery valve that is actuated by a change in the fuel-oil pressure.

Q Sketch a fuel-gas system for a diesel engine.

A See Fig. 10-30. Most installations of gas-diesel and dual-fuel diesel

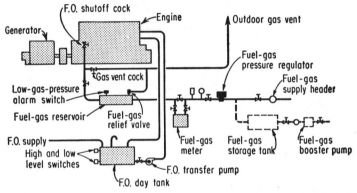

FIG. 10-30. Combination fuel-and-gas system for a gas-diesel or dual-fuel diesel installation.

engines are made adjacent to the main gas pipeline or gas distribution system. Clean, dry natural gas is usually supplied for such applications. Make sure that the pressure regulators, meters, reservoirs, valves, thermometers, and gages shown in Fig. 10-30 are used. Gas vent lines and lines from the relief valves should always be carried outside the building and should never be connected to drains or sewers. If the gas-supply pressure is below the engine manufacturer's requirements, compressors may be needed to boost the gas pressure to the required level. In some jobs, where the gas supply rate is a variable, such as sewage-disposal plants, large gas holders may be installed to store the gas during periods of heavy flow. This provides a steady fuel supply to the engine at all times.

CONTROLLING REVOLUTIONS PER MINUTE

Q What is a diesel engine governor?

A It is a speed-sensitive device used to control the speed of an engine under varying load conditions. The type of load and the degree of control desired determine the kind of governor to be used.

Q How are diesel engine governors classified?

A (1) Constant speed, which maintain the same engine speed from no load to full load. (2) Variable speed, used to maintain any desired engine speed from ideal to top speed. (3) Speed limiting, which control minimum engine speed and limit the maximum engine speed, or which limit maximum engine speed only. (4) Load limiting, used to limit the load that the engine will take at various speeds. Some governors perform two or more of these functions.

Q What is speed droop?

A Speed droop is the decrease in engine speed from no load to full load. It is expressed in revolutions per minute or as a percentage of the normal or average engine speed.

Q What is isochronous governing?

A Isochronous governing maintains engine speed at a truly constant rate, regardless of the load; thus, there is perfect speed regulation and zero speed droop.

Q What is hunting?

A A continuous fluctuation of engine speed, slowing down and speeding up from the desired speed, is called hunting. It is due to undercontrol or too high a sensitivity range of the governor.

Q What is stability?

A It is the ability of the governor to maintain the desired engine speed without fluctuations or hunting.

Q What is sensitivity?

A A change in engine speed required before the governor makes a corrective movement of fuel control is known as sensitivity. It is generally expressed as a percentage of the normal or average engine speed.

Q What is promptness?

A Promptness refers to the speed at which the governor acts. It may be expressed in terms of time in seconds needed for the governor to move the fuel control from the no-load to the full-load position. Promptness depends upon the power of the governor; the greater the power, the shorter the time needed to overcome resistance.

Q What are some causes of governor hunting?

A Governor hunting is due to the lag in action of the control mechanism, caused by poor sensitivity. This results in a large speed change before any governor action takes place. The engine slows down or speeds up too much. Then, once the controls begin to move, they continue to move, even after the correct speed is obtained. This results in an overcorrection of engine speed in the opposite direction.

Hunting may also be caused by a governor that is too small. The lag in action permits too great a change in engine speed to occur during the change in engine load before correction, even if the governor is very sensitive. Reducing the friction in the operating mechanism of the governor will tend to increase its stability.

Q   How is sensitivity determined?
A   Sensitivity can be determined by testing an engine with an increasing load, then by testing it with a decreasing load. Because of the lag in governor action, the speed corresponding to a certain load (obtained when the load is increasing) is always lower than the speed corresponding to the same load when it is decreasing. Sensitivity is expressed numerically as the difference between the two speeds divided by their average, in percent; the greater this figure, the less satisfactory is the sensitivity of the governor. The difference between the two speeds is usually greatest near one-half load conditions.

Q   What is a two-speed governor?
A   See Fig. 10-31. A two-speed governor is used when the engine has to run for prolonged periods without any load but cannot be stopped entirely. To reduce engine wear and fuel consumption, the engine speed is reduced while idling. This can be done with a direct-action governor having two springs. One spring is light and is used for idling when the centrifugal force is small. The stiffer spring acts at higher speeds when the engine is loaded. The springs may be arranged to act either separately or in combination.

Q   What is a proportional-action hydraulic governor?
A   See Fig. 10-32. It is a compensating device that anticipates the governor setting slightly before the new setting needed to maintain the control speed. The simplest method of compensating is to have a speed droop with an increase in load. Although this method prevents isochronous governing with this type of hydraulic governor, the speed droop can be held to a minimum and the governor will still possess the advantages of fine sensitivity and a large regulating force. When speed decreases, the flyballs draw closer together and the spring moves the valve downward, admitting oil under the large piston. Thus the piston is pushed up, compressing the spring and moving the fuel-control lever toward more fuel. A slight movement of the lever decreases the force of the small spring and returns it to its neutral position. This is called primary compensation. Speed-droop

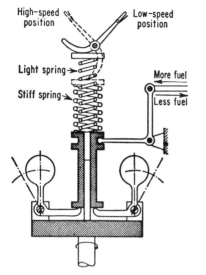

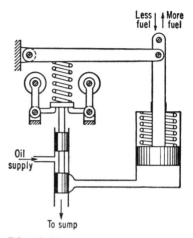

FIG. 10-31. Two-speed centrifugal governor reduces speed while engine idles.

FIG. 10-32. Proportional-action hydraulic governor anticipates setting.

governors are stable at any load change, but on variable-load service they need constant resetting to maintain a steady speed.

Q Explain how an isochronous diesel engine governor works.

A See Fig. 10-33. Oil from the gear pump of the governor is stored in an accumulator. The pressure in the accumulator is held constant by a spring-loaded piston and relief opening and is applied continuously through line *m* to lift a smaller surface of the differential piston. As speed

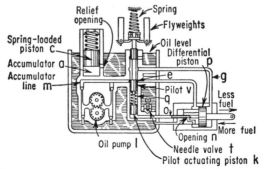

FIG. 10-33. Isochronous diesel-engine governor can adjust any load.

decreases, the spring overcomes flyweights and pilot v is forced downward. This admits oil past edge e to line g and the larger surface of the piston, moving the differential piston to the left, the direction of the greater fuel supply. The movement of the piston uncovers opening n to oil line o, and oil pressure acting on piston k compresses spring q opposing the action of the governor spring. Thus, pilot v raises and cuts off the oil feed at e. The oil bleeds through needle valve t. In time, the oil bleed or feed through t, under the push or pull of q, relieves the force of q and causes pilot v to come to set point.

An engine having an isochronous governor can carry any load between no load and maximum load or overload that the governor and engine will permit. If two engines are coupled to a single load, they cannot both be equipped with isochronous governors. An engine operated in parallel must use a governor with speed droop.

Q What is an overspeed governor?

A Overspeed governors are safety devices used to protect engines from damage due to overspeeding from any cause. If engine speed is manually controlled, the overspeed governor will work if speed increases beyond the safe limit before the operator can control it. Most overspeed governors cut off or limit the fuel supplied to the engine cylinders. In some two-stroke engines, the engine can run away by burning lubricating oil that may happen to be taken in with fresh air. If so, the governor is arranged to cut off the air supply to the cylinders, thus stopping the engine.

Q What is an overspeed trip?

A An overspeed trip is a governor that brings an engine to a full stop by cutting off the fuel or air supply.

PREVENTING CRANKCASE EXPLOSIONS

Q What is an explosive mixture in the crankcase of diesel engines?

A Hot oil and air vaporized to the right mixture are explosive. The motion of the crank, connecting rod, and crankpin, all spraying lube oil through the air in the crankcase, does the vaporizing. Lube oil usually enters the bearings at 20 to 30 psi and is sprayed out at 130 to 140°F. The warm oil being sprayed around has a blue-haze appearance. Lube oil in the sump cannot explode; its flash point is from 375 to 400°F, but it isn't vaporized. So, the oil vapor is the real danger, but only if it is ignited.

Q What causes oil vapor in the crankcase to ignite?

A (1) A spark, (2) a red-hot metal, (3) a piston blowby, or (4) an outside flame that has gotten into the crankcase.

A spark can result from bare metal striking against bare metal, as when an indicator gear comes adrift or when the telescope piping or lube-oil lines strike another metal part. Piston blowby is common but not dangerous unless red-hot gases blow past broken piston rings into the vaporized lube oil. Blowby is dangerous when it burns oil off the cylinder walls, causing a hot spot from the galled metal. Failure of the lube oil in the wrist-pin bearing, main bearing, or crankpin bearing also causes metal-to-metal contact; dry metal parts seize, causing sparks. If the vent pipe is unscreened (Fig. 10-34), an outside source may ignite the crankcase oil vapors. A vent connection from the intake manifold to the crankcase must have wire gauze and a drain, as shown in Fig. 10-35. If not, sparks from the leaky valves will work in reverse and find their way into the crankcase.

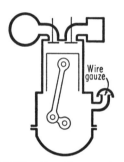

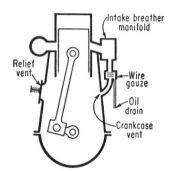

FIG. 10-34. Outside vent should be screened.

FIG. 10-35. Relief vent and wire gauze prevent explosions.

Q Explain the sequence of a crankcase explosion.

A The damaging crankcase explosion is always a double one. The first explosion is mild; it may rupture the crankcase or blow off a crankcase door. Then, air rushes into the crankcase through this opening and combines with the hot oil vapor, resulting in a big explosion.

To guard against explosion, some vapors are removed by a vent from the crankcase and intake manifold (Fig. 10-35). Other engines carry a slight vacuum in the crankcase. This vacuum is set up by suction to the scavenging blower, which removes vapors and air needed to support an explosion. Another precaution places spring-loaded relief ports on the crankcase. After the first explosion, the spring-loaded ports open to relieve the pressure, then snap shut, closing out the air needed to support the violent second explosion. Make sure that your relief ports work freely. Let the engine cool as much as practical before opening the crankcase for maintenance.

OPERATION AND MAINTENANCE

Q Why do crank bolts fail?
A Crank bolts that are repeatedly stressed beyond their elastic limit cause fatigue. Minute cracks develop and failure results without warning. Besides direct tension, misalignment causes serious shear and stresses in the connecting rod, crank-bearing bolts, and main bearing-cap studs. Lengthwise, the loads on the bolts put normal tension on the cross section and both normal and shear stresses on the incline section. Shear stress increases as the angle of incline increases.

Q What materials are used for crank bolts? Discuss iron and steel.
A Crank bolts are made of both nickel-chromium and molybdenum-alloy steel. These materials are stronger and tougher than plain carbon steel. Steels known as ASA 3125 and 3130 give good service for bolts up to 1¼ in. in diameter. Steels known as ASA 3230 and 3240 have higher physical properties than metals of a lower alloy content. When heat-treated properly, molybdenum steel, ASA 4140, has a minimum yield point of 100,000 psi and is elastic if stressed to 80,000 to 85,000 psi. Steel of this type is often used for larger bolts. Any steel that is loaded well below the yield point will stretch 0.001 in. for each inch of length when stressed to 30,000 psi and will return to its original length when the tension is removed. Iron and steel are composed of grains and crystals. Pure iron is soft, malleable, and can be worked cold, but it doesn't possess a high tensile strength. Free carbon crystals are easily seen in gray cast iron. Tensile strength falls off as the free carbon crystals get bigger. In the manufacturing of common or alloy steel, the carbon content is lowered, crystals get smaller, and tensile strength increases. Cold rolling produces small crystals, as in wire drawn down to very small sizes, where little ductility is left. But cold rolling may increase the tensile strength of common carbon steel to over 350,000 psi.

Q How should you tighten crank bolts?
A A box-type wrench is used to tighten crank bolts because it sets up less tension in tightening than does an open-end wrench. Draw down both sides evenly and as tightly as possible by hand. Then, two or three light blows with a hammer will stress the bolts sufficiently. Never use a piece of pipe to strike the wrench. After the bolts are set up, bar the bearing along the shaft with a small pinch bar, checking for movement fore and aft. There should be a 0.004- to 0.010-in. clearance, depending on the size and type of the engine. Too much side clearance causes a loss of oil pressure. If the nuts are tightened with a torque wrench, stress the bolts to the manufacturer's recommendations. Don't forget that a

torque wrench won't do much good unless all the threads on your bolts and nuts are in good condition and lubricated so that they turn freely.

Q What are some causes of compression loss in diesel engines?

A (1) Leaking piston rings, exhaust valve, air-starting valve, or air-inlet valve; (2) an increase in clearance volume caused by bearing-bushing wear; (3) the use of a thick head gasket; or (4) clogged air-inlet slots.

A leaky air-starting valve makes starting difficult because air gets into more than one cylinder at the same time. Then, when running, compression is lost because air leaks out of the starting valve. This effect is the same as that of increasing the clearance volume; it doesn't help starting.

Q How would you start a diesel engine if you had no starting air or electricity?

A You can use a few CO_2 bottles, obtained from a soda-fountain supplier, to start a diesel engine. CO_2 is bottled at 500 to 800 psi and liquefies at these high pressures. To use, break the discharge line between the compressor and the tank. To help the CO_2 expand, wrap burlap around the bottles and soak the rags in boiling water.

Q How would you start a diesel engine in cold weather if it had bad piston rings that caused poor compression?

A To start a diesel engine under these conditions, seal the cylinders with heavy oil or, if need be, lift the cylinder heads and smear heavy grease between the piston and cylinder walls. This helps to seal compression for those all-important revolutions before firing. Engines using a heavy fuel oil can be very hard to start in cold weather. Before shutting down, cut out the heavy fuel and run the engine on kerosene for a few minutes. When starting, switch back to the heavy oil as soon as the engine starts to turn over by itself. Also, preheat the lube oil if possible.

Q Discuss cooling water that is needed for diesel engines.

A Heavy-duty diesel engines need cooling water of 0.25 to 0.6 gal/ (min)(hp), depending on the type of engine, its fuel consumption, and the type of cooling system. Water should have less than 5 grains per gal hardness; up to 8 grains is OK if (1) the water is under 150°F with a pH value of 7, (2) various chemicals are used to reduce scale and corrosion, or (3) the water contains animal or vegetable matter.

Certain conditions call for the use of an atmospheric cooling tower, a spray cooling tower, a cooling pond, or evaporative coolers. The makeup water for each of these devices varies from 2 to 3 percent of the water circulated. If water temperature is a problem, use air-cooled coolers. Figure on the pump to circulate cooling water through the engine at about 0.5 gal/(min)(hp). Keep the pressure loss per 100 ft under 1 psi by using the right size of pipe. When water velocity is 2 ft/sec, use a 2-in. pipe; 3

ft/sec, use a 3-in. pipe; and 10 ft/sec, use a 10-in. pipe. Don't exceed 10 ft/sec in lines having more than a 10-in. diameter.

Q How much air does a diesel engine need?

A A four-cycle diesel engine needs about 2.8 ft³/min of air/hp, while a two-cycle engine needs 6 ft³/min of air/hp. Air velocities through the piping should be from 1500 to 3300 ft/min, depending on the type of air filter. Make sure that stack exhaust doesn't enter the intake.

Q What happens to the heat generated in either a diesel or a gas engine?

A See Fig. 10-36.

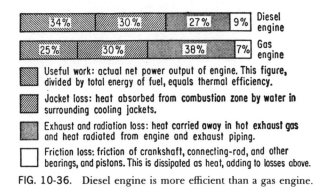

FIG. 10-36.   Diesel engine is more efficient than a gas engine.

Q What should you know about engine exhaust?

A Diesel-engine exhaust is about 6.7 ft³/(min)(hp) for a four-cycle machine and 8 to 13 ft³/(min)(hp) for a two-cycle unit. To keep the exhaust-pressure drop under 12 in. of water pressure on a four-cycle engine and less on a two-cycle unit, here are the approximate velocities: 6000 to 16,000 ft/min for four-cycle engines, 4000 to 6000 ft/min for two-cycle engines, and 4000 to 6000 ft/min for four-cycle supercharged engines. The exhaust line should leave the building at the highest point. Place it far enough from the cooling tower or pond so that exhaust gases won't contaminate the cooling water and set up corrosion.

Q What major equipment is needed for a heavy-duty diesel engine?

A See Fig. 10-37. A heavy-duty diesel engine needs an exhaust silencer, an air-intake filter, starting-air storage tanks, a lube-oil reclaimer, lube-oil coolers, a cooling tower, and a crane for servicing.

Q If one cylinder receives more fuel than the others, how is the engine operation affected? How can you prevent more fuel in one cylinder?

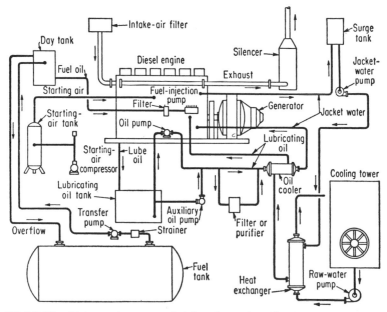

FIG. 10-37.   Major equipment needed for a heavy-duty diesel-engine installation.

A   Excess fuel in one cylinder causes incomplete combustion in that cylinder because too much oil is injected for the air supplied; incomplete combustion causes smoky exhaust. If the excess fuel isn't stopped soon, carbon builds up around the piston rings, causing them to stick. If the rings stick, the piston won't compress enough air to maintain the right temperature for proper combustion. Combustion gas will blow by the stuck rings, burn the oil off the cylinder walls, and score or even seize the piston. Excess fuel may also cause combustion knock, and because of power loss in the cylinder, fuel is wasted. With the remaining cylinders doing more than their share of the work, the engine starts to overheat.

The best way to avoid excess fuel is to check the cylinder-exhaust temperatures with a pyrometer every hour. Then, adjust the fuel oil so that all cylinder-exhaust temperatures are within 10°F of each other.

Q   Why do diesel engines overheat?

A   Overheating may be caused by (1) not enough cooling water, (2) deposits of scale on the cylinder and in the cylinder-head water jackets, (3) a bypass valve in the cooling tower being open, (4) not enough piston lubrication, (5) faulty lube oil, (6) lube-oil filters that need cleaning, (7) a worn lube-oil pump, (8) incorrect fuel-injection timing, (9) a fuel nozzle that is carbonized, or (10) an after-dribble condition.

Q What are some causes of a noisy diesel engine?

A Mechanical and fuel knocks are the two basic causes of noise in a diesel engine. Mechanical knocks may be from a worn piston pin or bearing, too much clearance in the crankpin bearing, a loose flywheel on the shaft, or worn pistons or liners that cause piston slap. Fuel knocks may result from early fuel injection, an injection system that is out of order, improper fuel, or too high an injection-air pressure.

Q What causes a diesel engine to stop suddenly?

A If an engine stops suddenly, you will probably find air in the fuel, that the tank is out of fuel, or that someone has closed the fuel valve by mistake. Water in the oil usually causes the engine to sputter before it stops. Broken valve heads, rings, or nozzle tips that enter the combustion space can prevent the piston from passing to tdc, but this is unusual. Piston seizure will also stop an engine suddenly. This can result from cylinder-oil failure and combustion gases blowing past the stuck piston rings.

Q What would you do if you couldn't stop a diesel engine in the usual way?

A In an emergency, cut off the air supply to the cylinders or stop the supply of fuel oil. Then check the governor-control mechanism. A worn control rack or weak springs will cause trouble.

Q Name and describe several diesel engine starting systems.

A 1. Compressed-air-starting systems (Fig. 10-38) are used on medium- or large-sized stationary and marine engines. Air from 100 to 300 psi is admitted to the cylinders on their firing strokes. The air works on the pistons until the engine fires.

2. Electric-storage batteries are used to energize the motor. They are either gear- or clutch-connected to the engine's flywheel. If the engine is directly coupled to the generator, the series-wound field in the generator windings will allow the generator to work as a starting motor.

3. A gasoline-engine system employs a small gas-cranking engine that is either gear- or clutch-connected to the diesel's flywheel. When the gas engine is started, it turns the diesel engine.

4. Compressed-air motors, gear- or clutch-connected to the diesel's flywheel, are used in mines and factories where there is enough air and where fire hazards must be avoided.

5. Hand-starting systems are used for small diesel engines. Here, a crank on the diesel engine's crankshaft is turned by hand until the engine fires.

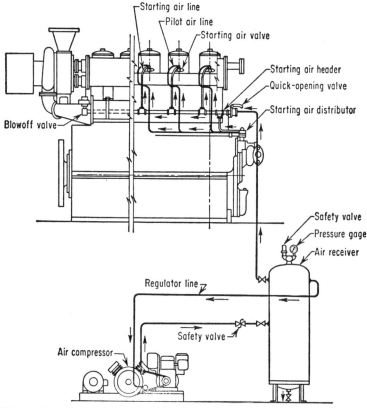

FIG. 10-38.   Air-starting system for a diesel engine needs these basic components.

Q How much heat is wasted by a diesel engine? How can some of it be recovered?

A About 65 percent of a diesel engine's heat is wasted through exhaust, cooling water, and radiation. Figure 10-39 shows one of the many ways to recover this heat. Exhaust from the engine boils water in the low-pressure steam boiler and preheats feed water for the boiler. Hot water is also heated in other systems.

Q How would you take over a watch in a diesel plant?

A When taking over a watch, first check the plant thoroughly. Check the cylinder temperatures; the lube, fuel, and cooling pressures; lube discharge; cooling-discharge temperature; governor-oil level; crankcase-oil level and shaft revolutions. Then, look over the log sheet to see if every-

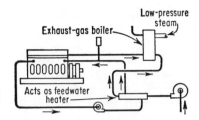

FIG. 10-39. Exhaust heat makes steam while jacket water heats the feed water.

thing went right on the previous watch. Examine the instrument readings on the control board. If everything is OK, you can relieve the watch. If not, the operator you are relieving usually stays until the watch is straightened out.

Q How is lubrication supplied to the cylinder walls?

A The cylinder walls of diesel engines are lubricated by oil thrown off from the crankshaft or by a separate lubricating system. The most reliable source is a separate system which permits the cylinder walls to be lubricated with a higher-viscosity oil in order to stand up under high temperatures, while the bearings can be lubricated with a lighter oil from the crankcase. With a separate system, the operator can also keep better control over the oil supply fed to the cylinder walls from the lubricator. This is important and often means the difference between trouble-free engine performance or stuck piston rings and resulting blowby, or, even worse, seized pistons.

Q Does lube-oil viscosity increase under higher pressures?

A Lube-oil viscosity increases a little under higher pressures, which compensate slightly for the higher running temperatures. But you can't merely use heavier oils to reduce wear because heavy oils on the cooler portions of the lower cylinder wall have a large viscosity excess and increase piston-ring friction. Thus, bearing friction also increases.

Q How would you locate a diesel engine cylinder causing smoke if the engine has no pyrometer?

A Smoky exhaust can result from poor compression, an overloaded engine, water in the fuel, the wrong type of fuel, not enough fuel-valve lift, etc. The fault might lie in one cylinder or in a number of cylinders. A quick way to find the faulty cylinder is to shut off the fuel to one cylinder. Then go outside and look at the exhaust. If the exhaust clears, it is evident that the trouble is in that cylinder. If there is no difference, keep cutting out one cylinder at a time while checking on the exhaust. If there is no change in the exhaust when all cylinders have been tested, the trouble is common to more than one cylinder. An exhaust pyrometer also gives you this information.

Q What components of internal-combustion engines are the most likely to fail?

A The Hartford Steam Boiler Inspection and Insurance Company provided the statistics below, based on 180 engine failures during a 1-year period several years ago (some variations from year to year should be expected). Types of internal-combustion engines are (1) diesel, (2) dual-fuel, (3) spark-ignited gas, and (4) gasoline engines. Most of the larger engines of 2000 hp and over drove electric generators; so their failure resulted in very costly work stoppage.

Initial part to fail	No. of losses
1. Bearing, sleeve	41
2. Piston	29
3. Cylinder head	19
4. Crankshaft	11
5. Cylinder liner	10
6. Valve, engine operating	9

NOTE: The remaining 32 parts to fail resulted in six losses per part, or less. The average cost of *each* failure, before deductible costs, was about $11,300. Bearing failures head the list, causing ruined bearings to result in crankshaft failures. Usually, the crankshaft is the most costly part of any engine. For trouble-free operation, preventive maintenance should be based upon the above figures.

RATING ENGINE EFFICIENCY

Q What is the indicated thermal efficiency of a diesel engine?
A The indicated thermal efficiency is the ratio of the heat equivalent of 1 hp·hr to the number of heat units actually supplied per indicated horsepower-hour. This may be calculated from either the high or low heat value of the fuel.

Q What is the brake thermal efficiency of a diesel engine?
A The brake thermal efficiency is the ratio of the heat equivalent of 1 hp·hr to the number of heat units actually supplied per brake horsepower-hour. This may be calculated from either the high or low heat value of the fuel.

Q What is the mechanical efficiency of a diesel engine?
A The mechanical efficiency is the ratio of the bhp to the ihp.

Q What is the horsepower rating of a diesel engine?
A The horsepower rating is the net horsepower after making adjustments for engine auxiliaries.

Q What is the sea-level rating of a diesel engine?
A The sea-level rating is the net bhp that the engine will deliver continuously when operating (1) in good condition, (2) at an altitude of not over 1500 ft above sea level, (3) with atmospheric temperature not over 90°F, and (4) with barometric pressure not less than 28.75 in. Hg.

Engine makers offer diesels with enough conservative sea-level rating so that they will deliver an output of 10 percent in excess of their full-load rating. Diesels have safe operating temperatures for 2 continuous hr. However, do not run at this rating for more than 2 hr out of any 24 consecutive hr of operation.

Q Does intake-air temperature affect the rating of a diesel engine?
A The power that any engine delivers decreases as the intake-air temperature increases, and a higher air-intake temperature decreases the horsepower capacity of an engine because the hotter air is less dense. As a result, a smaller quantity of oxygen is available for the combustion of fuel in the engine cylinder. Very few localities exceed 90°F air temperature for more than a few hours a day. If the air temperature at the engine intake is over 90°F, the engine capacity is reduced according to the curve in Fig. 10-40.

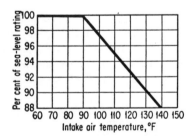

FIG. 10-40. Diesel-engine output decreases as intake-air temperature increases.

Q What kind of fuel-oil-consumption guarantees are made with new engines?
A Fuel-oil-consumption guarantees are usually made in pounds per net brake horsepower-hour at one-half, three-quarters, and full load when the diesel is operating at its rated revolutions per minute. Gas-burning and dual-fuel-engine gas-consumption guarantees are made in Btu per net brake horsepower-hour and are based on low heat value. Fuel-oil and

pilot-oil guarantees are based either on a high (gross) heat value of 19,350 Btu/lb or on average diesel-fuel consumption. When gas-diesel and dual-fuel engines operate with gas as the primary fuel, fuel-consumption guarantees are made on the basis of the total fuel (gas at low heat value plus pilot oil at high heat value) consumed by the engine in Btu per net brake horsepower-hour. The pilot-oil rate is usually stated in the guarantee and expressed in Btu at high heat value per net brake horsepower-hour.

Q Does a heat engine utilize the low or high heat value of oil?

A All heat engines utilize the low heat value of whatever fuel is used. The high heat value of fuels containing hydrogen includes some heat not available for conversion into work in any internal-combustion engine. But, because the high heat value of a fuel is easier to find, oil refiners and distributors sell oil on high heat values exclusively. The difference between high and low heat values of fuel oils is a fairly constant percentage. For this reason, fuel-oil-consumption guarantees are based on high heat value.

Q Why are gaseous-fuel guarantees based on low heat value?

A Gaseous-fuel guarantees are based on low heat value because the percentage difference between high and low heat values may range from 0 to 15 percent because of the varying hydrogen content.

Q Why don't manufacturers guarantee fuel consumption at one-quarter load?

A Fuel consumption is not guaranteed at one-quarter load because the small difference in cooling-water temperature or in internal friction has a disproportionate effect at such a low load, especially if the engine is new. So tests for one-quarter-load fuel consumption are inaccurate. Generator builders don't make one-quarter-load efficiency guarantees either; so the result cannot be expressed in terms of fuel per kilowatthour.

Q What are some things to keep in mind when selecting a building for your diesel engine?

A See Fig. 10-41. A concrete-block or brick building is better than a metal or wood, because noise doesn't carry so easily. Walls and ceilings may have to be treated acoustically, and the engine's foundation may have to be placed on spring mountings. The soil must be water-free and capable of supporting the engine's static-bearing loads of 3000 lb/ft^2. However, foundations can be designed for static loads down to 2000 lb/ft^2. If the soil can't support these loads, piles must be driven. Since about 5 percent of the heat input is radiated from diesel engines, plan room ventilation for a complete change of air every 3 to 5 min.

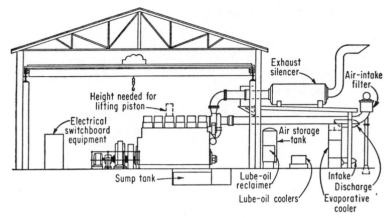

FIG. 10-41. Proper building and good layout are essential for efficient engine operation.

CALCULATIONS

Q What is meant by engine displacement per minute?
A The engine displacement per minute is the number of cubic feet per minute swept by all pistons during the power strokes. The displacement is equal to the number of cylinders times the area of the piston (square feet) times the stroke (feet) times the number of power strokes per cylinder per minute divided by 1728 (number of cubic inches in one cubic foot).

Q What is the engine displacement of a two-cycle engine having four 12-in.-diameter cylinders, a 24-in. stroke, and operating at 200 r/min?

A $\dfrac{12 \times 12 \times 0.7854 \times 24 \times 200 \times 4}{1728} = 1256 \text{ ft}^3$ *Ans.*

Q What is the ihp (indicated horsepower) of a diesel engine?
A The ihp of an engine cylinder is the horsepower developed in a cylinder. It can be found from the mip, engine speed, and cylinder dimensions. The formula is as follows:

$$\text{ihp} = \frac{\text{mip} \times LAN}{33,000}$$

where mip = mean indicated pressure, psi
$\quad L$ = stroke of piston, ft
$\quad A$ = net piston area, in.^{2}
$\quad N$ = number of power strokes per min

Q What is the mip of a diesel engine?

A The mip is the average pressure, in psi, acting on a piston for each stroke during one complete cycle. Pressures are positive when acting in the direction that the piston moves and negative when acting in opposition to piston movement.

NOTE: See steam engine indicator.

Q What is the bhp (brake horsepower) of a diesel engine?

A The bhp is the horsepower delivered by the shaft at the output end. The name is derived from the fact that it is determined by a brake.

$$\text{bhp} = \frac{2 \times \pi \times r \times \text{r/min} \times W}{33{,}000}$$

where r = distance between the center of the shaft and the point of application of weight to the brake arm, ft
r/min = revolutions per minute of brake shaft
W = effective weight on brake arm, lb
$\pi = 3.1416$

NOTE: See Chap. 6, "Instruments," for a discussion of the prony brake.

Q What is the brake mean effective pressure (bmep) of a diesel engine?

A The bmep is figured by the following formula:

$$\text{bmep} = \frac{\text{bhp} \times 33{,}000}{LAN}$$

where bhp = brake horsepower per cylinder
L = stroke of piston, ft
A = net piston area, in.²
N = number of power strokes per min

Q What is meant by piston speed?

A Piston speed is the total number of feet that a piston travels in 1 min. The formula is

Piston speed = stroke (ft) × r/min × 2

Q Find the speed droop of a governor if an engine has a normal speed of 1400 r/min and a no-load speed of 1450 r/min.

A Speed droop $= \dfrac{100\ (n_1 - n_2)}{n_2}$

n_1 = no-load speed
n_2 = normal speed

$$= \frac{100\ (1450 - 1400)}{1400} = 3.57 \text{ percent} \qquad Ans.$$

Q Find the sensitivity of a governor which at one-half load begins to act with an increasing load at 1417 r/min and with a decreasing load at 1429 r/min.

A $\text{Sensitivity} = \dfrac{200 \, (n_{max} - n_{min})}{n_{max} + n_{min}}$

n_{max} = decreasing load
n_{min} = increasing load

$= \dfrac{200 \, (1429 - 1417)}{1429 + 1417} = 0.84 \text{ percent}$ *Ans.*

Q How much heat must be absorbed by the cooling system of a 500-hp engine when it is running at full load? The fuel consumption is 0.35 lb/bhp·hr; the heat value of the fuel is 19,100 Btu/lb. The heat input lost to the cooling system is 28 percent.

A Heat input = 500 × 0.35 × 19,100 = 3,342,500 Btu/hr
Heat lost to cooling system = 0.28 × 3,342,500 = 935,900 Btu/hr

NOTE: This can also be calculated in Btu per brake horsepower-hour thus:

$\dfrac{935,900 \text{ Btu/hr}}{500 \text{ bhp}} = 1872 \text{ Btu/bhp·hr}$ *Ans.*

SUGGESTED READING

Elonka, Stephen M.: *Standard Plant Operators' Manual*, 3d ed., McGraw-Hill Book Company, New York, 1980 (has chapter on diesel engines in addition to examination questions and answers).

Elonka, Stephen M.: *Standard Basic Math and Applied Plant Calculations*, McGraw-Hill Book Company, New York, 1978 (has chapter on heat engines and also a chapter on metric conversion).

11

AIR CONDITIONING

To most people, air conditioning means only cooling. But today in many factories, office buildings, hospitals, shopping centers, etc., 10 factors affecting both physical and chemical conditions of the atmosphere within a structure are controlled by air-conditioning systems: (1) temperature, (2) humidity, (3) motion of air, (4) air distribution, (5) air pressure, (6) dust, (7) bacteria, (8) odors, (9) toxic gases, and (10) ionization.

Today, all the above are put under one label, HVAC (heating, ventilating, air conditioning). But these two volumes have chapters for several subjects dealing with HVAC, covering boilers, building heating, air conditioning, heat exchangers, etc.

In this chapter we cover basics and latest information on trouble-free operation, heat pumps, and the health hazards you must avoid.

BASICS

Q What is air conditioning?
A It is the process of conditioning the air to a given temperature, humidity, and cleanliness.

Q How is the temperature controlled in such a system?
A Figure 11-1 shows a typical air-conditioning system for a large plant. The temperature is kept at a set, comfortable level by the addition or

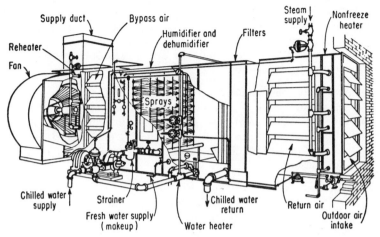

FIG. 11-1. Central plant has all conditioning elements except refrigeration.

removal of heat. To do this, two heat exchangers are used—one for heating in winter, the other for cooling in summer. The heating medium may be hot water or steam. Steam or hot water flows through coils placed in the airstream to be heated. The temperature is usually regulated by controlling steam or water temperature in the coil by means of a thermostat. Another way is to pass unconditioned air past a damper, thereby mixing heated and unheated air. The cooling medium is chilled water, brine, or a direct-expanding refrigerant. Cooling is also done by passing unconditioned air through cold-water sprays. Outdoor air is heated by steam coils, then humidified or dehumidified as needed. After the air is washed, it is distributed by a fan through ducts.

Q What is air?
A Pure, dry air is a mixture of oxygen and nitrogen, plus small amounts of rare gases, such as argon. The air around us also contains moisture in varying amounts. Air to be conditioned might therefore be called a mixture of air and steam.

Q How can we have steam in the air at atmospheric pressure and low temperatures?
A The air-moisture mixture, but not the water vapor, is at atmospheric pressure. The temperature at which water boils or vaporizes gets lower as the pressure goes down. Thus, at extremely low pressures, water can exist in the form of steam, even at usual temperatures of around 70°F.

Q What is saturation temperature?

A For any given pressure, there is one temperature—the saturation temperature—at which steam starts to vaporize or condense. Let us say that 1 ft³ of moist air at 70°F contains 0.0004 lb of moisture. But the same air can hold 0.0011 lb of steam. The reason why it is less is that the steam is superheated. In this case, 70 − 40 = 30°F of superheat.

Q What is relative humidity?

A Because our cubic foot of air in the above problem holds less moisture than it is capable of holding, we have relative humidity. Here, we have 0.0004 lb of moisture when we could have 0.0011 lb. So the ratio is 4 : 11, or 36 percent relative humidity. This is based on volume, which is cubic feet of moist air.

Q What is dew point?

A If we take our mixture, with 0.0004 lb of moisture in a cubic foot, and cool it down to 40°F, it will hold all the moisture that 1 ft³ can hold at that temperature. Then we say it has 100 percent relative humidity because the mixture is completely saturated. If the mixture is cooled still further, some of the steam will condense. In this case, condensation will start at 40°F, which is the dew-point temperature. The dew point of any mixture of air and water vapor therefore depends on the amount of moisture present.

Q What is wet-bulb temperature?

A To take the wet-bulb temperature, you need a wet-bulb thermometer and a psychrometric chart. The thermometer has a bulb that is covered with a wetted silk gauze and placed in the airstream. Some of the water in the gauze will evaporate. Because vaporizing takes heat from the remaining water, the water temperature will drop. The amount of this temperature drop depends on the dryness and temperature of the air. The thermometer reads wet-bulb temperature and tells us the amount of moisture in the air. Then, by checking a psychrometric chart, we learn the other things we need to know.

Q What is latent heat?

A Heat must be added to vaporize water into steam, but heat must be removed to condense steam back into water. In each case, the same amount of heat is removed or added. This heat is called latent heat. Since the amount of latent heat varies with the dew point, it is used to change a liquid to vapor, or a vapor to liquid, without changing the temperature.

Q What is sensible heat?

A Any heat needed to change the temperature of a liquid or vapor is sensible heat. The amount of sensible heat depends on the temperature, and specific heat of the substance.

Q What is total heat?
A For completely dry air, the sensible heat would be the total heat. For water vapor alone, its total heat would be sensible heat plus latent heat. Total heat depends on the wet-bulb temperature, just as sensible heat depends on the dry-bulb temperature and latent heat depends on the dew point.

USING PSYCHROMETRIC CHARTS

Q What is a psychrometric chart?
A See Fig. 11-2. Because the moist-air mixtures always follow the same rules, a psychrometric chart has their conditions plotted. This saves time in calculations. The chart shows percentage of humidity (some charts show relative humidity), wet- and dry-bulb temperatures, and dew point. By using auxiliary scales, many useful data can be obtained from the chart.

Q What does a psychrometric chart show?
A The skeleton chart (Fig. 11-2a) is a Trane psychrometric chart. Lines of the constant dry-bulb temperature are almost vertical. Lines of the constant dew-point temperature are horizontal. Lines of the constant wet-bulb temperature slope downward to the right. Lines of the constant percentage humidity are curved. Before using the chart, any two of the above values must be known. The remaining two can then be found on the chart.

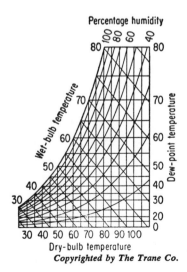

FIG. 11-2. Psychrometric chart plots moist-air conditions.

Copyrighted by The Trane Co.

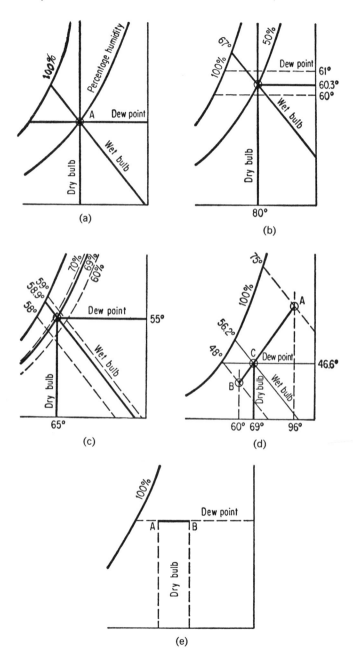

(a)

(b)

(c)

(d)

(e)

Q How do you find humidity on a psychrometric chart?

A EXAMPLE: Given air having a dry-bulb temperature of 80°F and a wet-bulb temperature of 67°F, find the dew-point temperature and the percentage of humidity. Refer to the skeleton chart in Fig. 11-2b. Then try this problem on the psychrometric chart in Fig. 11-2. You will find that the dew-pont temperature of the air is 60.3°F and the humidity is 50 percent.

Q How do you find a wet-bulb reading?

A EXAMPLE: Given air having a dry-bulb temperature of 65°F and a dew-point temperature of 55°F, find the wet-bulb temperature and the percentage of humidity. Refer to the skeleton chart in Fig. 11-2c. Then try this problem on the psychrometric chart. You will find that the wet-bulb temperature is 58.9°F and the humidity is 69 percent.

Q How do you find air mixtures on the Trane chart?

A EXAMPLE: The chart can be used to determine resultant wet-bulb and dew-point temperatures of a mixture of two streams of air at different conditions. Suppose that 25 percent of the mixture has a dry-bulb temperature of 96°F and wet-bulb temperature of 75°F, as represented by point A in Fig. 11-2d. The balance, or 75 percent, has a dry-bulb temperature of 60°F and a wet-bulb temperature of 48°F, as shown by point B. The resultant dry-bulb temperature of the mixture is figured as follows:

$0.25 \times 96 = 24°F$
$0.75 \times 60 = 45°F$
$24 + 45 = 69°F$, the resultant dry-bulb temperature of the air mixture

Now, draw a straight line between points A and B. The intersection of the vertical line of 69°F dry bulb with the line from A to B gives point C. The wet-bulb and dew-point lines running through point C are the resultant wet-bulb and dew-point temperatures of the mixture. In this case, the wet-bulb temperature of the mixture is 56.2°F and the dew-point temperature is 46.6°F.

Q How do you use the Trane chart to trace air-conditioning cycles?

A Besides giving the properties of air, the Trane chart can be used to trace air-conditioning cycles. Processes involving heating or cooling and humidification or dehumidification can be clearly followed on the chart. In tracing any process, keep this fact in mind: The dew-point temperature is constant as long as there is no change in the moisture content of the air. Thus, the heating of air without changing its moisture content takes place along a horizontal line of the constant dew point. The dew-point line is determined by the initial condition of the air. In Fig. 11-2e, the air that is initially in the condition designated by point A is heated to point *B* along the horizontal line *AB*. Also, if the air is to be cooled without the moisture being condensed, the process is represented by a straight line drawn from point *A* to *B* in Fig. 11-2*e*.

Q How do you find air volumes on the Trane chart?
A See Fig. 11-3. To find the volume of 1 lb of air having any temperature

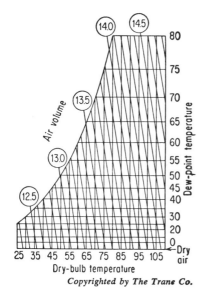

Copyrighted by The Trane Co.   FIG. 11-3. Trane volume chart.

and humidity, you must know the dry-bulb and dew-point temperatures of the air. The diagonal lines on the Trane chart give the volume of 1 lb of dry air. Thus, using the volume chart, air at a dry-bulb temperature of 71°F and at a dew-point temperature of 59°F has a volume of 13.6 ft³/lb.

AIR PURIFICATION

Q What is spray humidifying?
A Spray humidifying is the process of adding moisture to the air by passing it through water sprays (washers). The sensible heat of air changes into latent heat, which supplies heat needed for vaporizing some of the water. While the air's dry-bulb temperature goes down, the total heat of the air doesn't change (only proportions of sensible and latent heat change).

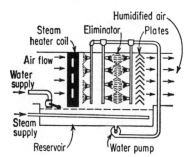

FIG. 11-4. Typical air washer used for conditioning air.

Figure 11-4 shows a typical air washer. The air flows through filters that separate dust from the airstream and then to the water sprays that remove the remaining impurities by washing.

Q How do human beings affect the air they live in?

A Human beings (1) use up oxygen in metabolism, (2) exhale carbon dioxide, a waste product of metabolism, (3) increase the dry-bulb temperature of the air because energy liberated in metabolism is partly lost as heat, (4) increase the humidity of the air because of the evaporation of moisture from their body surfaces and through respiration, (5) give off odors to the air, and (6) decrease the number of small ions in a unit volume of air.

Q What is air purification?

A Just as air temperature is controlled by heating or cooling in an air-conditioning system, dust, fumes, pollens, odors, and other contaminants may be controlled through various air-cleaning devices. This is done by placing filters, activated carbon, washers, etc., in the air ducts.

Q What are packaged air-conditioning units?

A See Fig. 11-5. Packaged air-conditioning units come with all the needed equipment in a single cabinet. They are usually made in smaller sizes and placed in various zones around a plant or office. Larger packaged units have ductwork for fully automatic room conditioning that is too large for one outlet.

Q Describe a few devices used for air purification.

A See Fig. 11-6 *a* to *c*. The devices used for air purification include (1) centrifugal collectors, (2) air washers, (3) dry-type filters, (4) viscous filters for manual operation, (5) viscous filters for automatic operation, (6) electrostatic precipitators, and (7) absorption equipment.

Centrifugal collectors remove heavy airborne contaminations and cope with the waste from woodworking machines, the exhaust from sanding, grinding, fly ash, etc.

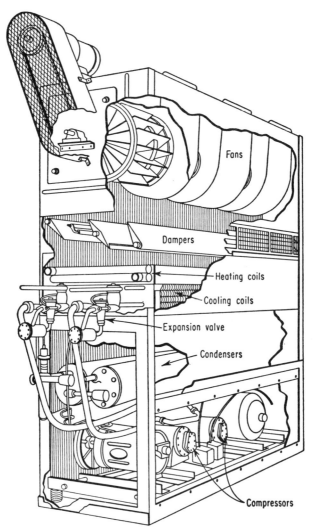

Fans

Dampers

Heating coils

Cooling coils

Expansion valve

Condensers

Compressors

FIG. 11-5. Packaged unit conditions air.

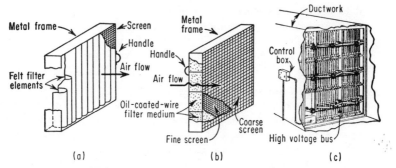

FIG. 11-6. Three types of popular filters.

Air washers are banks of spray nozzles that arrest entrained particles. Surface scrubbers have large surfaces that are constantly washed down by spray nozzles. Impurities are removed with spray.

Dry-type filters are either throwaway or semipermanent. Throwaway types are discarded when saturated with airborne impurities. Semipermanent filters are cleaned and used over a number of times.

Viscous filters usually have wool or fiber, screen wire, metal punchings, etc., and are treated with a sticky oil that captures and holds particles in the air.

Electrostatic precipitators arrest airborne particles under the influence of a high-tension electric field. The particles become charged or ionized and will precipitate when they contact an electrode of the opposite polarity.

Absorption equipment is used to absorb odors, organic gases, and vapors.

Q How are air mixtures handled in air-conditioning systems?

A In many systems, the air returning from the conditioned space is mixed with incoming fresh air. In most systems, a certain quantity of air is discharged from the system and replaced with fresh or new air. The balance of the air is recirculated through the conditioner. It is recooled or reheated and humidified or dehumidified. In systems where the contaminated air is very slight, recirculated air isn't cleaned but is mixed with fresh air that is cleaned before it enters the system. Where contaminating is heavy, both fresh and recirculated air are treated. In some systems, even the air wasted must be cleaned before it may be discharged to the atmosphere. Fresh air is air taken from outdoors to replace the air discharged from the system; but the degree of freshness may vary widely. It may even be less pure than the air discharged from the conditioned system. So cleaning is important.

Q What are pan or surface humidifiers?
A Pan or surface humidifiers are often used in small room coolers. Steam or electrical heated tubes in the bottom of the pan heat the water for vaporization. An airstream, sweeping over the pan, carries the moisture off with it.

Q What is direct humidification?
A In direct humidification, the humidity is increased by adding moisture to the airstream on its way to the conditioned space. This is usually used where humidity control is part of an overall conditioning problem, as in a usual comfort system. In industrial jobs, like textile mills, a high relative humidity may be needed, temperature control and ventilation being only incidental. Here, adding water directly to the air in conditioned spaces is often practical.

Q How is air dehumidified?
A Air is dehumidified either by cooling or by chemical adsorption. When the final water temperature is held below the initial dew point of the air, both cooling and dehumidification take place. The cooling coils for dehumidification should have finned surfaces separated enough so that the moisture condensing on them can roll off. Drip pans and drains should be provided to catch the condensate. Both spray devices and cooling coils are used, depending on the job.

Q What is dehydration?
A Dehydration is a form of dehumidifying, without the removal of heat at the same time. Here, latent heat entering the air is converted into sensible heat in the leaving air. The job is done with absorbents, which are materials having the ability to extract and hold water vapor from the surrounding air. Absorbents may be divided into two classes according to the way they behave in use.

HEATING-COOLING SYSTEMS

Q Sketch the piping system of a simple heating-cooling system.
A See Fig. 11-7. A packaged liquid cooler, with either manual or automatic controls, supplies the needed cooling capacities. When interconnected to the heating system, manual or motorized valves installed in the bypasses permit one pump to be used for both the heating and cooling cycles. But the water temperature must be reduced to less than 100°F before the cooling system is started. If not, the chiller or compressor may be damaged. Here, the mixing tank and venting system help remove air from the system wash. The mixing tank permits the use of a single compression tank for both heating and cooling, as shown.

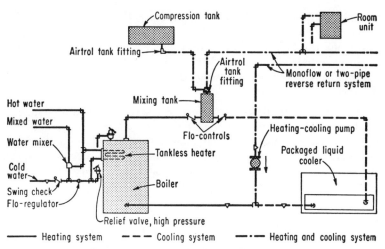

FIG. 11-7. Simple heating-cooling system.

Q How would you hook up a packaged cooler for dual heating-cooling air conditioning if you had only a steam supply for heating and no boilers? **A** See Fig. 11-8. For this hookup, use heat exchangers heated with steam for both domestic-water heating and space heating, as shown. Here, the

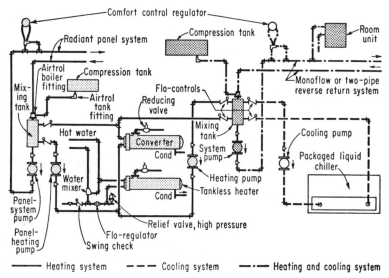

FIG. 11-8. Converters supply steam in this system.

cooling is provided by a packaged liquid cooler. If your old heating system has radiators, you might replace them with modern heating-cooling convectors. Water can be used as the conveying medium. Each room, office, or area can be individually controlled in this way to meet specific heating and cooling requirements. Converters, shown in the sketch, take the place of a boiler.

Q Are refrigerants allowed to be expanded directly into the cooling coils installed in air-conditioned spaces?

A Local codes permit certain refrigerants (Group 1, American Standards Association) to be used directly in the cooling coils. In such direct-expansion coils, the liquid refrigerant vaporizes and, in so doing, extracts heat from the passing airstream.

Q Name the two basic control methods used in direct-expansion coils.

A The flooded coil (not widely used in air conditioning) and the thermal-expansion valve method. In the flooded-coil control, a float keeps the liquid refrigerant at the desired level in both the coil and the surge tank. In the thermal-expansion system, a valve feeds just enough liquid into the coil to hold the refrigerant at the coil's suction outlet at about 6 to 10°F superheat. The temperature is measured by a temperature bulb, which actuates the valve; see Fig. 11-9.

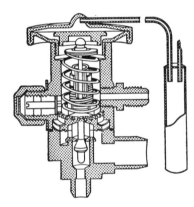

FIG. 11-9. Thermal-expansion valve controls evaporation.

Q Explain how chilled water is used for air conditioning.

A Chilled water is the most common air-conditioning method, especially in larger installations. The refrigerant is expanded in an evaporator, which, in turn, cools the chilled water. This chilled water is then circulated by a pump to the various units doing the space cooling. Because temperatures below 40°F are seldom needed, water is usually used instead of brine.

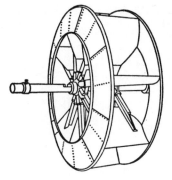

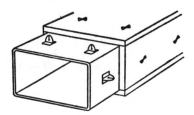

FIG. 11-10. Centrifugal wheel pushes air through ducts where needed.

FIG. 11-11. Ducts distribute treated air.

Q How is conditioned air distributed?
A Conditioned air is distributed by fans (Fig. 11-10) that provide the pressure head needed to overcome resistance to the airflow. Trunk ducts and branches (Fig. 11-11) then guide the air to its destination. Outlets, grilles, registers, and diffusers (Fig. 11-12) introduce the air into the conditioned spaces.

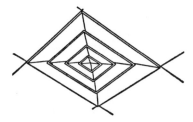

FIG. 11-12. Diffusers introduce air into spaces.

Q What is the ice system of air conditioning?
A See Fig. 11-13. Here, cooling is done by melting ice. This was a practical air-conditioning method for churches, theaters, and public halls that had short operating hours and relatively high peak loads. Since the investment in mechanical refrigeration equipment is expensive for short periods, ice fits the need. A small quantity of ice in a water-cooling tank can release refrigeration at a rapid rate.

Q How can natural groundwater be used in air conditioning?
A Some groundwater remains at a low constant temperature, around 55°F or cooler. This water can be pumped through cooling coils to precool

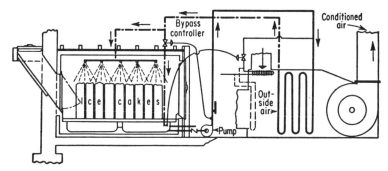

FIG. 11-13.   Ice is used in this air-conditioning system.

the air before it's cooled by the chilled refrigerated coils. This slightly heated water is then returned to a disposal well some distance away to conserve groundwater.

Q   What is a central air-conditioning system?
A   A central air-conditioning system has all the major equipment—filters, air washer, fans, and refrigeration machinery—in one centrally located space, removed from the area to be conditioned. Ducts distribute the conditioned air to the desired spaces.

Q   What are some advantages of a central air-conditioning system?
A   (1) The space occupied by the equipment need not be as valuable as the conditioned spaces. (2) For a large conditioned load, the equipment may cost less. (3) The maintenance and inspection of a central system does not disturb the people in the conditioned areas. (4) The exhaust air can be returned and partly reused, with obvious savings in heating and refrigeration.

Q   What is the main disadvantage of a central air-conditioning system?
A   The ductwork needed in a central system is costly and often impossible to install in old buildings.

Q   What is meant by zoning?
A   Zoning is used to cope with different conditions in various parts of large buildings or plants. For example, more air conditioning may be needed on the sunny side of a building than on the shady side. Thus, areas are broken up into zones, and each is fed by separate ducts.

Q   How is air blended?
A   See Fig. 11-14. To blend air, an air washer in front of the supply fan is bypassed in hot weather. The supply fan discharges through a split duct; the top is a heating coil and the bottom is a cooling coil. The air

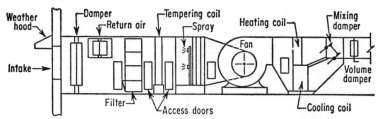

FIG. 11-14. Supplying air at two separate temperatures.

leaving these coils goes into separate chambers, with branch ducts running from each chamber. Hot and cold ducts run side by side. At each takeoff, there is a double-bladed, mixing, damper control of a room thermostat or other control device. This blends warmer and cooler air as needed to give the desired conditions in each space. In the winter, this system does not use a refrigerant in the cooling coil; in the summer, there is no heat in the heating coil. Because air leaving the warm chamber may be high in relative humidity, it may not compensate for the nearly saturated cool air. Closer control over the relative humidity may be obtained by placing a reheater in a cold-air chamber for summer service.

Q How is air cooled?
A Most of the refrigeration systems described in Chap. 9 are used for air-conditioning purposes.

Q What is a high-velocity air-conditioning system?
A See Fig. 11-15. To save space and installation cost, air can be forced through relatively small conduits at high speeds. Here, high-velocity conditioned air acts as a jet to induce room air with the incoming conditioned air. The mixture sweeps over a heating or cooling coil for final conditioning. The water supply and return lines leading to these coils run parallel to the air conduits, which are furred in along the outside walls.

Q What is reverse operation?
A Room conditioners having refrigeration equipment inside a room may be used for heating during the winter months. Here, the cooling coil becomes the condenser and the condenser acts as the evaporator. In this way the heat of compressing the refrigerant is used as a heat source for heating a space, while the outside air-cooled condenser coil is now used as the evaporator coil. But, remember that the outside-air temperature must be at least 45°F for a reversed-cycle operation of this kind.

Q What is a heat pump?
A A heat pump is a refrigeration compressor which provides both cooling and heating by using the heat of compression that is rejected at the con-

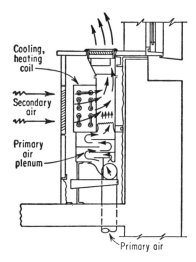

Cooling, heating coil

Secondary air

Primary air plenum

Primary air

FIG. 11-15. High-velocity air is mixed with room air.

denser (Fig. 11-16). During the cooling cycle, the heat pump operates as a straight compression-refrigeration cycle. Whenever heat or cooling is needed, a changeover switch of summer or winter operation is provided, and this causes the function of the condenser and evaporator-heat exchanger to be automatically reversed by a changeover valve. By rerouting flows, the air-cooled condenser becomes an evaporator and picks up heat from the outside air.

Extracting heat from outside air at 0°F, for example, requires a pressure drop in the refrigerant. Some newer units include a second compressor in series to boost pressure for heating. In these systems, a centrifugal compressor may handle the base load, with reciprocating units supplying the second compression state.

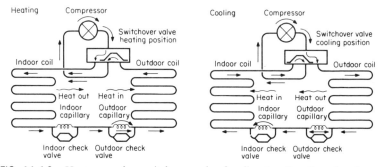

FIG. 11-16. Heat pump has switchover valve for directing flow from heating to cooling, or to cooling from heating. *(General Electric Co.)*

Q Considering today's high costs of fuel and equipment, name some advantages of a heat pump.

A (1) Long-range availability of coal for generating electricity to power the heat pump and overall first-cost saving. For many new buildings a single system can be installed to serve both cooling and heating. The cost of a boiler plant and auxiliary equipment including a smokestack can be saved. (2) Space saving—through the elimination of boiler plant, smokestack, fuel storage, etc. (3) Nuisance elimination—does away with ash removal, smoke, soot, and ash dust damage. (4) Single energy source—electric power—simplifies accounting and service problems. (5) Increased safety—through elimination of handling of fossil fuels. (6) Fire insurance rate reduction—by elimination of fire hazards. *And,* a refrigeration cycle can be applied first to provide heating only, with conversion to complete year-round air conditioning carried out later.

OPERATION AND MAINTENANCE

Q Most air-conditioning system failures occur on preseason start-up or shortly thereafter. How can they be avoided?

A The Hartford Steam Boiler Inspection and Insurance Company, which has paid millions of dollars for such failures, suggests the following checklist:

PRESEASON MAINTENANCE AND START-UP
CHECKLIST FOR AIR-CONDITIONING SYSTEMS

Compressors

1. Energize crankcase heaters for at least 8 hr before start-up and before taking insulation resistance readings of hermetic motor windings.

2. If insulation resistance tests indicate less than 1 MΩ resistance, don't start the compressor (hermetic-type motor-compressor).

3. Crankcase heaters should be left energized for the rest of the season so that, whenever the compressor is idle, the heater will prevent refrigerant "migration" to the crankcase.

4. Examine all valves for signs of wear, cracking, and fatigue. Valves that show any signs of stress should be replaced. (Valve failures comprise a large percentage of compressor breakdowns.)

5. Test the lubricating oil for color and acidity.

6. Check the crankcase oil level.

Motors

1. Check the air passages of open motors for cleanliness and obstructions.
2. Check the condition of bearings.
3. Lubricate the bearings.
4. Take insulation resistance readings. If the readings indicate less than 1 MΩ resistance, don't start the motor. Check for the cause of the low resistance.

Motor Controls

1. Inspect starter contacts for deterioration from short cycling, arcing, or corrosion.
2. Check terminal connections for tightness.
3. Examine the overload protection for defects. Determine that the protection is of the proper size.
4. Check mechanical linkages for binding and excessive looseness.
5. Check timing devices for correct operating sequence.

Operating and Safety Controls

1. Determine that the controls are properly calibrated and in working order.
2. Test thermostatic controls by immersing the sensing elements in a bucket of ice water to verify both the calibration and the setting.
3. Test oil pressure differential safety switches both mechanically and electrically.
4. Examine flow switches by removing them and checking for corrosion and proper linkage operation.

Refrigerant Circuits

1. Be sure that the circuit is equipped with a moisture indicator.
2. If moisture is indicated, install new liquid-line filter/drier cores. Determine and correct the source of the moisture.

Thermostatic Expansion Valves

1. Check the expansion valve for proper operation and superheat settings over the full range of operation.

Condensers

1. Air-cooled condensers: Clean with a solution marketed for this specific use. Be careful to protect the fan motors from moisture.

Q How do you control compressor capacity?

A Compressor capacity is controlled by the unloader or bypass valves. Most compressors have two to three steps; or, if there is more than one compressor, they may be started or stopped in any order to give the required capacity. Multiple-compressor jobs may use bypass valves on each compressor.

Q How are drafts avoided in conditioned spaces?

A To avoid drafts in conditioned spaces, use ceiling diffusers with bottom grille dampers. With this system, the air velocity can approach 3000 ft/min and will be diffused with lowered noise in spite of the machines, columns, and other obstacles.

Q How do you prevent vibration from traveling through the ducts?

A Vibration in ductwork can be minimized by setting all air-conditioning equipment on shock absorbers. Separate the equipment foundations from the main building foundations. Install sound-absorbing linings inside the ducts and felt-line the dampers. Use flexible joints between the ducts and air diffusers, and keep the air diffusers tight against the ducts to prevent air leakage; leakage adds noise to the system. Air diffusers placed in the ceiling are quieter than those located in the walls, even if the wall outlet is 1 ft below the ceiling. Separating the ducts of both supply and return lines prevents noise from traveling from one area to another. When passing ducts through the walls, you should insulate them at the cross-through points to avoid wall noise pickups. Floating-construction duct mounting also eliminates duct noise. Keep the duct elbows from branching too close to the fan outlets.

Q What are some causes of odors in conditioned spaces?

A Odors in conditioned areas may be caused by refrigerant leaks, brine leaks, no trap in the air-washer drain to the sewer, a dirty cooling-coil surface, or odor-producing units located near the air intake.

Q What conditions would keep a compressor from stopping?

A (1) Too high or too low a temperature in the conditioned rooms, (2) too high a discharge pressure, (3) not enough refrigerant, and (4) new heat loads in the conditioned spaces.

Q Name the "eight pillars" of air-conditioning (refrigeration) trouble-shooting.

A If the cause of the trouble is not known, the first action is to record significant conditions as found. This method will indicate the areas in which performance is ailing, or even disrupted. Data so collected often point with reason to the underlying cause. Record these data: (1) Note the temperature of each conditioned space. For zoned installations, record the temperature of each zone. (2) Note the status of each control thermostat. List as satisfied or not satisfied and calling for cooling. (3) Note the temperature of the air from the discharge of the air handler. Also note the temperature of return air entering the handler. (4) Note the refrigerant suction pressure and temperature. Compare these with the setting of the low-pressure cutout. (5) Note the liquid pressure and temperature leaving the condenser. Compare with control settings of the cutout switch. (6) Note condenser conditions. If the condenser is air-cooled, note air-in and air-out temperatures. If it is water-cooled, note temperatures of water in and out. (7) If the compressor seems to be short-cycling, note the length of run in minutes. (8) Note the presence of any unusual sounds. If possible, designate the apparent source, such as compressor, blower, or expansion valve.

ANNUAL SHUTDOWN MAINTENANCE

Q What maintenance should be given to centrifugal compressors during annual shutdowns?

A First consult the operating log and maintenance record for problems experienced during the operating season. Bearings are especially vital. Measure thrust-bearing seal gaps and compare them with the original gaps. Excessive wear over 0.005 in. in 1 year (0.127 mm) indicates the need for replacement before 0.010 in. (0.254 mm) of wear has been reached. All compressor manufacturers have specific details on what maintenance is needed in their units, including checking of purge units, pump down procedures, seal maintenance, and journal checking. It is recommended that the maintenance manual of the compressor manufacturer or the service organization be consulted for full details. Each manufacturer has a particular design, which must be considered in the maintenance program.

Remove water from the oil cooler if it is in an area subjected to subfreezing temperatures. First close the water valves, and remove the plug in the end of the cooler shell, and then drain, or break the flared inlet fitting and blow out the water coils.

Q What attention must be given to the lubrication oil in compressors?

A Lubrication oil must be drained from the seal-oil reservoir, atmospheric float chambers, and main oil sump. As soon as service operations have been completed, replace with new oil if tests have proved that it is required.

CAUTION: If oil is not removed, do not shut off oil heater.

Q What maintenance do the chilled water coolers require during shutdown?

A All water in the chilled water circuit should be drained to protect the lines and cooler tubes from freezing during winter shutdown. At the end of the operating season for a new unit, clean the tubes if necessary. If required, start water treatment in the chilled water circuit.

Q Detail the needed winter maintenance for heat-rejection equipment.
A If cooling towers and condensers are subject to freezing, remove all water to protect tubes, water boxes, and piping. Remove all sludge and accumulated dirt from the cooling tower; then paint it. Inspect spray nozzles and strainers in the waterline to the condenser; clean if needed. Check blade roots of fans for cracks and gears for wear, and also the condition of the oil in the gear case. Swelling and shifting of the cooling tower may have misaligned the motor and gear case.

Inspect the condenser tubes for effectiveness of water treatment. Coated heat-transfer surfaces greatly increase power costs.

Q What checks should be made on air-handling equipment during shutdown?
A Inspect the fan blading and bearings for wear and corrosion. Clean or replace filters, check motor belts, clean fan dampers, and check circulating piping connections for tightness.

Q What safety controls must be checked during winter shutdown?
A Pressure controllers, water-regulating valves, the evaporator pressure regulator, the condenser high-pressure cutout, the low refrigerant temperature cutout, the purge high-pressure cutout, the low chilled water temperature cutout, the low-oil-pressure switch, the solenoid valves, and the float switches should *all* have their setting checked and their sequence of operation corrected, if needed.

Q Where would you check for leaks in an air-conditioning system?
A The most likely places are around the cooler rupture disk or the relief valve, in the cooler-condenser expansion joint, in the suction damper seal, at the low refrigerant cutout bulb in the cooler and valves, and also around the flare and gage connections in the purge. At the same time, check the purge system for tightness and make an operational check.

REMEMBER: The leak test is one of the most important checks during winter shutdown inspection. Be sure to repair all leaks found.

Q Name some common problems often overlooked during cold weather.
A There is no substitute for alertness at *all* times. Consider freezing of sprinklers, water piping, heating stacks, steam condensates, and wherever water might be exposed to cold air.

HEALTH HAZARDS

Q What material is forbidden by OSHA in ducts, plenums, and ceilings where there is human occupation?
A Asbestos; this material can cause lung cancer.

Q What are fire dampers? Describe.
A Fire dampers are automatic dampers and are usually rectangular "flaps" or else louvers. They act when either heat or smoke is sensed in the system, as in the ducts, plenums, or intakes.

There are several problems. Internal air being recirculated may carry fumes or fire into other areas. Fresh-air intakes may carry fire and smoke from an adjacent building fire. Many modern materials and building contents are either made of or coated with plastics, which release heavy smoke and extremely lethal gases during combustion. These plastic materials are confined in a sealed air-conditioned building, and it is necessary to consider including pressurized fireproof stairwells, areas of refuge, and video (TV) as well as voice communication systems as part of the system. The blower systems may automatically either start or stop depending on their function in smoke and heat emergencies.

Q How do the dampers trigger themselves?
A Refer to both instrumentation and sprinkler systems for various schemes.

Q It seems impossible to stop the occupants from wedging swinging smoke fire doors open. What is a solution to this problem if the local codes permit?
A Electromagnetic holdbacks that are both fail-safe and wired to open the circuit both automatically and manually. The circuits should have a small supervisory current wired to a central control much like an internal fire signal system.

Q Are there other health hazards to an air-conditioning system?
A Yes, harmful bacteria sometimes build up in parts of the system, especially in cooling towers. Bacterial problems are ordinarily part of water treatment, and both the manufacturer and the water-treatment service will have instructions. Local emergencies will be the concern of health officials.

CALCULATIONS

Q When air contains 75 gr of moisture/lb of dry air, and the temperature is 80°F, what is the relative humidity?
A Table 11-1 shows that when air of 80°F is saturated with water vapor, the moisture contained is 155.8 gr/lb of dry air.

Thus $\dfrac{75}{155.8} \times 100 = 48.14$ percent   *Ans.*

NOTE: Multiply by 100 so that the result may be expressed as a percentage.

Q The first fan law states that the amount of air delivered by a fan varies in direct proportion to the speed. Consider a fan delivering conditioned air of 10,000 ft³/min at a speed of 600 r/min. How much air will it deliver if the speed is increased to 700 r/min?

TABLE 11-1   Moisture Contained in Saturated Air

Temperature °F	Weight of moisture, gr/lb of dry air
40	36.41
50	53.47
60	77.3
70	110.5
80	155.8
90	217.6
100	301.3
110	415
120	569

A Expressed as a formula:

$$\text{Ft}^3/\text{min at new speed} = \frac{\text{new r/min} \times \text{ft}^3/\text{min at old speed}}{\text{old speed, r/min}}$$

Thus

$$\text{Air at new speed} = 10,000 \times \frac{700}{600} = 11.667 \text{ ft}^3/\text{min} \qquad Ans.$$

Q How much cooling water per ton of refrigeration is required for an air-conditioning system if the water's inlet temperature is 66°F and the outlet temperature is 98°F?

A For estimating the water required in gallons per minute per ton of refrigeration, divide 30 by the difference in water temperature between condenser inlet and outlet.

Thus

$$\frac{30}{98 - 66} = 0.94, \text{ about 1 gal/(min)(ton) of refrigeration} \qquad Ans.$$

SUGGESTED READING

Elonka, Stephen M.: *Standard Plant Operators' Manual,* 3d ed., McGraw-Hill Book Company, New York, 1980 (has chapters on air conditioning and refrigeration, and questions and answers on license examinations).

Elonka, Stephen M., and Quaid W. Minich: *Standard Refrigeration and Air Conditioning Questions and Answers,* McGraw-Hill Book Company, New York, 1973.

12

FUELS AND FIRING

Today an operator who knows fuels and how to fire efficiently is a valuable employee to management. Never since the industrial revolution (which started with the Newcomen engine in the eighteenth century) have fuels been so expensive. With our earth containing a finite supply and demand growing yearly, fossil-fuel prices can go only one way—*up*. Thus the operator who can obtain the last Btu from fuel (without polluting the atmosphere) is invaluable.

Here we cover the various kinds of fuels, equipment needed for burning them, storage and handling, how to avoid smoke and soot, drafts needed for efficient combustion, combustion control systems, and calculations.

BASICS

Q What is burning?

A Burning or combustion is a form of oxidation. When iron and oxygen combine to form an oxide, known as rust, a slow burning process takes place. When oxygen combines rapidly with fuels, heat is liberated. Combustion may be self-starting. For example, when coal is piled outdoors, it combines slowly with the oxygen in the air and gives off heat. If this heat cannot get away, the temperature rises gradually until the coal bursts into flame. This is known as spontaneous combustion.

Q What must happen before a fuel can burn?

A A fuel must be turned into a gas before it can burn because nothing truly burns unless or until it is a gas. For example, to make the wax in a candle burn, it is first turned into a gas in the wick. After this, the burning wax gives off enough heat to continue the melting process, vaporizing, and igniting. You can't burn wax in a candle by holding a match to it; the match will only burn the gas that forms in the wick. All other fuels must also be turned into gas before they can burn.

Q What must happen before gas burns?

A Before gas burns, there must be a gas-air mixture that will ignite and raise the mixture to the ignition temperature.

Q Where does air enter the picture?

A Each element or compound needs a certain amount of oxygen for complete combustion. The exact amount is easy to calculate. If the right amount is mixed, we have a perfect or theoretical mixture. The relationship between gas and air is called the fuel-air ratio.

Q What are the chief fuel components in a hydrocarbon?

A Hydrogen and carbon are two basic fuel elements. Hydrogen is usually a gas, liquefied at 400°F below zero, while carbon vaporizes at around 6300°F. Their heating values are high: 62,000 Btu/lb for hydrogen, and 14,500 Btu/lb for carbon. Many hydrocarbons are compounds, such as methane (CH_4); they are normally gaseous and form important fuel gases.

Q Where does the ignition temperature come in?

A When the fuel-air ratio is right, we have a combustible gas that needs only heat to ignite. Heated gradually, the rate of the fuel-air chemical combination increases until no additional outside heat is needed. This is the ignition temperature, at which point the fuel mixture will continue to burn as long as the fuel mixture lasts. For each gas there is a range of flammable mixtures that ignite and continue to burn.

Q What is the main source of oxygen?

A Oxygen is the sole supporter of combustion. The main source of oxygen is the air or atmosphere. Air has 23.15 percent oxygen by weight and 76.85 percent nitrogen. To supply 1 lb of oxygen for combustion, we must therefore use $1 \div 0.2315$ or 4.320 lb of air. This means that for each pound of oxygen supplied, 3.320 lb of nitrogen is also used. But nitrogen serves no useful purpose in combustion and is a direct loss.

Q Why is the proper fuel-air mixture important?

A To burn properly, the carbon particles in a fuel must be thoroughly mixed with oxygen. In any flame or combustion space, there can be widely different mixtures. In one area the mixture may be too rich to burn, while in another area it may be too lean with almost all air. The nearest practical approach to a perfect fuel-air mixture is in the cylinder of a gas engine.

Q What is primary air and what is secondary air?
A Primary air is mixed with a fuel at or in the burner. Secondary air is, usually, air brought in around the burner or through the openings in a furnace wall or floor.

Q What condition is needed to burn solid fuels completely?
A Each atom of oxygen must contact the carbon surface, form carbon monoxide (CO) gas, then move away so that more oxygen can move in. The combustion of solid fuels needs diffusion (oxygen moving to the surface and CO moving away from the surface), mixing, and chemical combination to form carbon dioxide (CO_2). Solid fuels may be pulverized in order to burn at high rates nearing that of gaseous and liquid fuels so that each carbon particle is more completely surrounded by the air needed for combustion. Pulverizing a solid fuel is similar to atomizing a liquid fuel.

Q Name three elementary fuels.
A (1) Gaseous hydrocarbons, (2) solid carbon, and (3) a mixture of carbon monoxide and hydrogen are three general groups of fuels. They are contained in many fuel substances, such as charcoal and coke in a solid-carbon class. But each group has a similar pattern of combustion. Coal gas is a mixture of gaseous hydrocarbons and carbon monoxide plus hydrogen. Fuel oil volatilizes into gaseous hydrocarbons before combustion. Coal also decomposes into elementary fuels before combustion. This takes place when the coal contacts the heat of the fire. Gaseous hydrocarbons, carbon monoxide, and hydrogen are distilled off, leaving solid carbon behind.

Q Why is the sulfur content of fuels so important to the plant operator?
A Sulfur has a highly corrosive effect, and sulfur dioxide and water vapor in combustion products may unite to form acids. These are highly corrosive in breechings. Sulfur has heating value and must be accounted for in calculations.

Q How does carbon burn?
A Oxygen penetrates the carbon surface to break away atoms which, in turn, combine with the oxygen to form an unstable carbon-oxygen compound. Depending on the temperature and other conditions, this compound breaks up into carbon dioxide and carbon monoxide. Excess oxygen causes the carbon monoxide to oxidize to carbon dioxide. If combustion is incomplete, carbon monoxide is present in waste gases.

Q What do we mean by the term "available carbon"?

A This is the carbon in the fuel that does not combine chemically with the oxygen in any way. Complete combustion of 1 lb of carbon (C) yields a total heat of 14,500 Btu. So, 1 lb of C plus $2\frac{2}{3}$ lb of O_2 produces $3\frac{2}{3}$ lb of CO_2 plus 14,500 Btu. But incomplete combustion that produces carbon monoxide instead of carbon dioxide yields only 4350 Btu/lb of carbon. That is, 1 lb of C plus $1\frac{1}{3}$ lb of O_2 produces $2\frac{1}{3}$ lb of CO plus 4350 Btu. The further addition of oxygen and reignition would yield 14,500 minus 4350, or 10,150 Btu for each pound of the original carbon, so that $2\frac{1}{3}$ lb of CO plus $1\frac{1}{3}$ lb of O_2 produces $3\frac{2}{3}$ lb of CO_2 plus 10,150 Btu, or a total of 14,500 Btu.

Q Name the steps required in the combustion of fuel in a furnace.
A See Fig. 12-1. The job of burning fuel in a furnace includes (1) preparing the fuel and air, (2) converting the complex fuel into elementary fuels,

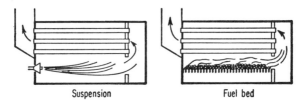

Suspension   Fuel bed

FIG. 12-1.   Fuel burning takes two forms: (1) suspension or (2) fuel bed.

(3) bringing these fuels and air together in the right proportions and at the right temperature for ignition and combustion, and (4) transferring heat from the combustion products to the boiler or other surfaces while retaining enough heat in the combustion zone to maintain volatilization and ignition. There are two ways to handle this job: in suspension or with a fuel bed.

Q Explain suspension firing.
A Suspension firing involves ejecting gas, liquid, or pulverized fuels from a burner. Since gas is ready for quick mixing with air, gas burners need to proportion only the volume of air and gas to ensure thorough mixing. But, oil or coal burners, in addition to proportioning the fuel and air, must mix them. This means converting the oil from a liquid to gaseous hydrocarbons. For coal, it involves distilling off the volatile matter (gaseous hydrocarbons, plus hydrogen and carbon monoxide). This is done in the instant after the fuel enters the furnace.

Q What is the furnace's job?
A The furnace provides the proper conditions for continuous, complete combustion. The fuel must be vaporized or distilled in the combustion

zone, mixed with air, and ignited. The furnace must also maintain a heat supply to prepare and ignite the incoming fuel.

Q What is the advantage of turbulent mixing?

A When fuel and air whirl and eddy in irregular paths instead of streaming for the furnace outlet, (1) the time available for combustion increases; (2) the fuel and air mix more thoroughly; and (3) the fuel and air move past each other at a higher velocity, helping to sweep away combustion products and to expose fresh surfaces. Good combustion depends on three "Ts"—temperature, time, and turbulence.

Q What causes ash and slag?

A Ash and slag are impurities (especially in coal) that do not burn. The particles that are carried out of the stack with gas in suspension firing are known as fly ash. When ash contacts relatively cold surfaces in the furnace while the ash is in a plastic state, it forms a slag coating that reduces the heat-transfer rate and slows down the passage of gas through the furnace. Slag must be broken up and removed from the furnace.

Q What is fuel-bed firing?

A In fuel-bed firing, the fuel is thrown, pushed, or dropped onto a grate inside the furnace. Air flows upward through the grate and fuel bed; the green coal is heated, volatile matter distills off, and coke is left on the grate. The volatile matter of the coal and the carbon monoxide from the coke burn over the fuel bed with the air that has come up through the fuel bed. Secondary air is usually admitted over the grate. From 40 to 60 percent of the coal's heat is in gas that is liberated over the fuel bed.

Q Explain overfire burning.

A Here, about one-half of the burning takes place above the fuel bed. But stratification (separate streams of gas and air leaving the furnace without mixing) is a problem. Excess air is supplied so the air and gas will mix more thoroughly.

Q What is natural gas?

A Natural gas is colorless and odorless. It is composed mostly of methane (CH_4) and usually contains some ethane (C_2H_6) and a little nitrogen. Gas, known as sour gas, contains hydrogen sulfide and organic sulfur vapors. The heating value averages about 1000 Btu/ft³ (20,000 Btu/lb). Natural gas is sold by the cubic foot or therm (100,000 Btu).

Q What is manufactured gas?

A Manufactured gas is seldom transmitted, except for small consumers such as homeowners, and is seldom used for steam generation other than at the point of manufacture. Coal gas and coke-oven gas are produced by carbonizing high-volatile bituminous coal in retorts. Cleaned of impurities, these gases are roughly one-half hydrogen and one-third methane, plus carbon monoxide, carbon dioxide, nitrogen, oxygen, and illuminates. Their heating value is only about 550 Btu/ft³. Water gas and oil gas are other forms of manufactured gas. Producer gas has a low heating value of 125 to 550 Btu/ft³. By-product gases, blast-furnace gas, sewage gas, and sewage-sludge gas are used in some areas.

FUEL OIL

Q What is fuel oil?

A Fuel oil is a decomposition of tiny marine growths or vegetable matter trapped in pools between the layers of the earth's crust. Crude oil is from 83 to 87 percent carbon and from 10 to 14 percent hydrogen, with traces of oxygen, nitrogen, and sulfur. The hydrogen and carbon combine as hydrocarbons.

Refining separates and often recombines the hydrocarbons into gasoline, fuel oil, etc. Distillation separates the hydrocarbons into groups or fractions having the same boiling points. Typical fractions are: (1) naphtha, (2) gasoline, (3) kerosene, and (4) gas oil. These are the distillates; the remainder, or residual, is a heavy fuel oil. Products of simple distillation are called straight run. Fuel oils may be either distillates or residuals and either straight run or cracked. Refinery wastes, which have little value, are acid sludge, tars, and tank cleanings or bottoms; they are usually burned at the refinery. Cracking is a chemical process that rearranges the oil molecules into more desirable forms.

Q How is crude petroleum classified?

A Crude petroleum is referred to by the following three general classes: (1) paraffin, (2) intermediate (mixed), and (3) asphalt. Crude oil must be refined to be usable.

Q What are the properties of commercial grades of fuel oil?

A Commercial fuel oil is numbered from grade 1 to grade 6. Its common characteristics are: (1) viscosity, Seconds Saybolt Universal (SSU), or Seconds Saybolt Furol (SSF); (2) specific gravity, in degrees API and Bé; (3) flash point; (4) coefficient of expansion; (5) fire point; (6) vanadium content of ash; (7) heating value; (8) sulfur content; (9) moisture and sediment, in percentage by volume, which should be kept below 1 percent; and (10) pour point.

Q How is viscosity measured?

A To measure viscosity, heat a 60-mL sample of oil to a standard temperature of 100°F, 122°F, or 210°F. Allow the oil to flow through a tube of a given length and diameter. The number of seconds it takes for the oil sample to flow through the tube is the oil's viscosity. This is expressed in SSU or SSF, depending on the size of the orifice used at the base of the tube. The measurement is made with a viscosimeter.

Q Define the specific gravity of oils.

A The specific gravity is the weight of a unit volume of oil compared with the weight of an equal volume of water, with the temperatures of both the oil and the water at 60°F. Two types of hydrometers are used to determine specific gravity. (1) The Baumé (Bé) hydrometer is used mostly in foreign countries, while (2) the American Petroleum Institute (API) scales are used in the United States. Light oils have a low specific gravity but are high on the Bé and API scales; the reverse is true for heavy oils.

Q How do you calculate specific gravity?

A When the weight of a unit quantity of oil is known and its temperature is 60°F, you can find the specific gravity by dividing the weight of the unit quantity of oil by the weight of an equal quantity of water at 60°F.

EXAMPLE: If the weight of 1 gal of oil at 60°F equals 7.986 lb and the weight of 1 gal of water at the same temperature is 8.328 lb, then $7.986 \div 8.328 = 0.9589$, the specific gravity.

Q What does flash point mean?

A The flash point of a fuel is the lowest temperature at which the fuel can be heated so that the vapor given off flashes momentarily when an open flame is passed over it.

Q Name the five common grades of fuel oil and the preheating temperatures needed for each grade to burn properly.

A Lighter oils numbered 1, 2, and 3 usually need no preheating. The commercial grades 5 and 6 give best combustion efficiency when heated enough to introduce the oil to the atomizer tip between 150 and 200 SSU (Seconds Saybolt Universal viscosity).

Q What is specific heat?

A Specific heat is the amount of Btu needed to raise the temperature of 1 lb of oil 1°F. It varies from 0.4 to 0.5, depending on the oil's specific gravity. In short, specific heat indicates how much steam it takes to heat an oil to a desired temperature. Light oils have a low specific heat, whereas heavier oils have a higher specific heat.

Q How does oil expand and contract with change in temperature?

A The coefficient of expansion is the increase or decrease in the volume of 1 gal of oil caused by raising or lowering its temperature 1°F. The constant allowed for expansion for each degree Fahrenheit increase or decrease, above or below 60°F, is 0.0004. The difference in the volume of an oil at 60°F and 120°F is $(120 - 60) \times 0.0004 = 60 \times 0.0004 = 0.024$. So, 200 gal of 60°F oil heated to 120°F has a volume of 200×1.024 or 204.8 gal—an increase of 2.4 percent. If a 200-gal oil storage tank is full when that temperature rise takes place, 4.8 gal will spill over. When receiving hot oil, this factor must be used to determine the amount actually purchased.

Q What harm does sulfur in fuel oil do?

A The sulfur content of a fuel oil is determined in percent by weight; the allowable limit is 4 percent. If an excessive amount of sulfur is present in a fuel, sulfurous or sulfuric acids are apt to form in the boiler breechings and uptakes, corroding the economizer, air heater, and stack. It also may affect EPA stack discharge SO_2 limits.

Q What harm will moisture or sediment do in a fuel?

A If allowed to enter the atomizer, the moisture or sediment in a fuel will cause sputtering, possibly extinguishing the flame, reducing the flame temperature, or lengthening the flame. Sediment is very annoying because it clogs strainers and sprayer plates. If there is a lot of sediment, frequent cleaning of the strainer and atomizer is necessary. If water, sediment, or both are present to any great extent, they can be separated from the oil by heating. This is done while the oil is in the settling tanks or, occasionally, by passing the oil through a centrifuge. Strainers are always used.

Q What is pour point?

A The pour point is the lowest temperature at which an oil will flow under set conditions. It indicates the difficulty which will be met in handling a fuel at its minimum temperature.

SOLID FUEL

Q What is coal?

A Coal is a black or brownish-black combustible mineral formed by the partial decomposition of vegetable matter without free access of air and under the influence of moisture, pressure, and temperature. Coal is found in beds or veins in the earth's crust and is mined for use as a fuel.

Q Does the carbon in coal vary?

A Different kinds of coal contain different amounts of carbon substance, depending on age, etc. Next to original peat—the youngest form of coal— is lignite, which is high in moisture and low in fixed carbon. Older coals, high in rank, contain more fixed carbon.

Q What properties of coal are determined in a "proximate analysis"?

A The proximate analysis shows the percentage of (1) moisture, (2) ash, (3) volatile matter, and (4) fixed carbon. These percentages add up to 100. You may also determine the total amount of sulfur as a separate percentage, the ash-fusion temperature, and the heating value.

Q How would you report a coal analysis?

A There are five ways to report a coal analysis, but only the first three are used in power-plant work: (1) as received, (2) air-dried, (3) moisture-free, (4) moisture- and ash-free, and (5) moisture- and mineral-free. These analyses report the condition of the coal as it is delivered to the laboratory. They are important because they give the condition of the coal as it is shipped or as it is fired—the values needed for practical work.

Q Do all coals contain moisture?

A All coals contain some natural moisture, varying from 1 to 5 percent in eastern coals and up to 40 percent in some lignites.

Q What is the difference in inherent moisture and surface moisture?

A Inherent moisture lies in the pores of the coal and does not leave the coal when it is air-dried. Surface moisture is absorbed by the coal after being mined, depending on the conditions in the mine and during transit or storage.

Q Is moisture in coal wasteful?

A Moisture in coal must be transported, handled, and stored. Since it replaces combustible material, it decreases the heat content per pound of coal. Further, some heat liberated in the furnace is wasted since it goes to evaporating the moisture in the fuel and superheating the vapor. There are charts for figuring this moisture loss.

Q What is coal ash?

A Like moisture, coal ash is an impurity that will not burn. It must be removed from the furnace and plant; this increases shipping and handling costs. Because ash causes clinkering and slagging, it is regarded as the no. 1 fuel-bed and furnace problem.

Q What volatile matter is found in coal?

A Methane and other hydrocarbons, hydrogen and carbon monoxide, and incombustible gases like carbon dioxide and nitrogen are found in coal. The volatile matter in coal is an index of the gaseous fuels present. Firing, furnace volume, and heating surfaces are all dependent on the percentage of volatile matter.

Q What is fixed carbon?

A A solid fuel is left in the furnace after the volatile matter distills off.

It consists mostly of carbon but also contains some hydrogen, oxygen, sulfur, and nitrogen not driven off with the gases. When you discount the percentage of moisture, ash, and volatile matter, the percentage left is fixed carbon.

Q Why is sulfur in coal undesirable?

A Although sulfur burns, it causes clinkering and slagging and corrodes air heaters, economizers, breeching, and stacks. It also is a factor in spontaneous combustion during coal storage. Sulfur shows up as iron sulfide (pyrites), as organic sulfur, and as sulfates. However, you measure only the total sulfur content. It also may affect EPA limits on sulfur dioxide amounts.

Q Explain ash fusion of coal.

A Heating cones are used to measure the temperature at which ash fuses. These are ceramic cones that fuse down to a round lump at the softening or ash-fusion temperature. Other temperatures sometimes noted are where (1) the cone tip starts to bend (initial deformation temperature) and (2) the cone spreads out in a flat layer (fluid). These temperatures are the best means of learning the clinkering and slagging tendencies of a coal under given fuel-bed and furnace conditions. See the discussion of the pyrometric cone under Refractories in Chap. 2.

Q How do you measure the heating value of coal?

A Heating value is determined by burning a coal sample in a "bomb" calorimeter filled with oxygen under pressure. The heating value in coal is what you pay for, depending on the type of coal. The next problem is to convert all the possible heating value into energy.

Q How are the grindability qualities of a coal measured for pulverizing?

A The ASTM (American Society for Testing and Materials) approves the following two methods: (1) ball-mill and (2) Hardgrove. The ball-mill method measures the energy needed to pulverize different coals by finding the number of ball-mill revolutions needed to grind a sample so that 80 percent passes a 200-mesh sieve (74 μm). The ball-mill grindability index, in percent, is found by dividing the number of revolutions into 50,000.

In the Hardgrove test, a prepared sample receives a set amount of grinding energy in a miniature pulverizer. The results are measured by weighing the coal that passes a 200-mesh sieve. To find the Hardgrove grindability value, multiply the weight of the coal passing the sieve by 6.93 and add 13 to the product.

Q What are caking and coking of coal?

A Most operators are confused by the terms "caking" and "coking." When coal is heated, the volatile matter is driven off, leaving a pure carbon known as coke. This may be in the form of small powdery particles, or it may fuse into lumps. Coke represents a stage in fuel-bed combustion. Coals that form lumps or masses of coke are called caking coals. Coals showing little or no fusing action are known as free-burning.

Q How is anthracite coal sized?

A Size stability is the ability of a coal to resist breakage; it is opposite to friability (the tendency of a coal to break or crumble into smaller pieces). Standard anthracite sizes are: (1) broken, passing a 4⅜-in. screen, retained on 3¼-in.; (2) egg, 3¼ to 2⁷⁄₁₆ in.; (3) stove, 2⁷⁄₁₆ to 1⅝ in.; (4) chestnut, 1⅝ to 1³⁄₁₆ in.; (5) pea, 1³⁄₁₆ to ⁹⁄₁₆ in.; (6) no. 1 buckwheat, ⁹⁄₁₆ to ⁵⁄₁₆ in.; (7) no. 2 buckwheat (rice), ⁵⁄₁₆ to ³⁄₁₆ in.; and (8) no. 3 buckwheat (barley), ³⁄₁₆ to ³⁄₃₂ in. Culm or river coal is refuse from screening anthracite into prepared sizes.

Q How is bituminous coal sized?

A There is little standardization of either screen openings or the names given to the sizes of bituminous coal. Run of mine is unscreened coal as it comes from the mine. A 2-in. nut-and-slack usually takes in all the coal passing a 2-in. screen. Between-screen sizes are everything passing one screen and retained on another.

Q Why are coal sizes important?

A Coal size affects the fuel-bed nature, draft required, density of the coke formed, and amount of the unburned-carbon loss. All these factors are important to efficient firing. Retention on grates is another factor.

HAND FIRING

Q What is the first thing a fireman should learn about hand firing?

A See Fig. 12-2. A fireman should assume the right position or right

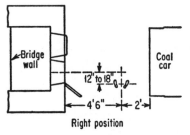

Right position

FIG. 12-2. Distance and position are important when hand firing.

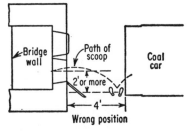

Wrong position

FIG. 12-3. Standing in the wrong position prevents coal from getting where it belongs.

stance for hand firing. He should stand so that he can see all the parts of the grate upon which he is throwing coal. Dark glasses protect his eyes and allow him to see what is being done. Raking and leveling may be needed rather than more coal, or certain spots may need building up with fresh coal. Cracks and air holes may need covering to prevent excess air from flowing through the furnace. So, it is important for the fireman to watch the entire grate area. See Fig. 12-3.

Q   What is the correct way to sprinkle coal over a fire bed?
A   See Fig. 12-4. To sprinkle coal over a fire bed, raise the tip of the

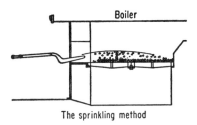

The sprinkling method

FIG. 12-4.   Raise the tip of the scoop slightly to sprinkle coal.

scoop slightly at the instant of delivering the coal. This helps you spread the coal smoothly, even on the furthest part of the grate.

Q   What should a fireman look out for if the furnace has stokers?
A   In stoker-fired furnaces, the fireman should make the same observations to detect air leaks as he makes for hand-fired boilers. But, instead of looking for air leaks in the corners, he should look in the hoppers. A feature of a stoker is its observation door: the door does not have to be opened and, thus, excess air is kept out. Tramp iron or debris going to the stoker must be removed to prevent stoker damage.

Q   Should you always sprinkle coal evenly over a fuel bed?
A   If the fuel is growing thin on one section of the grate, give it more coal. Otherwise, you will have to rake the fire to level off the fuel and to cover the thin places. As the coal cools or cakes, it fuses into islands of coke so that air cannot get to it unless it is broken up.

RESULT: The fuel bed soon gets seamed with air fissures, causing both the CO_2 and furnace temperature to drop sharply.

Q   What care should be taken when using a rake?
A   When raking a fire don't penetrate the fuel bed to any great depth and don't disturb the fuel more than is needed to break up the coke and level off the fire. Use a light rake; a three-prong rake is better than one with two prongs.

Q   What are the two general methods of hand-firing coal?

A Coal can be hand-fired by (1) the coking method or (2) the spreading method.

Q Explain the coking method of hand firing.

A The coking method is sometimes used to fire caking coals, especially in low-pressure heating plants; it is not used for high-pressure boilers because of the time needed to break up the coke bed. In this method of hand firing, the coal is pushed to the rear and a new bed of fuel is arranged in position for coking. Heating plants make good use of the coking method as it gives the fireman time to do other work between firings. Unless the grates are arranged to dump, or at least to shake the fire, cleaning will be troublesome.

The coking method is not suited to fluctuating loads because the fireman cannot see and correct the faults in the fuel piles at the rear of the coking coal. Most modern stokers use the coking method.

Q Explain the spreading method of hand firing.

A In this method of hand firing, coal is spread or sprinkled over the burning fuel. An alternate-door system has a separate door, or doors, on each side of the boiler. This allows green coal to be spread evenly over one-half of the fuel bed through one door. This door is then closed, allowing a few minutes for coking. The other side of the fuel bed can then be treated in the same way.

REMEMBER: Green coal must be heated to its ignition point before it can burn; until it reaches that point, it absorbs heat from the furnace.

Under heavy firing, the furnace temperature can drop hundreds of degrees, allowing a drop in steam pressure. The advantage of an alternate-door system is that only one-half of the furnace is affected by the green coal; the other side maintains steam pressure and promotes combustion.

Some firemen prefer to open both doors and spread coal on the rear half of the grate, close the doors to allow for coking, and then open both doors to treat the front of the grate. They claim that this creates less smoke because there is better distribution of air to the volatile gases. The objection to this method is that both furnace doors must be opened at each firing, admitting more air than is introduced by the alternate-door method.

Q How is a coal fire cleaned?

A There are two ways to clean a coal fire. (1) Push or "wing over" the unburned coal from one side of the furnace to the other and rake out the ashes and clinkers. Then wing back the burning fuel to the clean grates and clean the other side in the same manner. (2) Push the unburned coal back against the bridge wall and rake the clinkers and refuse out at the front. Then, rake back the burning coal and distribute it over the grates. One side of the furnace is now clean and the fuel can be distributed for a new fire before the other side is cleaned. This method is quicker than the first, but it is not as thorough because the ashes and clinkers under the fuel near the bridge wall cannot be removed; they may fuse. Use this method only when the cleaning job must be done in a hurry.

Q When should coal fires be cleaned?

A If possible, the cleaning job should be done with the least possible interference to plant routine. Clean the fires, therefore, when the load is light so that you will have clean fires to meet peak loads. Watch for clinkers. If you can pull them out with a hook or rake without making conditions worse, do so.

Q How and for what purpose is a slice bar used?

A A slice bar is used on a live fire to cut clinkers loose from the grates and to help fine ash fall through the grates. Don't use it to pry or lift clinkers clear of the grates or you will mix the ash with the fuel; then it will be necessary to clean the fires, whether the time is convenient or not. If possible, allow the fire to burn down before cleaning, but clean one side a little faster than the other. When pulling clinkers, first rake them forward near the dead plate. Stand back as far as the rake will permit and pull the clinkers out onto the floor or into a wheelbarrow. Quench the clinkers with a hose, or cover them with ashes. Be sure to sweep the floor clean of coal before pulling out clinkers.

Experience will help you to know when clinkers are present. Keep an eye on your draft gage; it tells you when the air supply is being shut off. If the fuel is too thick on the grates or if the air opening in the grates is stopped up with ash or clinkers, the "vacuum" above the grates will increase.

You can usually tell the condition of a fire as to ash and clinkers by looking into the ashpit. A bright ashpit indicates a clean grate, while a dark ashpit depicts a dirty grate. You can locate clinkers by dark spots or shadows on the ashpit floor after slicing the fires.

Q What types of grates are used in hand-fired boilers?

A Herringbone and Tupper grates are best adapted for anthracite and the freer-burning varieties of bituminous coals. Straight grate bars are better for burning coals with troublesome caking characteristics or with ash that fuses at a low temperature. Here, grooves in the bars and straight air spaces between them make using a slice bar easier. By shaking or rocking the grate by hand, fine ash can be shaken down without disturbing the fire. A fireman should watch the ashpits closely, gently agitating the grates from time to time when the bottoms of the pits begin to darken. Dumping the grate is also good, but it does not break clinkers. Be sure to remove any clinkers that get caught between the grates. A shaking or rocking grate is best suited for coal that produces ash which fuses at a low temperature. In this case, most of the ash can be removed as fast as it forms. These coals cannot be burned at high temperatures, and plenty of grate surface is needed.

Q What causes unburned coal in ashpits?
A Unburned coal in ashpits results from feeding more fresh fuel than can be oxidized by the air moving through the fuel bed. Common causes of this are: running the stoker too fast, shaking the grates too much, defective grate bars, letting the coal fall through the grates, or carelessness in cleaning the grates.

Q What is a common cause of warping grates?
A Failing to remove ashes from ashpits causes high heat to be reflected back to the grates, or else it simply interferes with air needed to cool the grates. Use of a water hose in the ashpit is dangerous, as well as harmful to the grates.

PULVERIZERS

Q How is pulverized coal burned?
A Pulverized coal is first ground to the fineness of flour. Then, it is made to flow through pipes and ejected into the furnace in a manner similar to fuel oil. The plant must have equipment for drying and pulverizing the coal, transporting it to the furnace in an airstream, and injecting it with air needed for combustion. Proper air-fuel ratios must be maintained to avoid furnace gas explosions from unburned fuel suddenly igniting.

Q How is pulverized coal burned by the suspension method?
A In suspension burning, because the finely ground coal particles are injected into the furnace and exposed to radiant heat, the temperature rises and the volatile matter distills off. Enough primary air enters at the burner to mix with the coal particles and to burn the gas resulting from separate distillation of each particle. The volatiles, mostly hydrocarbons, ignite more easily than the carbon remaining in the particle and heat the particle to incandescence. Secondary air enters around the burner, flows past the hot carbon particles, and burns with them in a flame several feet long.

Q What is the unit system of firing?
A In the direct-firing or unit system of firing, which is common in new plants, the pulverizers feed the burners directly. Since there is no storage, the pulverizer operation fluctuates with the steam demand. The advantages

of this system are its simplicity, need for less equipment, and elimination of storage-bin fire hazard. The heart of the unit system is the pulverizer which feeds raw coal at the rate needed, grinds the coal to the desired fineness, and classifies the finished product so that the oversized particles are returned to the mill.

Q How is air used in pulverized systems?
A Air is used to (1) dry the coal, (2) classify the pulverized fuel, and (3) transport the finished product to the burners.

Q How is air supplied for pulverized-coal firing needs?
A See Figs. 12-5 and 12-6. Fans are arranged in either of two basic

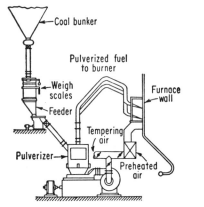

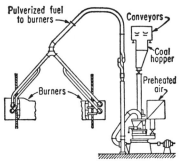

FIG. 12-5.   Forced-draft fan is outside the mill in this system.

FIG. 12-6.   Mill is under negative pressure from the exhaust fan.

ways. In one, a forced-draft fan outside the mill supplies the air. It has enough pressure to handle the air needed by the mill and to transport coal to the furnace. Here, the fan handles air only. In the second design, the mill is under a negative pressure that is developed by an exhauster fan. This fan is either combined with the pulverizer or mounted externally.

Q Explain pulverized-coal fineness.
A Fineness is very important; it is usually expressed as the percentage of pulverized coal passing through a sieve with openings of a specific size. The common sieve sizes for pulverized coal are 50-mesh for determining oversize and 200-mesh for powdered dust. The 50-mesh sieve has 50 openings per inch or 2500 to the square inch.

Coking coals swell in the furnace and form lightweight, porous coke particles that may float out of the furnace before burning; hence, they must be ground to size in order to make them burn more readily. Since free-burning coals don't have such a swelling characteristic, they don't require the same fineness.

Q How is pulverized coal dried?

A A problem common to all pulverizing is moisture, especially surface moisture. Most mills mix the incoming wet coal with the drier coal inside. This quick mixing prevents the mill-feed end from plugging with wet coal. Modern steam-generating units supply preheated air at about 500°F or higher to dry coal. There are many ways to dry coal, but conditions within the mill should be held at a relative humidity below that of saturation at the mill outlet, or roughly at 150 to 160°F.

Q Name three basic types of pulverizers.

A These machines are usually known by the forces that they use to crush the coal. Three basic types are (1) impact, (2) attrition, and (3) crushing. More common names are ball mill, whirling bowl, impact-attrition, etc. Today, fluid pulverizers are bidding in.

Q What are the functions of the burners?

A The burners must supply air and fuel to the furnace in such a way as to permit (1) stable ignition, (2) effective control of the flame shape and travel, and (3) thorough and complete mixing of fuel and air.

The air that transports the coal to the burners forms the primary air; secondary air may be introduced in the burners or around or near the burners. Figure 12-7 shows an intervane burner in which the primary air and coal whirl around a cylinder enclosing the auxiliary air passage and oil burner. To lick the problem of lighting off, an electrically ignited auxiliary oil or gas burner is used. The sketch shows that primary, secondary, and tertiary air, all under separate control, are used.

Q What is a slag-tap furnace?

A In a slag-tap furnace, part of the ash is removed from the combustion zone by directing the burner flame downward over a pool of molten slag. The slag pool is kept hot enough to remain molten so that the slag flows continuously over a water-cooled weir, or ring, into a quenching pit where it is broken up by water.

Q What is a cyclone burner?

A See Fig. 12-8. Here, the burner receives crushed, not pulverized, coal in a stream of high-velocity air tangent to the circular burner housing, which forms a primary water-cooled furnace. Coal that is thrown to the rim of the furnace by centrifugal force and held there by a coating of molten ash receives a scrubbing from the fast-moving air. Secondary air also enters at high velocity, parallel to the path of the primary coal-air mixture. Combustion of the volatile matter begins in the burner chamber

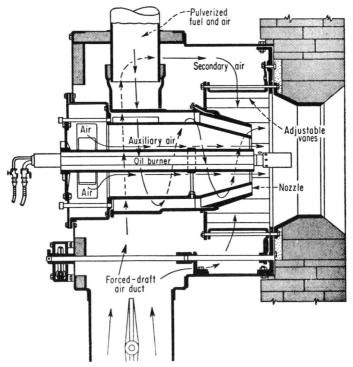

FIG. 12-7. Intervane burner has primary air and coal whirling around a cylinder.

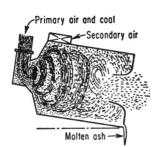

FIG. 12-8. Cyclone burner whirls crushed coal against the slagged walls.

and is completed in the secondary furnace into which the burner chamber discharges. The molten ash which is held under centrifugal force clings to the burner-chamber walls. The inclined furnace can then discharge slag continuously. The advantage of this design is that it tends to reduce the amount of ash carried in suspension; thus, less fly ash gets into the atmosphere.

Q Is more solid fuel burned in stokers or by suspension firing?

A Today, there is more fuel-bed firing than suspension firing, and most solid fuels are burned in stokers. Stoker operation involves (1) pushing, dropping, or throwing coal on a grate within a high-temperature region of the furnace; (2) distilling off part of the coal as a combustible gas so that it can burn above the fuel bed; (3) exposing the remaining red-hot solid coke so that it can be scrubbed by the air coming up through the fuel bed until it is burned; and (4) removing the ash from the furnace zone.

Q Name the various types of stokers.

A Stokers are divided into the following two broad classes, depending on how the raw coal reaches the fuel bed: (1) overfeeds, in which the fuels come from above, and (2) underfeeds, where the fuel comes from below. Overfeed designs make up two groups: (1) spreader stokers and (2) chain-grate and traveling-grate stokers.

Q How does a spreader stoker operate?

A In a spreader stoker, the raw coal is whirled into suspension within the furnace by paddles or wheels or by air or steam jets. The fines burn in suspension as they travel across the furnace, while the larger pieces fall to the grate to form a fuel bed. The fuel bed is usually thin, but it varies with the steam demand and the class of coal. There is seldom more than a few minutes supply of coal on the grate. A layer of ash under the fuel bed, together with the flow of air up through the grate, helps to keep the metal parts at a safe temperature. Air is preheated to 300 to 350°F.

Q Describe a chain-grate stoker.

A See Fig. 12-9. The grate in these stokers is a wide conveyor belt made of metal links, which moves slowly from the feed end of the furnace to the ash-discharge end. The coal feeds from a hopper under the control of a "guillotine" gate, which sets fuel-bed thickness. Coal is ignited by heat from the furnace; the coke formed is burned as the fuel bed moves along slowly and the bed gets thinner and thinner. At the far end, only ash remains, which falls off the grate as it goes around the end sprocket. Dampers under the grate supply air up through the fuel bed. The drive is from either the front or rear end, and a worm and wheel or a gear and pinion provide speed reduction. The power unit can be a constant-speed motor with a variable-speed transmission, a turbine, or a steam engine.

Q How does an underfeed stoker work?

A In an underfeed stoker, the raw coal comes to the fuel bed from below.

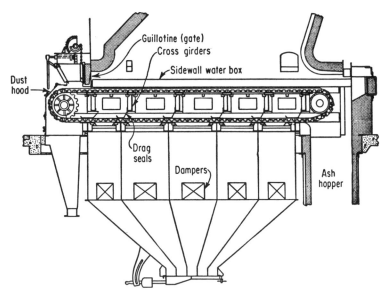

FIG. 12-9. Chain-grate stoker moves coal into the furnace and dumps the ashes.

The fuel is pushed along a feed trough, or retort. Fresh coal pressing from behind causes the coal to rise in the retort and spill over onto the fuel bed at either side. Air comes through tuyeres in the grate sections. Raw coal is dried by furnace heat and by incoming air at the top of the retort. The coal ignites as it moves from the retort area to the active burning area around it. The burning coke moves slowly to the ash-discharge area, from either the pressure of the incoming coal or the motion of the grate.

Q Name some underfeed-stoker types.
A Single-retort, twin-retort, multiple-retort, screw-feed, and ram-feed are common types of underfeed stokers.

Q What fuel capacities can retort units handle?
A Single-retort units can handle up to 40,000 lb/hr steaming capacity while multiple-retort designs can handle from 30,000 to 500,000 lb/hr steaming capacity.

Q How do single-retort stokers work?
A See Fig. 12-10. In small single-retort stokers, the coal is propelled into the retort by a worm or screw; in larger units, a ram, aided by pusher blocks or a sliding retort bottom, does the job. The simplest grate design uses stationary sections.

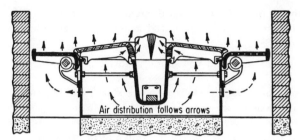

FIG. 12-10.   Single-retort unit has side-dump grates.

STORING COAL

Q Does stored coal lose heating value with time?
A Most coals can be stored for long periods. The loss of heating value is about 1 percent during the first year, although low-rank coals may lose up to 3 percent. The weather tends to make most coals slack, causing a reduction in size or crumbling. When coal is stored, the main thing to guard against is overheating and fires because of spontaneous combustion.

Q How can you guard against spontaneous combustion?
A There are two basic ways to prevent spontaneous combustion. (1) Make sure that air moves through the coal pile fast enough and uniformly enough to carry away heat. See Fig. 12-11. (2) Try to cut the airflow through the coal pile to a minimum. See Fig. 12-12.

Q What should power engineers know about outdoor coal-storage piles?
A Select a high, well-drained area for storage. If no such place is available, install drainage ditches. Build up the pile in successive layers, not more than 2 ft thick, and compact each layer. Dress the pile by sloping the tops of the successive layers and the top of the completed pile toward the sides. Make periodic temperature checks, especially at the edges and

FIG. 12-11. Loose dumping coal makes airflow easy.

Compacted layers reduce air flow

FIG. 12-12. Compact layers of coal reduce airflow.

sides of the slope, and do not let the temperature reach 160°F. Seal the pile; a 6-in. layer of fines, anchored against wind erosion by a coarse layer, is good.

Q What would you do if you found a hot spot or had a fire in a coal pile?

A In case a hot spot develops or a fire starts, cut away or isolate the heated coal, taking care not to disturb the remaining coal. Recompact the pile, starting at the edges and working inward; or if the pile is small and the area large enough, move the coal and respread it.

Try feeding CO_2 into the pile, using a pipe fitted with well-drilling points or with holes in the flattened end. Don't apply water to the heated area; the fire may appear to be quenched after soaking, but you have set up conditions likely to cause a recurrence of heating within a few days.

BURNING GAS

Q Describe a low-pressure (atmospheric) gas burner.

A Figure 12-13 shows a single-port atmospheric burner. A needle valve controls the gas flow through a spud; air is drawn in around the shutter

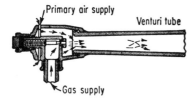

Primary air supply

Venturi tube

Gas supply

FIG. 12-13. Atmospheric gas burner pulls in primary air.

at the end. This gas-air mixture passes through the tube and burns at the end. Single-port burners are often grouped, several banks high and wide, to serve larger furnaces. Each burner pulls in primary air for combustion by the action of a stream of low-pressure gas expanding through an orifice.

Q What is meant by the premix percentage when referring to gas burners?

A With a fixed burner-port size and shape, the nature of burning depends a lot on the amount of primary air or premix. With the premix low, the flame is long and pale blue. It may have a yellow tip, which indicates some cracking and the presence of free carbon. When the primary air is increased, the burning becomes more rapid; the flame shortens and a greenish inner cone appears. When the speed of burning, or flame propagation, exceeds that of the gas issuing from the port, the flame flashes back into the mixing tube. About 30 to 70 percent premix is good; some burners use 100 percent primary air. Secondary air, which is often drawn in around the burner, can be controlled by varying the draft or by adjusting the opening area by shutters.

Q Describe a high-pressure burner.

A Figure 12-14 shows a high-pressure burner that mixes air and gas in

FIG. 12-14. Two-stage burner is for high-pressure air.

Two-stage inspirator action

a short distance. Most high-pressure burners use gas at 20 to 30 psig and air at atmospheric pressure, but some use compressed air.

Q What is a refractory burner?

A Figure 12-15 shows a burner that premixes the gas and air needed for combustion in a chamber outside the furnace. Multiple gas jets discharge into the airstream, causing a violent agitation in the short mixing tube, or tunnel, of the refractory.

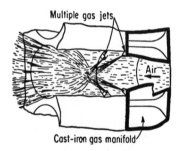

Multiple gas jets

Air

Cast-iron gas manifold

FIG. 12-15. Refractory burner premixes gas and air in a mixing chamber.

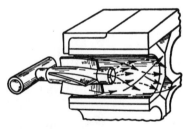

FIG. 12-16. Turbulence vanes impart a swirling motion.

In Fig. 12-16, turbulence vanes impart a swirling motion to the air entering the tunnel. Each small jet of gas issuing from the multiple-jet orifice entrains with the air and impinges it outward against the tunnel walls; the result is turbulent, thorough mixing.

Q What safety rules must you keep in mind when lighting off an oil or gas furnace?

A Before lighting off a furnace, always ventilate it to remove (purge) the accumulation of gas or vapors. Leave the drafts open until the burner is lit. Never stand directly in front of the firebox when lighting a burner; unless you stand to one side, you may be burned if there is a flareback. Wear goggles to protect your eyes. If an oil burner has leaked and oil has accumulated in the bottom of the furnace, *always* clean out the oil carefully before attempting to light the burner. Wipe all oil spills.

Q How would you light a gas burner manually?

A Before lighting a gas burner, make sure that the air and gas valves are closed. Then apply a torch to the burner, turn on the gas, and open the air valve slowly.

Q How would you light an oil burner manually?

A When lighting an oil burner, make sure that the oil valves are shut. Then open the steam or air valve slightly, depending on the type of burner used, place a torch below the burner, turn on the oil, and adjust the air flow.

Q Sketch and describe a safe hookup for purging a gas-fired furnace.

A See Fig. 12-17. An air-pressure switch in the ventilating duct prevents the ignition of the accumulated gas before the furnace is purged prior to relighting. A flame-failure device shuts off the gas if the flame fails unexpectedly. Many serious accidents occur when a furnace is not purged properly before lighting off the boiler, so make sure that your furnace has the flame-failure hookup shown in Fig. 12-17.

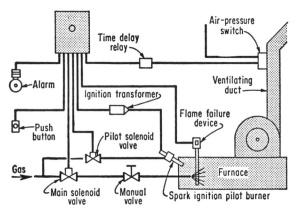

FIG. 12-17.   Safe hookup for gas must have automatic devices.

BURNING OIL

Q What is the function of oil burners?

A Oil burners proportion the fuel and air, mix them, and prepare the fuel for combustion. There are two basic ways to do this: (1) the oil may be vaporized or gasified by heating within the burner or (2) it may be atomized by the burner so that vaporization can take place in the combustion space. The first types, called vaporizing burners, are limited in the range of fuels they can handle. The oil must be broken into tiny particles to expose as much surface as possible to the heat.

Q Name three ways that oil is atomized.

A Oil is atomized by (1) using steam or air under pressure to break the oil into droplets, (2) forcing the oil under pressure through a nozzle, and (3) tearing an oil film into drops by centrifugal force.

Q How do steam-atomizing burners work?

A Steam-atomizing burners burn almost any fuel oil (including tarlike residues) of any viscosity at most temperatures. Air also is used, but it is more expensive than steam. Two types of burners are (1) internal-mixing or premixing, where oil and steam or air mix inside the body or tip of the burner before being sprayed into the furnace (Fig. 12-18), and (2) external mixing, where oil emerging from the burner is caught by a jet of steam or air (Fig. 12-19).

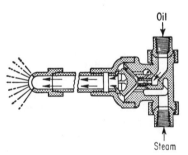

FIG. 12-18. Internal-mixing steam-atomizing burner.

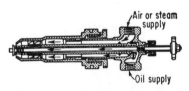

FIG. 12-19. Another steam-atomizing burner of the external-mixing type.

Steam used for atomizing averages about 2 percent of the steam produced. The pressure varies from 75 to 150 psi, and steam can be taken from a low-pressure line, from a desuperheater with a pressure reducer, or from a vent through an orifice and regulating valve.

Q What is a mechanical atomizer?

A See Fig. 12-20. In a mechanical atomizer, the oil is atomized while under a high pressure of 75 to 200 psi or higher. It is discharged through a sprayer plate (a small orifice with slots in the disk) that gives the oil a whirling motion. For a fluctuating boiler load, a number of burners are used and turned on or off, depending on the steam demand; or burner tips with different sized orifice openings and slots can be inserted in a single burner.

Bottom view of sprayer plate

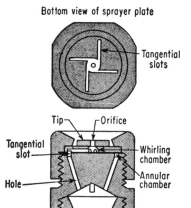

FIG. 12-20.   Mechanical atomizer for oil.

Q What do the numbers on a sprayer plate signify?

A The first two numbers on a sprayer plate identify the drill size of the orifice; the last two numbers are the ratio of the combined area of the tangential slots to the area of the orifice.

Q What is a wide-range oil burner?

A See Fig. 12-21. A wide-range oil burner delivers oil at a high pressure of say 350 psi, at constant rate, but discharges through the nozzle only the quantity needed to meet steam demand. The oil that is not needed goes back to the storage tank. The purpose of the wide-range design is to have a 4:1 range instead of a 1.4:1 range, as in the burner shown in Fig. 12-20.

Q What is a rotary-cup burner?

A See Fig. 12-22. In a rotary-cup burner, the oil is atomized by tearing

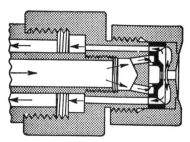

FIG. 12-21.   Wide-range, return-flow oil burner with fixed orifice size.

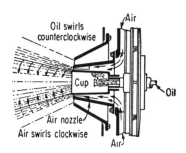

FIG. 12-22.   Rotary-cup burner tears oil into tiny drops.

it into tiny droplets. A conical or cylindrical cup rotates at a high speed of around 3500 r/min. Oil flowing along the cup reaches the rim where centrifugal force flings it into an airstream. Since the only oil pressure needed is that required to deliver the oil to the cup, this burner is ideal where only low-pressure steam is available. However, it should not be used at high oil-preheat temperatures; if it is, the oil may gasify. The rotary cup atomizes oils having high viscosities of around 300 SSU. Its range is 16:1—another important factor.

Q Can gas and oil burners be combined?
A Yes. A burner's ability to handle either gas or oil, or both at once, is important when both fuels are available.

Q What must be done to burn fuel oil economically?
A There are nine rules to remember when burning fuel oil. (1) Atomize the oil completely to produce a fine uniform spray. (2) Mix the air and fuel thoroughly. (3) Introduce enough air for combustion, but limit the excess air to a maximum of 20 percent. (4) Maintain a clean, steady supply of oil to each burner. (5) Keep the orifices and sprayer plates clean and in good condition. (6) Maintain the proper relation between the sprayer-plate nut and the diffuser hub. (7) Maintain the proper relation between the diffuser and the burner tile. (8) Keep the refractory throat tile in good repair. (9) Use the proper size of sprayer plate (for mechanical type) and the proper number of burners to accommodate the anticipated steaming load.

Q What is the first step in atomizing oil?
A When atomizing oil, be sure to heat it enough to get the desired viscosity. This temperature varies slightly for each grade of oil. The lighter oils, nos. 1, 2, and 3, do not usually need preheating. But the commercial grades, nos. 5 and 6, give their best combustion results when heated enough to introduce oil to the atomizer tip between 150 and 200 SSU.

Q Why is oil pressure important?
A The oil pressure helps to bring the oil up to full rotation within the sprayer plate. The best pressure depends on the load and the type of sprayer plate used; it varies from 75 to 300 psi. When a steaming load falls off and oil pressure falls close to the minimum recommended pressure, use a smaller sprayer plate to deliver the oil at a steady pressure. If you are using a piston-type, fuel-oil pump, place a large air chamber into the fuel line ahead of the oil heater and valve it in order to keep the system charged with air to dampen the pump pulsations.

Q How do you control combustion air for fuel-oil burners?
A See Fig. 12-23. Introduce air into the cone of the fuel spray, and

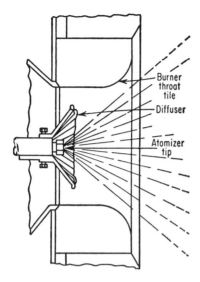

FIG. 12-23.   Position of the cone controls combustion air.

position the diffuser so that the register delivers air to the fuel spray at the right point, rotation, and velocity. This is controlled by the adjustable doors (vanes) on the register. Once the air registers are set for the right air rotation, adjust the airflow to load changes by varying the air pressure, adjusting the dampers, or changing the fan speed.

Q Today, low-excess-air burners (Fig. 12-24) are becoming popular. Explain why they save fuel.

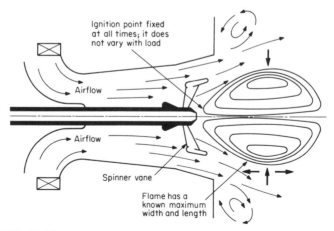

FIG. 12-24.   Low-excess-air burners use 0.5 percent oxygen, or less.

A These low-excess-air burners are of the axial-flow type, designed to operate on only 0.5 percent excess oxygen or less, between 70 and 100 percent of rated capability. Gas, oil, and coal burners are available; oil burners come in air-, steam-, and mechanical-atomizing types.

The main reason they operate effectively with low excess air is that they reduce the effects of wind-box maldistribution to a minimum. The venturi throat sends low-turbulence air into the fuel, and because this flow can be controlled precisely (see figure), the burner does not have to be flooded with excess air to make up for inefficient mixing as in older burners. That is why many burners of the swirled-flow type are being replaced with these new axial-flow types.

In comparison, conventional swirled-air register burners in oil-fired boilers are designed for 15 percent excess air. On load swings, they may use 20 percent or more. The answer is to install the proper control system with these burners.

Q How do you check a furnace for efficient combustion?

A Take CO_2 readings to determine whether your furnace is operating efficiently. A theoretically perfect CO_2 reading for fuel oil is 20.9 percent, but if you can hold 13 to 14 percent, you are doing very well. Here are the reasons. Air leaks into the furnace gas if the furnace setting or air casing is not tight. The reading then shows high excess air (low CO_2) at the boiler exit as there is a deficiency of air through the burners and in the furnace. When the boiler uptake shows a high excess of air, yet furnace conditions show a deficiency, take readings at the top of the first pass. A drop in CO_2 of over 0.5 percent from the first pass to the boiler exit shows a need to seal against leaks. Air entering through the walls or floor, especially at reduced capacity, cools the flame and may cause smoke or carbon.

Q What causes a furnace to pant or pulsate?

A Panting is caused by firing with a considerable air deficiency through the registers. You can usually prevent this by raising the air supply or by cutting down the fuel supply, but it's hard to do if the setting is leaking badly. Too high an oil temperature also causes panting, and the resulting vibration makes loose dampers change their position. A constantly varying backpressure at the driving turbine may cause the fan to hunt.

Q What attention should be given to sprayer plates?

A The sprayer plate and nozzle or orifice plate should be handled carefully. Use a piece of wood or copper wire for cleaning. Soak the carbonized atomizer ends in kerosene to soften the deposit before cleaning. Look for enlargement and out-of-roundness of the sprayer-plate orifice, nicks in the orifice, and burrs on the matching surfaces. Burrs allow oil to get into the whirling chamber without passing through the tangential slots in the plate. What is worse, they cause leaks that drool.

Q How do you check the capacity of sprayer plates?

A Make regular checks for sprayer-plate capacity by pumping oil or cold water through two atomizers—one with a new sprayer plate, the other with a worn plate. Spray downward into separately covered containers. For an accurate check, keep a constant inlet pressure on both atomizers for a specified time. When you are through, measure the contents of each can. If the worn plate pumps 15 percent more liquid than the new one, discard the worn plate.

Q What is a flame scanner?

A A flame scanner or monitor is a device that detects the presence or absence of a stable flame by means of certain physical characteristics of a flame that can be measured with electronic circuitry, and thus can determine whether a good flame is present. Among these devices are (1) conductivity flame rods, (2) radiation detecting tubes or cells, (3) visible light phototubes, and (4) infrared photocells.

Q Describe three ways that these cells operate.

A (1) A lamp is focused on a distant photocell, and anything passing between the lamp and the cell stops the beam and creates a signal. (2) Photovoltaic cells create current when exposed to light. (3) Color-sensitive cells (for example, the flame scanner) and some photocells are designed to detect very small color changes. All deal with small currents that need amplification for applied use.

OIL STORAGE AND HANDLING

Q What precaution should be taken before installing oil burners?

A Learn the recommendations and requirements of the National Board of Fire Underwriters (NBFU) and check your local ordinances.

Q Trace the flow of heavy oil from the storage tank to the burners in a typical system.

A See Fig. 12-25. The oil is drawn up through the suction line, extending about 6 in. from the bottom of the storage tank. This space allows solids and sludge to settle out of the oil. The fuel pump draws oil through the suction strainer and pumps it through the oil heaters and discharge strainers into the burners on the furnace. The oil that is not needed is returned to storage for recirculation.

Q What should you know about the oil-storage tanks?

A Oil-storage tanks should be installed in enclosures having walls at least

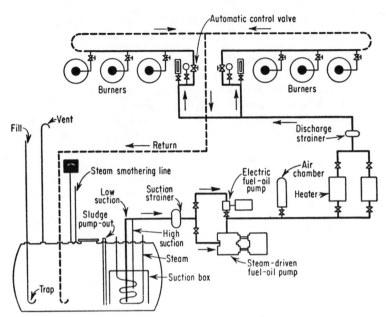

FIG. 12-25. Oil-handling system for heavy fuel needs these basic components.

6 in. thick, if reinforced concrete, or 8 in. thick, if brick. The tanks should rest on a fire-resistant floor, preferably concrete. The tops of the enclosures should be reinforced concrete, at least 5 in. thick, or an equivalent fire-resistant material, except where the floor and roof construction outside of the enclosures is concrete. The openings should be of the approved type and properly ventilated.

The gross capacity of an oil-storage tank can reach 15,000 gal in a fire-resistant building or 50,000 gal where the tank room is cut off vertically and horizontally from the other floors of the main building. Consult your local code, insurance company, and fire as well as casualty companies.

Q What should you know about venting fuel-oil tanks?

A All fuel-oil tanks must have a vent pipe that opens to the outside air; this lets the tank breathe as it fills or empties. The NBFU states that (1) vent pipes should be sized to prevent abnormal pressure within the tank during filling and (2) they should never be smaller than 1½ in. for 500 to 10,000-gal tanks, 2½ in. for tanks up to 25,000 gal, and 3 in. for tanks up to 50,000 gal. When oil tanks are filled by pumping, a good rule of thumb is to make the vents at least equal to the pump-discharge lines. If the vents are less than 10 ft long or greater than 2 in. inside diameter, their outlets should carry a vacuum- or pressure-relief device or an approved flame arrester.

Q What should you know about preheating fuel oil?

A For efficient handling and combustion, all no. 6 oils and most no. 5 oils have to be preheated. For mechanical-atomizing burners, the best viscosity is 150 SSU at 100°F. The temperature required to produce this viscosity depends on the type of fuel oil used. A general rule, used by the Navy, puts this temperature at 125°F plus SSF viscosity at 122°F.

Rotary-cup burners handle oils having viscosities up to 300 SSU, while steam- or air-atomizing burners permit a wider range. There is a danger of vapor locking in the suction side of the oil pump if the preheating is done before the pump. The top temperature in a suction line should not exceed 80 to 110°F. The factor of low oil temperature from a defective heater must be considered by the installation of a low-oil-temperature cutout on the fuel line. Oil preheaters using steam must be provided with double tubes or detectors for identifying oil leaking into the condensate.

Q How can you prevent fuels from sludging in storage tanks?

A Sludging can result from mixing oils of a different character from two sources. To avoid sludging remember that (1) straight-run residuals can be mixed with any straight-run product, and cracked residuals can be mixed with straight-run residuals and (2) cracked distillates can be added as a third constituent but cannot be added to straight-run distillates. Water is a prime troublemaker, but wax is worse.

SMOKE AND SOOT

Q When fuel oil is burning, what causes heavy black smoke?

A The main cause of black smoke is operating with insufficient air or with excess fuel. As the air needed for combustion is increased, the smoke lightens until it turns into a light-brown haze; this corresponds to the best operating conditions. A further increase in air will cause a clear stack; dense, white smoke indicates far too much air. So, regulate the air until you have a faint, light-brown haze issuing from the stack.

Smoke can also be caused by the following factors: (1) Sprayer plates that are of an unequal size. (2) Oil spray on the diffuser, carbon formation on the throat tile, a dirty atomizer, improper atomizer position, a damaged diffuser, worn plates or nozzles, no sprayer plate in the atomizer, a loose nut holding the plate in position, and too much throttling of the air-register doors—all are causes of smoke. If carbon forms on the throat tile and cannot be punched off without damaging the throat, it is better to remove the atomizer, crack the air-register doors, and let it burn off. (3) The atomizer may be in too far, causing an incomplete mixture of fuel, air, and flame fluttering. If the atomizer is out too far, carbon forms on the burner throat. Both these conditions cause smoke. (4) The fuel viscosity may be too high (oil too cold). (5) The air register and burner throat may not be centered, or the double front may be too deep, which results in air leaking into the throat without passing through the register doors. (6) There may be faulty air distribution in the double front; check the air pressure at various points in this area.

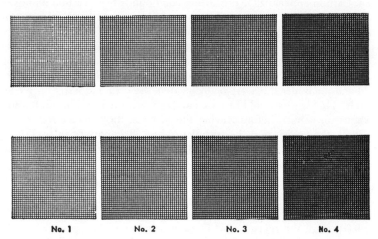

No. 1   No. 2   No. 3   No. 4

FIG. 12-26. *Power's* microRingelmann chart roughly measures the density of smoke. These grids are a direct facsimile reduction of the standard Ringelmann chart as issued by the U.S. Bureau of Mines. Copyright 1954 by McGraw-Hill Publishing Company, 1221 Avenue of the Americas, New York, N.Y. 10020.

Q How is smoke density measured?
A See Fig. 12-26. Ringelmann charts are used to measure the density of smoke. Older charts had to be positioned 50 ft from the viewer, making them awkward to use. However, *Power* magazine has a microRingelmann chart which can be read at arm's length. Grids on the chart, numbered 1 through 4, indicate the density of the smoke. To use this chart (which may be obtained from *Power* magazine), do the following: (1) Hold the chart at arm's length and view the smoke through the slot in the chart. (2) Be sure that the light shining on the chart is the same as that shining on the smoke being examined; for the best results, the sun should be behind the observer. (3) Match the color of the smoke as closely as possible with the corresponding grid on the chart. (4) Enter the density of the smoke and the time of each observation on a record sheet. (5) Make repeated observations at regular intervals of one-quarter or one-half of a minute. (6) To compute the smoke's density, use the formula: Equivalent units of no. 1 smoke $\times$ 0.20 $\div$ number of observations = per-

centage of smoke density. (7) Note and record the distance to the stack, the direction of the stack, the shape and diameter of the stack, and the speed and direction of the wind. Most major cities have codes regulating the permissible smoke density. Fines are imposed on offenders.

Q What causes soot in a furnace?

A Solid fuel is difficult to ignite and burns slowly unless it is finely pulver ized. Carbon appears as hydrocarbon compounds or as carbon monoxide in liquid or gaseous fuels, and improper burning causes these hydrocarbons to crack and form soot. With gaseous and liquid fuels the soot problem is overcome by proper design of the burners and combustion chamber. These provide enough air, turbulence, and proper preheating of fuel before combining with air. However, if the furnace is small and comparatively cold and the boiler tubes are badly located, the carbon doesn't burn completely. That is why a cold furnace smokes when the fire is lit off. Because carbons must burn before leaving the furnace, the distance traveled by the fuel, the speed, and the turbulence are all important in preventing soot and smoke. Soot can burn, and if wet or under certain other conditions, it can explode.

Q How should you observe smoke in a furnace?

A A colored glass, mounted in a welder's shield, helps the operator to detect a smoky flame and protects against furnace puffs. By watching the flame through the register and furnace peepholes, the operator may be able to spot improper combustion. When combustion is right, the flame is smooth and tends to have light wisps of smoke on the ends. Too little air gives a long, smoky flame which tends to fill the furnace. Too much air gives a ragged, bright, white flame and often a shower of sparks. With fuels containing much ash, it may be impossible to completely eliminate the incandescent particles even with low excess air.

AIR NEEDED FOR PERFECT COMBUSTION

Q What must the power operator know about draft?

A Every fuel and rate of combustion have a certain draft for the best results. A light draft is best for free-burning bituminous coals, but it increases as the percentage of volatile matter in the coal diminishes and as the fixed carbon increases. The depth of the fire bed, the percentage of ash, and the total area of air spaces in the grates have a direct bearing on the draft needed for a given combustion rate. When burning oil, combustion rates and amount of draft depend a lot on furnace volume.

Q What causes natural draft in a boiler?

A Natural draft, or air movement, is caused by the difference in the pressure of the stack gases and the atmosphere. When the gases in a stack are heated, each cubic foot expands, and the weight of the heated gas will be less than the cold air outside the stack. The difference in pressure causes the stack gases to rise. Outside air then flows into the furnace, is heated, and continues up the stack. This creates a condition known as the chimney effect. Actually, the heated stack becomes an air pump. But as soon as the boiler is cut out and the stack and gases inside cool to the temperature of the atmosphere, the stack loses its draft. The reason for this is that the weight of the air inside and outside the stack is balanced.

Q How do you measure draft?
A Draft is measured in terms of inches of water. Let us say that the atmosphere is 62°F, while the temperature of the stack gases is 500°F. (We shall forget about the difference in the densities of the stack gases and the air.) The difference between the outside air and the gases in the stack per cubic foot is:

Weight of 1 ft^3 of air at 62°F = 0.0761 lb
Weight of 1 ft^3 of air at 500°F = 0.0414 lb

Then, 0.0761 − 0.0414 = 0.0347 lb, the difference between the outside air and the stack gases. Therefore, the pressure exerted on each square foot of a 200-ft stack at the base of its cross-sectional area is 0.0347 × 200 = 6.94 lb. Since 1 ft^3 of water at 62°F weighs 62.355 lb, 1 in. of water will exert a pressure of 62.355 ÷ 12 = 5.196 lb/ft^2. So, draft in the 200-ft stack is 6.94 ÷ 5.196, or about 1.34 in. of water. See Chap. 6, "Instruments," for data on draft gages, etc.

Q Will a draft gage read the same at any point along the gas flow in a furnace?
A Draft densities grow less as you get farther away from the stack. In a boiler ashpit, with the ashpit door open to admit air freely, the draft gage reads very low, because the breeching, stack dampers, baffles, tubes, and coal on the grates all retard the passage of the gas through the furnace. So the draft from the stack must be strong enough to overcome the resistance created by these factors. The draft at the boiler breeching, where the connection is made to the stack or to the uptake, may be 0.5 in.; but the furnace directly above the fire draft may not be more than 0.15 in. The difference shows the draft needed to overcome the resistance of forcing the gases through the tubes and around the baffling.

Q What is available draft?
A The available draft is the difference in the theoretical draft (determined by formula) and the draft lost by friction in the stack proper. Since it is indicated by connecting a draft gage at the base of the stack, the sum of

the losses in the uptake, boiler, and furnace must be equivalent to the available draft.

Q Why is forced or induced draft used instead of natural draft?

A The weakness of natural draft is that it depends on many variables, such as the temperature of the atmosphere, height of the stack, thickness of the fire bed, and direction and force of the wind. Blowers or fans supply a constant draft without depending on these variations. See the discussion of fans and blowers in Chap. 2.

COMBUSTION CONTROL SYSTEMS

Q What three elements must be regulated in boiler plants?

A (1) Fuel supply in proportion to steam demand, (2) air supply, and (3) the ratio of air to fuel supply must all be regulated in boiler plants.

Q What three methods of regulation are used in boiler plants?

A Three methods of regulating boiler plants are (1) hand, (2) base load, and (3) automatic control.

Q Explain the hand-regulating method.

A In hand regulation, a fireman usually attends a battery of boilers. He looks after the fuel bed, fuel supply, water, ash removal, etc., and adjusts the stoker speed and damper positions for uniform furnace conditions. His big job is to keep steam at the right gage pressure so that there is no fluctuation in load.

Q Describe the base-load regulating method.

A In base-load regulation, a group of boilers is operated at a steady, high rate. An effort is made to maintain uniform fuel-bed conditions and an even air supply. But, one or more boilers are operated at a variable rating to handle peak loads.

Q Name three types of automatic combustion control.

A (1) On-off operation, (2) positioning control, and (3) metering control.

Q What are the advantages of controlling combustion automatically?

A See Fig. 12-27. (1) Feed-water regulation is better because the airflow through the fuel bed is more even. Because of smoother firing, the water level fluctuates less. (2) Superheat is more even because changes in the combustion rate are narrowed down to those needed to meet plant load changes. (3) There is less trouble from clinkering because high combustion rates are eliminated. (4) Fewer boiler tubes need replacing because the water circulation in the boiler is more even. (5) Combustion is better, and there is very little smoke or soot because an efficient fuel-air ratio

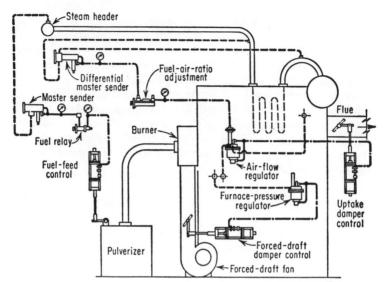

FIG. 12-27. These basic combustion-control elements are needed for a complete system.

is maintained and shown by the CO_2 recorder. (6) Stoker parts last longer because they are more evenly air-cooled. (7) Refractory troubles are cut because there is less fluctuating in the load. (8) Firemen have time to stand a more attentive watch. (9) Sudden, unexpected, or unusual demands for peak loads are met as soon as they crop up.

Q What is an on-off system control?

A An on-off system is used widely on small boilers fired by oil or gas and on some stoker-fired units. Normally, the fuel feed and airflow don't vary, and operation is intermittent. Control comes by varying the relative lengths of the "on" and "off" periods. The primary element of control is a device that responds to the steam pressure in the steam header. It develops enough force to operate a relay element, which turns the blower on and off and starts and stops the fuel feed.

During the "off" period, natural draft causes some air to flow through the furnace. This carries off heat, cooling the boiler and its contents. Thus, the overall efficiency is reduced. For this reason, the system may have a power unit for operating the boiler's outlet damper. The power unit interlocks with a relay element to close the damper during periods when the firing equipment is off. It also opens the damper wide when the primary element calls for steam and releases the relay to start the firing equipment.

This system operates between two steam-pressure levels. When the pressure drops below the lower level, the firing equipment starts. When the pressure rises above the upper level, it shuts down the firing equipment. Because of the two-level operation, the system does not offer close pressure control. During "on" periods, the firing equipment maintains the fuel-air ratio for which it has been set. With stoker firing, some airflow, and possibly fuel feed, is needed during the "off" periods to keep the fire in a banked condition. A device called a "hold-fire" control usually does this job. In on-off systems, the relaying is often done electrically. Small oil burners use a draft-actuated damper. (Barometric-damped instead of using a relay and motor.)

Q   Describe a positioning control.

A   A positioning control is commonly used on small- and medium-sized boilers. A device responds to the steam-header pressure and operates a sending-relay element. The relay system may use cables and linkages, compressed air, oil under pressure, or electric circuits to actuate the receiving-relay elements at the power units and to control the fuel- and air-feeding devices. The power units (regulators) position the lever, rheostat, valve, etc., that fix the operating rate of the stoker, feeder, burner, fan, or damper involved. The entire system has to be adjusted so that changes in the steam pressure produce proportional changes in the fuel and air feeds. The primary element can be designed to run the system either on a drooping steam-pressure characteristic or to maintain a constant steam pressure. With a drooping characteristic, the fuel and air controls take a definite position for each steam pressure. Hence, the pressure may vary by about 2 or 3 percent from zero to full load.

The positioning method of control assumes that one setting of a given control—for instance, a rheostat regulating the fan-motor speed—always produces the same result, which is in this case the same airflow. Yet, at any rheostat position, the airflow will be influenced by voltage variations at the motor terminals, changes in the resistance to flow through the boiler caused by soot or slag, or variations in barometric conditions. Similarly, the actual fuel feeds may differ for any one control setting.

Though the system will hold the steam pressure constant, the combustion efficiency may drop off. Usually the system can be adjusted to hold a desired fuel-air ratio over part of the load range, but it will drift off in either direction at other loads. A manual adjustment can restore the proper fuel-air ratio.

An automatic controller maintains a constant-furnace draft by measuring the draft and resetting the power unit operating the damper or fan control whenever the draft deviates from normal.

Q   What is the best means of assuring continuous low-excess-air operation?

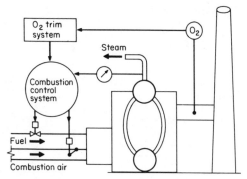

FIG: 12-28.   Oxygen trimming combines with the correct burner to assure efficient combustion.

A Oxygen trimming. The heart of an efficient low-excess-air combustion system is the burner, but it must be coupled with a suitable sensing and control system (Fig. 12-28). Here an oxygen (O_2) analyzer and other sampling equipment provide an electrical output signal that can be used to "bias" the preset air-fuel ratio in a combustion-control system.

Biasing, or O_2 correction signal, provides a variable set point for the oxygen controller. This system complements the venturi design burner of Fig. 12-24, which promotes intimate air-fuel mixing for efficient low-excess-air operation on power and industrial boilers.

Q Explain the Coen single-point-positioning control system in Fig. 12-29, used for trimming oxygen in smaller single-burner industrial boilers of up to 100,000 lb/hr.

A This newer type of single-point-positioning combustion-control system has a damper drive lever with an adjustable control arm. By combining this with a rapid O_2 set-point control (which depends upon the firing rate) within the "black box" between the O_2 sensor and control arm, this control method becomes precise enough so that only 5 percent excess air, for control functions, is adequate, even with rapidly changing load swings.

Q Describe the metering control system.

A The metering control system is a further development of a positioning control. Instead of relying on the assumption that the control-level position is directly proportional to the resulting fuel or airflow, this system measures the flows and balances them against signals for more or less steam flow. This eliminates the effects of the power unit, damper, and rheostat operating characteristics and the influence of variations in supply voltage, resistances, and air pressures and temperatures. Thus, it makes it possible to hold a fuel-air ratio over a wide load range.

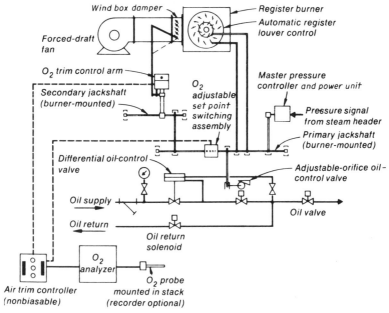

FIG. 12-29.   Coen system of single-point-positioning control can utilize oxygen trim on industrial boilers.

The system includes metering or measuring elements that work with the receiving-relay elements at the power units or with the sending-relay element at the primary element. In the latter scheme, a signal is sent to the receiving relay and is modified in accordance with the existing flow conditions.

As in the positioning system, the metering control scheme can either work on a drooping steam-pressure characteristic or hold a constant steam pressure. Pressure variations are small, and the fuel-air ratio is essentially constant.

CALCULATIONS

Q   If the manufacturer of your burner requires viscosities of 100 to 150 SSU at the burner nozzle, how do you determine the best temperature range for pumping and atomizing a fuel oil with a viscosity of 75 SSF at 122°F?

A For this problem, we must know (1) the viscosity of the unheated oil, and (2) the viscosity desired at the burner nozzle. Then we need the ASTM viscosity-temperature chart (Fig. 12-30) to help determine the approximate temperatures to which any fuel oil must be heated for best pumping and atomizing results. Usually, viscosity of bulk oils is expressed in Saybolt Seconds Furol (SSF) at 122°F. But the atomizing viscosities are in Saybolt Seconds Universal (SSU) at 100°F.

To find the pumping temperature, return to the diagonal line and read upward where the diagonal line crosses through the zone marked "Easy Pumping." The temperature range is 72 to 93°F.

Now to find the atomizing temperature, just follow the diagonal line downward where it crosses through the "Atomizing Viscosity Range." The temperature for best atomization for the fuel in this problem is indicated to be between 184 and 209°F.   *Ans.*

Q If it takes about 10 tons of air to burn 1 ton of coal, calculate the stack loss in the dry hot gas from each pound of coal, where stack temperature is 575°F, boiler room temperature is 75°F, firing is done with 30 percent excess air, and it takes about 0.25 Btu to heat 1 lb of flue gas 1°F.

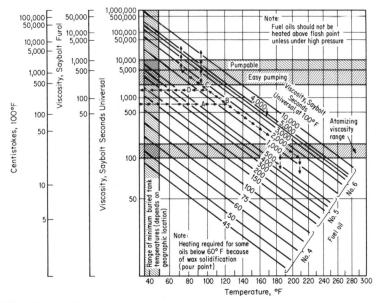

FIG. 12-30. Viscosity-temperature chart helps determine best temperature range for pumping and atomizing of fuel oil.

A Temperature rise is 575 − 75 = 500°F. With 30 percent excess air, the furnace would use up 13 lb of air/lb of coal fired. Thus, 13 + 1 lb (fly ash; matter is indestructible) = 14 lb of hot "gas" for each pound of coal. Then, stack loss in hot dry gas is 500 × 0.25 × 14 = 1750 Btu/lb of coal fired.   *Ans.*

Q Calculate the wattage needed to heat 52 gal/hr of fuel oil from 100 to 210°F.

A Watts = 1.25 × gph × T
where gph = gallons per hour
   1.25 = constant
      T = temperature difference of inlet and outlet oil, °F
Watts = 1.25 × 52 × (210 − 100)
     = 1.25 × 52 × 110
     = 7150 W.   *Ans.*

SUGGESTED READING

Elonka, Stephen M.: *Standard Plant Operators' Manual,* McGraw-Hill Book Company, New York, 1980 (has chapter on fuel, also chapter on license examination questions, answers, and problems).

Elonka, Stephen M., and Anthony L. Kohan: *Standard Boiler Operators' Questions and Answers,* McGraw-Hill Book Company, New York, 1969 (has chapter on firing and combustion).

Elonka, Stephen M., and Alonzo R. Parsons: *Standard Instrumentation Questions and Answers,* Krieger Publishing Company, Melbourne, Fla., 1979.

13

COMPRESSED AIR

Like electricity, compressed-air power is used by industry to perform many tasks because it can be piped far away from the compressor. Since the first edition of this book appeared, many power plants are using compressed air instead of steam for blowing soot from boiler tubes. Today's compressors have greater reliability and higher efficiency and are of compact design and lighter in weight. They can also provide oil-free air where needed, and better control because of advances in instrumentation.

This edition covers the latest OSHA noise standards, the newer rotary-screw compressor, integral gear designs, and the newest diaphragm type. Tips on maintenance and operation, along with calculations, are given for obtaining the best possible performance.

BASICS

Q When speaking of air compressors, what is meant by atmospheres?
A An atmosphere is generally taken to be 15 psia, or the absolute pressure of the atmosphere at sea level. It is a convenient way to describe pressure above atmosphere. For example, a compressor that compresses air to 90 psig has compressed it to $105 \div 15 = 7$ atmospheres of pressure. Note that absolute pressures must be used to convert to atmospheres.

Q What is atmospheric pressure?

A Atmospheric pressure is caused by the weight of free air, as measured by a barometer. The weight of a vertical column of air, under normal conditions, 1 in. square, extending from the earth's surface at sea level up to the limit of the atmosphere, is equal to the weight of a column of mercury 1 in. square and 29.92 in. high. Where the earth's surface extends above sea level, such a column of air is shorter and weighs less. Normally, atmospheric pressure at sea level is about 14.7 psi. The table in Fig. 13-1 shows atmospheric pressure at various altitudes.

Q What is the difference between static pressure, total pressure, and velocity pressure of air?

A The static pressure of air is measured so that the velocity of the air has no effect on the reading. The total pressure of air is the pressure produced by stopping a moving airstream. The velocity pressure of air is the total pressure in a moving airstream minus the static pressure.

Q Does the temperature of air or gas change during compression and expansion?

A Yes. Part of the work needed to compress the air or gas is converted into heat, raising the temperature, pressure, or volume. During expansion, the heat is reconverted into energy and the temperature drops.

Altitude	Barometric pressure	
	Lb per sq in.	Inches Hg
0	14.7	29.92
1000	14.16	28.86
2000	13.66	27.82
3000	13.16	26.81
4000	12.68	25.84
5000	12.22	24.89
6000	11.77	23.98
7000	11.33	23.09
8000	10.91	22.22
9000	10.50	21.38
10,000	10.10	20.58
11,000	9.71	19.75
12,000	9.34	19.03
13,000	8.97	18.29
14,000	8.62	17.57
15,000	8.28	16.88

FIG. 13-1. Atmospheric pressure depends on altitude.

Q What is isothermal compression?

A When the compressed air or gas has the heat of compression removed as rapidly as it is generated, so that the temperature of the air or gas doesn't change during compression, you have a state of isothermal compression.

Q What is atmospheric air?

A Air is a mechanical mixture of gases, mainly oxygen and nitrogen. Atmospheric air always contains some water vapor and consists of widely separated, individual molecules of oxygen and nitrogen. Traveling at high speed, they strike against any enclosing surfaces and thus produce pressure.

Q What comparisons are used for compression efficiency?

A Compression efficiency is compared against two theoretical standards—isothermal and adiabatic. Neither occurs in an actual compressor because of unavoidable losses. The plot of a compression process on a pressure-volume diagram (Fig. 13-2) shows how an actual unit works between these two standards. Isothermal compression has perfect cooling, and the air remains at the inlet temperature while being compressed. The work input to the compressor, measured by the area *ABCD,* is the least possible. Adiabatic compression has no cooling; the temperature rises steadily during compression. The discharge pressure is reached sooner than with isothermal compression. Since air pressure is higher during every part of the piston stroke, more work input is needed, as shown by area *ABCD* in the illustration.

Q How does intercooling affect compression?

A If compression is divided into two or more steps or stages, air can be cooled between them. This intercooling brings the actual compression line closer to the isothermal line (Fig. 13-3). The area *BCDE* shows the power that is saved.

Q What is meant by the term "free air"?

A "Free air" is defined as air at atmospheric conditions at any specific

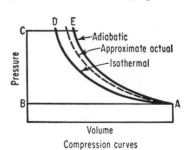

FIG. 13-2. Efficiency is the comparison between isothermal and adiabatic.

Volume

Compression curves

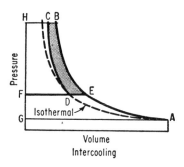

Volume
Intercooling

FIG. 13-3.   Intercooling saves power shown by area *BCDE*.

location. Because the altitude, barometer, and temperature may vary at different localities and at different times, it follows that this term does not mean air under identical or standard conditions. Free air as a measure of volume may be applied to either displacement or capacity and in no way distinguishes between these two terms.

Q   What is meant by the term "standard air"?

A   "Standard air" is defined as air at a temperature of 68°F, a pressure of 14.7 psia, and a relative humidity of 36 percent (0.0750 density). This agrees with the definitions adopted by the ASME (American Society of Mechanical Engineers), but in the gas industries the temperature of "standard air" is usually given as 60°F.

Q   What is the ratio of compression?

A   The ratio of compression is the ratio of the absolute discharge pressure to the absolute intake pressure. If the discharge pressure is 114.7 psia (100 psig) and the intake pressure is atmospheric at sea level, the ratio of compression is 114.7 to 14.7, or 7.8.

Q   What is the compressor piston displacement? How is it computed?

A   Piston displacement is the volume displaced by the piston; it is equal to the net area of the piston multiplied by the length of stroke and the number of strokes per minute. If the compressor is a single-stage unit with several cylinders, its displacement is the sum of the displacements of all cylinders. But, if the compressor is a multistage machine, the displacement is only that of the first-stage cylinder or cylinders. If it is a double-acting machine, deduct the volume occupied by the piston rod. Piston displacement is expressed in cubic feet per minute.

Q   What is the clearance in an air cylinder? How does it affect the performance of the compressor?

A   The clearance in an air cylinder is the volume of the space in the end of the cylinder, measured when the piston is at the end of its stroke. It includes the space between the piston and head, valve cavities, counter bore at the end of the cylinder, etc. You cannot avoid clearances. At the end of the compression stroke, the clearance space is filled with air at the maximum discharge pressure. As the piston starts on its return stroke, this air expands, preventing the entrance of inlet air until the cylinder pressure is slightly less than that of the outside air. This portion of the stroke is wasted. The higher the compression ratio, the greater is the loss of capacity due to reexpansion of the air in the clearance space. Most of the power used in compressing air in the clearance space is regained during the reexpansion.

Q How does water vapor affect atmospheric air?

A Water vapor exerts a pressure separate from that of the air alone. The total atmospheric pressure is the sum of the air pressure and the vapor pressure. For example, when 80°F air is saturated with water vapor, the air contains all the moisture it can hold at this temperature. Any additional vapor will condense. If the total atmospheric pressure is 14.7 psia, the pressure exerted by the air alone must be the difference between 14.7 and the vapor pressure at 80°F. This is the same as saturated steam pressure at 80°F and is shown in the steam tables as 0.507 psia. Here, the air pressure is 14.7 − 0.507 = 14.19 psia.

Q Explain the effect of partially saturated air.

A Air containing less than the maximum amount of water vapor that it can hold is partially saturated air. The amount of moisture is measured by relative humidity. If 80°F atmospheric air has a relative humidity of 70 percent, it holds only 0.7 as much water as it could. The vapor pressure is 0.7 × 0.507 = 0.355 psia. The air pressure is 14.7 − 0.355 = 14.35 psia. The water vapor in the air entering the compressor leaves as a super-heated vapor because its temperature is in excess of that corresponding to its pressure. It can be converted to water only by cooling it to a temperature below the saturation temperature corresponding to its pressure. The air should be cooled immediately after it leaves the compressor so that the vapor does not reach the distribution system. Either air- or water-cooled heat exchangers, called aftercoolers, can do the job.

Q What is compressor volumetric efficiency? How is it determined?

A Because of cylinder clearance, the air actually discharged per stroke isn't the volume swept by the piston. Expressed in percentage, the volumetric efficiency is the ratio of the air actually delivered to the amount of piston displacement. The higher the ratio of compression, the lower the volumetric efficiency because the air trapped in the clearance space reexpands to a greater volume. The actual capacity and, therefore, the volumetric efficiency of a compressor is found with a low-pressure orifice test of the ASME. The volume of air delivered by the first stage of a multistage compressor must pass through the various stages. So the volumetric efficiency of a multistage compressor is the volumetric efficiency of the first-stage cylinder and is affected only slightly by variations in the final discharge pressure.

REASON: The first-stage discharge pressure (intercooler pressure), which affects the ratio of compression in the first stage, varies only slightly as the discharge pressure of the final stage varies.

Q What is the mechanical efficiency of a compressor?

A Mechanical efficiency is a measure of the power lost because of mechanical friction (not including air friction), as in bearings. It is the ratio of the power consumed in the compressor cylinders (shown on indicator cards) to the power delivered to the shaft of a power-driven compressor (bhp) or to the power applied to the steam cylinders of a steam-driven machine (ihp in the steam cylinders).

Q Define compression efficiency (adiabatic).

A This is a comparison of the power needed theoretically and the power actually expended in the cylinder of a compressor. Hence, it is a measure of the efficiency of the air end of a compressor. Friction losses in the frame and running gear aren't used. Compression efficiency (adiabatic) is the adiabatic horsepower for the volume of air delivered, divided by the actual horsepower in the air cylinders as revealed by indicator cards (ihp). The latter is equal to the mechanical efficiency multiplied by the bhp of a motor-driven compressor or by the ihp in the steam cylinders of a steam-driven compressor.

Q Why should cylinder heads, as well as cylinder barrels, be water-jacketed?

A During compression, the more heat extracted, the less power is needed to compress the air. Therefore, you should jacket the cylinder heads because during compression the air is in contact with the head longer than it is in contact with the cylinder barrel. So cooling here is more effective.

Q Explain the overall efficiency (adiabatic) of a compressor or compressor efficiency.

A Overall efficiency or compressor efficiency is the adiabatic horsepower divided by the bhp at the shaft of a motor-driven compressor or the ihp in the steam cylinders of a steam-driven unit. It is equal to the compression efficiency multiplied by the mechanical efficiency. Overall efficiency includes the friction losses in the frame and the running gear; compression efficiency does not include the friction losses.

Q Does it take more or less power to run a compressor at high altitudes? Why?

A Power needed for operating a given sized compressor, either multistage or single stage, is less at upper altitudes than at sea level, because of the lower mass of air being compressed.

TYPES OF COMPRESSORS

Q Name six older types of air compressors and explain briefly how each one works.

A See Fig. 13-4.

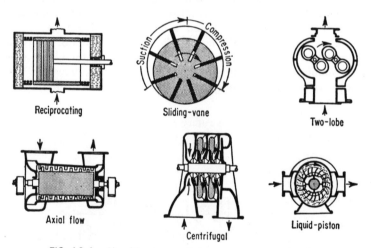

Reciprocating   Sliding-vane   Two-lobe

Axial flow   Centrifugal   Liquid-piston

FIG. 13-4.   Six older types of air compressors used today.

1. Reciprocating compressors suck air into the cylinders through suction valves during the suction stroke. At the end of the discharge stroke, the air leaves the cylinders at a higher pressure.

2. Sliding-vane rotary compressors trap the air between the vanes as the rotor passes the inlet opening. As the rotor turns toward the discharge port, the volume of the cell between any two vanes decreases. This causes the air pressure to rise to the rated discharge value. The vanes slide in

and out of slots as the rotor turns and are held against the casing by centrifugal force.

3. Two-lobe rotary units have two identical impellers that are held in a fixed relationship to each other by external gears. When the impellers rotate, they trap air between their outer surface and the casing. When the upper tip of an impeller passes the edge of the casing, it permits air discharge to begin. The bottom tip of the impeller pushes the enclosed air into the discharge piping, compressing it against the backpressure.

4. Axial-flow compressors accelerate air in a direction parallel to the shaft. These units resemble turbines; each set of moving and stationary blade rows forms a stage. The pressure rise per stage is relatively small.

5. Centrifugal compressors usually take in air at the eye of the impeller and accelerate it radially. Some static pressure rise occurs in the impeller, but most of it is in the diffuser section of the casing where velocity converts to static pressure.

6. Liquid-piston rotary units have a round multiblade rotor revolving in an elliptical casing that is partly filled with liquid, usually water. When the rotor turns, it carries the liquid around with it. The blades form a series of buckets. Because the liquid follows the contours of the casing, it alternately leaves and returns to the space between the blades (twice each revolution). As the liquid leaves the bucket, air is drawn in. When the liquid returns to the bucket, it compresses the air to the discharge pressure.

Q   Describe the newer type of rotary-screw compressor.

A   See Fig. 13-5 and the discussion in Chap. 9, under Compressors.

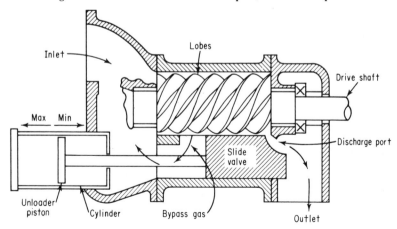

Operation of slide valve

FIG. 13-5.   Slide valve of helical rotary-screw compressor is hydraulically actuated to regulate compressor capacity.

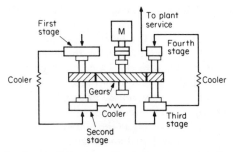

FIG. 13-6.   Integral-gear centrifugal compressor has four stages.

Q Describe the newer integral-gear centrifugal compressor (icc).
A Figure 13-6 shows a four-stage design. Icc units have between one and four impellers, all directly geared by pinions to a bull gear. Where greater capacity is desired, a large fifth first-stage impeller may be directly connected to the main shaft at the motor end.

One advantage of gearing lies in permitting the pinions to rotate at different speeds, driving each pair of impellers near their optimum specific speed. Rotative speeds may reach 70,000 r/min. Coolers are outside the compressor casing, usually in the machine's base.

Designs range from 1400 to more than 26,000 ft³/min with pressures from 20 to 450 psig. Typical application is in general plant service where large volumes of oil-free air are used, such as for blowing soot.

MULTISTAGING AND BOOSTING

Q What are the advantages of multistage compression?
A In multistage compression the air is compressed to some intermediate pressure in the first-stage cylinder, passed through an intercooler to reduce the air temperature to the initial intake temperature, and then sent into the second-stage cylinder (if only two stages are used) where it is compressed to the final discharge pressure. Where other stages are used, the air is discharged from the second stage, through a second intercooler, into the third-stage cylinder. Here the air is further compressed and discharged into a third intercooler and into the fourth stage, etc. The cylinders must be so proportioned that the ratio of compression and the power needed are about the same for all stages. Multistage compression has the following advantages over single stage, where the compression ratio is high enough to justify multistage:

1. There is lower power consumption per unit of air delivered. The

saving depends on the total ratio of compression and the intercooling efficiency.

2. There is higher volumetric efficiency, because the actual capacity of a multistage machine is controlled by the first-stage cylinder. Since the number of compressions in the latter is highly reduced (compared with a single-stage cylinder operating at the same pressures), reexpansion losses are reduced and the volumetric efficiency is increased.

3. Discharge temperatures are decreased, since the number of compressions in each cylinder is less than the number in a single-stage cylinder operating between the same initial and final pressures.

4. Most of the moisture in the air is condensed in the intercooler.

Q At what capacity is it desirable to use multistage compression?

A This depends on a number of factors including: (1) the kind of gas used, (2) the ratio of compression, (3) the amount of power saved by two-stage compression, (4) the cost of power per kilowatthour, (5) the continuity of operation, (6) the greater initial cost of a two-stage compressor, and (7) the fact that more floor space is usually needed. For a compression ratio of less than 5:1 (60-psi discharge, with a sea-level atmospheric intake), power saving does not justify two-staging. For a compression ratio between 5:1 and 8:1 (60- to 105-psi discharge, sea-level intake), a single-stage is usually preferable in sizes up to 60 or 75 hp and a two-stage in larger sizes. For a higher compression ratio, multistage compression is preferable and usually mandatory in order to avoid excessive discharge temperatures. This includes mostly the slow-speed double-acting stationary compressors. Smaller high-speed single-acting units are built in two-stage types. The reason for this is that the discharge temperatures of these machines, if built single-stage, would (on account of high speeds) be too high for sustained, satisfactory, efficient operation. The power saving of two-staging is offset by the extra power consumed because of their high air velocities and single-acting operation. The power consumption per unit of air delivered at 100-psi discharge pressure is about the same or slightly higher than that for some single-stage compressors.

Q What is a booster compressor?

A A booster machine compresses air or gas from a pressure above atmospheric to a still higher pressure. Booster machines have many uses, especially in oil and gas fields and related industries. Compression may be either single or multistage, depending upon the ratio of compressions, horsepower, and gas analysis. With gases having a low *n* value (see *Compressed Air Handbook*), multistage compression is usually used above five compressions.

REASON: The lower the *n* value, the lower the volumetric efficiency and the greater the need for multistage compression.

Q Why are steam-compression boosters used?

A Where a small volume of steam is required at a pressure or temperature higher than that available from the boiler, boosters can do the job. This saves installing a higher-pressure boiler. The cylinder of such steam boosters is usually lagged with a magnesium insulation in order to minimize heat loss and to evade boiler or license requirements, as on a steam cleaner used on building walls.

Q What is the relation between the pressure and the number of stages needed?

A The Compressed Air and Gas Institute gives the following relations: 0 to 150 psig, single stage; 80 to 500 psig, two stages; 500 to 2500 psig, three stages; and 2500 to 5000 psig, four stages. These ranges are for the usual positive-displacement units.

FILTERING, COOLING, AND STORING AIR

Q Why are intake filters needed? Describe a few types.

A See Fig. 13-7. Intake-air filters prevent dust and other atmospheric impurities from entering the compressor. Dust, for example, may cause sticking valves, scored cylinders, and excessive wear.

Some of the common types of intake filters are: (1) Oil-bath filters, which have a reservoir of oil agitated by incoming air. Oil-coated dust collects in this oil reservoir. (2) Traveling-screen filters, which have air blowing through a screen that is continuously coated with oil by passage through a reservoir. Dust caught on the screen is washed off in an oil bath. (3) Dry-type filters use felt or some other filtering media which is held in a rectangular or cylindrical frame. Some types of filtering materials may be vacuumed; others are throwaways. (4) Viscous-impingement filters are packed with fine strands of oil-coated wire. Air passing through the filters impinges on the wires, and the oil film traps any dust.

Q Where should air-intake lines begin?

A See Fig. 13-8. Air-intake lines should begin at the cleanest, driest, and coolest place available. An outside intake is usually the best because cooler air takes up less volume and the machine compresses a greater weight of air on each stroke. Also, the compressor stays cooler. For every decrease of 5°F in the incoming air, there is a 1 percent increase in the mass of air compressed or the volume of compressed air.

Q Why is compressed air reheated? Where should reheating take place?

A The volume of air is increased if the pressure is constant. Or, if the volume remains constant, the pressure is increased in proportion to the

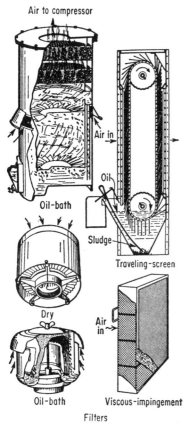

Air to compressor

Air in

Oil

Oil-bath

Sludge

Traveling-screen

Dry

Air in

Oil-bath

Viscous-impingement

Filters

FIG. 13-7. Filters prolong compressor life by removing abrasives.

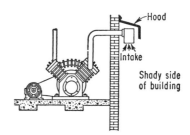

Hood

Intake

Shady side of building

FIG. 13-8. Outside intake is usually best for a compressor.

increase in absolute temperature. Reheating should take place as near to the point of consumption as possible. The success of reheating depends on the air reaching the working apparatus at as close to the final reheated temperature as possible. Reheating also has the effect of decreasing the condensation of the moisture when air passes through tools. This is from the increased moisture-carrying capacity of air at higher temperatures.

Q Why is an air receiver used? Where should it be placed?
A See Fig. 13-9 *A* and *B*. An air receiver dampens pulsations and acts as a reservoir to take care of sudden demands. It also knocks out some oil and moisture.

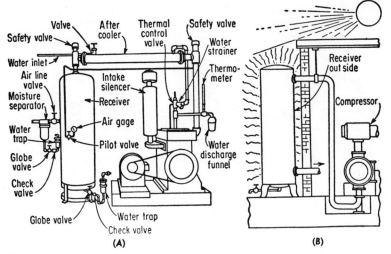

FIG. 13-9. Inside receiver is close to the machine; outside receiver is on the shady side of the building.

Place the receiver as close to the compressor as possible *(A)*. Install it in the coolest place available so that the air can help it cool. If the air lines are long with a small diameter or if the equipment is far from the compressor, install extra receivers at the points of maximum demand to prevent sharp drops in pressure when demands are high. Avoid pockets in the line from the compressor to the receiver, or moisture will collect. If the receiver must be placed outside *(B)*, place it on the shady side so that the cooler outside air can help knock out moisture and furnish drier air at the same cost.

Q Why do you need large air receivers with an automatic start-and-stop control compressor?

A Large air receivers are used here so that the compressor won't have to start too often. Repeated starting may be objectionable to the power company and may cause the starter to overheat.

Q What causes moisture in air lines? How can it be prevented?

A Compressing air packs the original moisture into a smaller space. Moisture remains in vaporized form while the air is hot but condenses as the air cools. This moisture should be removed before the air enters the lines to avoid (1) freezing in the discharge ports of tools, (2) washing away the lubricant from tools, (3) contaminating work, and (4) interfering with the proper operation of controls. The best way to remove moisture is by aftercooling and hooking up the piping properly.

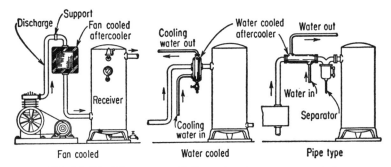

FIG. 13-10.   Three types of aftercoolers in common use today.

Q What is an aftercooler? Where should it be installed?
A See Fig. 13-10. An aftercooler is installed between the compressor
and the receiver to cool compressed air or gas. Cooling the air reduces
its temperature and causes moisture and oil vapor to drop out.

Q Does aftercooling represent a loss of energy?
A No. If the air were not cooled in an aftercooler, it would be cooled
in the discharge line where the moisture would drop out and cause trouble.
With an aftercooler, all precipitation can be drawn off before it gets into
the discharge line.

Q How would you install air piping in order to avoid moisture troubles?
A See Fig. 13-11. Air lines should run as directly as possible, with pockets
and drains at the points where the branch is taken from the main. Branches
should be taken from the top side, as shown in the figure. The main

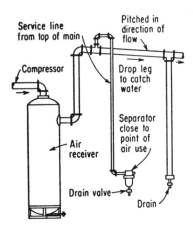

FIG. 13-11. Slope air lines; take
branches from the top of the line.

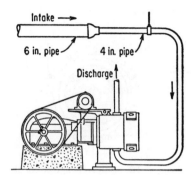

FIG. 13-12. Increase the pipe diameter and size for every 10 ft.

should drop gradually toward the point of use. When installing air lines, take care to avoid short-turn elbows; in long lines, the pipe must be large enough. The intake pipe diameter should increase one size for every 10 ft of length. See the *Compressed Air Handbook* for sizes of air pipes and also Fig. 13-12.

Q What are some rules to follow for laying out air piping systems?
A (1) Make the piping sizes large enough so that the pressure drop between the receiver and the load will not exceed 10 percent. Provide for future growth. (2) Where possible, use a loop system around the plant and inside each shop and building. This gives two-way distribution where the air demand is greatest. (3) Install good-sized air-storage receivers at the far ends of the long lines and at points of occasional heavy use. Many peak demands for compressed air are either instantaneous or relatively short; so storage capacity avoids excessive pressure drop. (4) Provide frequent outlets on each header or main for attaching air-operated equipment. Always put the outlet at the top of the pipeline in order to prevent condensed moisture from reaching the tools. (5) Slope all piping toward a drop leg or moisture trap so that moisture can be drained.

MOTORS AND CONTROLS

Q What types of motors are usually used for compressor drive?
A Both induction (Fig. 13-13) and synchronous (Fig. 13-14) motor types are used for alternating current. Because of its lower cost and simpler, more rugged construction, the squirrel-cage motor rather than the slip-ring wound rotor motor is used in the induction type. The slip-ring type is used only where the starting current must be severely restricted.

The synchronous motor is more complicated and more expensive than the squirrel-cage type, but it improves the power factor of the line. In

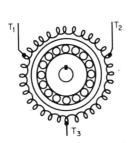

FIG. 13-13. Squirrel-cage induction motor is simple, rugged.

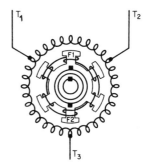

FIG. 13-14. Synchronous motor can be built for any power factor.

some cases this is a must, while in most cases it earns a better rate from the power company. A synchronous motor is always used for slower-speed direct drive because it gives power-factor correction and because direct current and induction motors are not always available in such low speeds. These synchronous motors are called engine type; they come without shaft or bearings, using the shaft and bearings of the compressor.

The shunt-wound dc motor is preferable when using direct current because it is cheaper, but it does have a drooping speed characteristic with load. The compound-wound dc motor costs more, but has a steady speed characteristic under load. The compound-wound type costs more and speeds up a little when running light. The lower starting torque of the shunt-wound type is OK since the compressors are started unloaded. The series-wound dc motor has high starting torque, but it must have load or it will run away from overspeeding. If it is used under possible no-load conditions, an overspeed trip device should be incorporated into the control system.

Q   What controls are used with squirrel-cage and synchronous motors for compressor service?
A   Full-voltage (or line starter) and reduced-voltage starters are used for this service. The full-voltage starter is cheaper and simpler. It is automatic and operated by a push button or by a pressure switch for automatic start-and-stop service.

Q   What special equipment is needed for automatic start-and-stop operation?
A   The motor must have an automatic starter and a pressure switch. The compressor must have a starting unloader so that it can start and stop without load. The compressor, if water-cooled, should also be equipped with an automatic water-control valve to start and stop the water flow as the compressor starts and stops. If the compressor is water-cooled, it should have a high-temperature jacket water alarm in case water is inadver-

tently shut off during operation. Where freezing is possible, a low-temperature room alarm should also be considered.

Q How is compressor capacity controlled on larger types?

A There are two general methods of controlling compressor capacity: (1) speed and pressure regulation, which varies the compressor speed according to the air demand, and (2) constant-speed regulation, which runs the compressor at a constant speed and changes its capacity by regulating the amount of air entering the cylinder. For general industrial use, the pressure does not have to be held closer than 5 percent of normal, from no load to full load. But equipment with closer regulation is available.

When possible, select and adjust the pressure regulators so that the large units carry the base load and unload only after the smaller units shut down. When load requirements drop to a point where one small machine can do the job, shut down the large unit to get the best overall economy.

Q Where are dual controls used?

A A plant having abnormally high peak loads for short periods needs dual control. If the peak load lasts an hour or two, a dual control is the answer. A simple hookup sets the start-stop switch at values outside an unloader pilot-valve setting. In other words, if the switch is set to cut in at 145 psi, it should be out at 175 psi. At this pressure, the pilot valve is set to load at 150 psi and to unload at 170 psi. Then, with one simple cutout valve, the change from one to the other is made easily. Also, the constant-speed unloader is used only during peak load.

SAFETY VALVES AND OTHER FITTINGS

Q What fittings must an outside receiver have? Where must they be located?

A See Fig. 13-15. An outside receiver must have a safety valve and a pressure gage. They both must be located on the inside of the building to keep from freezing.

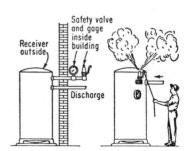

FIG. 13-15. Outside receiver has a relief valve and gage on the inside.

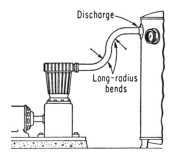

FIG. 13-16. Discharge line has large-radius bends to save energy.

Q How large should the discharge line on a compressor be?
A See Fig. 13-16. The discharge line should be either the same size or larger than the opening on the compressor. Unless long-radius bends are made to reduce friction, the compressor will have to work too hard.

Q Where do you install the discharge-line safety valve if there is a shutoff valve between the compressor and the receiver? Can you set the safety valve at the discharge pressure?

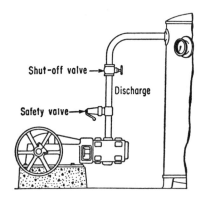

FIG. 13-17. Safety valve must be between the shutoff valve and the compressor.

A See Fig. 13-17. With a shutoff valve in the discharge line, install the safety valve between it and the compressor. Set the safety valve at 5 to 10 psi above the discharge pressure. This is very important; be sure that the receiver is a properly constructed, unfired pressure vessel suitable for your purpose and pressure. Do not exceed the safe working pressure of the vessel. It is recommended that the ASME code on unfired pressure vessels be consulted, as well as the compressed air industry standards on proper compressor-receiver installations. Boiler and machinery insurance inspectors can also advise on jurisdictional requirements.

Q What type of valves are used in air compressors?
A See Fig. 13-18. Channel, strip, and plate valves are commonly used

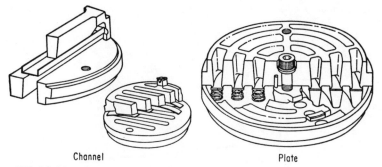

Channel   Plate

FIG. 13-18. Channel, strip, and plate valves are used in air compressors.

in air compressors. Known as the automatic type, they open and close on the pressure difference. Some types have springs. Cam-operated poppet-type valves are used on some single-acting compressors.

Q What are the advantages of a central air system?
A See Fig. 13-19. This system has one or more large compressors in a more or less central location. The supply piping often forms a loop and runs to areas needing air. The advantages claimed for central systems include (1) low investment cost per unit of capacity, (2) low unit power cost, (3) a chance to use synchronous motors to correct the power factor, (4) good pressure regulation, and (5) minimum wiring for motor drive.

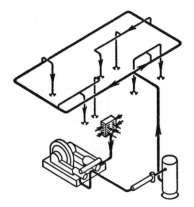

FIG. 13-19. Central air system has one machine room, air outlets where needed.

Q What are the advantages of a unit system?
A See Fig. 13-20. A unit system spots the compressors in the areas that use the air. In most plants, each compressor serves the area in which it is located, with only emergency connections between the different areas. The advantages are (1) low initial investment, (2) less pressure loss in the piping, (3) reduced engineering and planning, (4) simpler installation,

Extra receiver at
point of heavy use

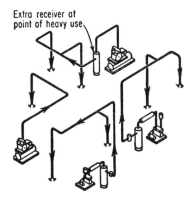

FIG. 13-20. Unit air system is made
up of independent systems.

(5) greater flexibility, (6) easier financing for plant expansion, and (7) simplified purchasing.

Q How would you look for valve trouble in a two-stage compressor?

A The quickest way to spot valve trouble in a two-stage compressor is to check the pressure of the intercooler. This pressure varies with the size of the cylinders and the intake pressure; it is usually 26 to 30 psi

Name	Function
Relief valves	On compressor discharge side to relieve excessive pressure. Don't use any shutoff valves between compressor and the safety valve.
Overspeed shutdown	Trips out drive when compressor exceeds predetermined safe speed.
Oil-failure shutdown	For large compressors fitted with pressure lubrication, this device protects bearings by stopping unit when oil pressure fails for any reason.
Jacket-water valve	Shuts down compressor if water pressure fails. It is operated by either pressure or temperature.
Overpressure shutdown	Stops compressor when discharge pressure goes above preset safe value.
Excessive-temperature shutdown	For isolated compressors this gives protection against high discharge temperature by automatically stopping unit.
Main-bearing protection	Thermal shutdown devices stop compressor if bearing temperature goes too high.
Multistage temperature protection	Recording thermometers for each stage are good for this, give continuous reading of each stage's outlet temperature.

FIG. 13-21. Eight typical compressor safety devices needed for reliable service.

for a machine with atmospheric intake at 100-psi discharge. The right intercooler pressure is easy to figure within a few pounds.

EXAMPLE: Suppose that a compressor has a 26-in. low-pressure cylinder, a 15-in. high-pressure cylinder, and the machine's intake is at atmospheric pressure of 14.7 psia. To find the correct intercooler gage pressure, divide the low-pressure cylinder by the high-pressure cylinder (26 ÷ 15) = 1.73; square 1.73 (1.73 × 1.73) = 3.0; subtract the constant *one* (3 − 1) = 2.0; and then multiply the intake pressure (2 × 14.7) = 29.4 psig, the intercooler pressure.

Q   Name some typical compressor safety devices.
A   See the table in Fig. 13-21.

OPERATION AND MAINTENANCE

Q   What effect does varying the intake pressure have on the power needed by a compressor or vacuum pump?
A   A common error is the assumption that a higher intake pressure, with a fixed discharge pressure, lowers the power needed by the compressor. A typical horsepower curve for a single-stage machine is shown in Fig. 13-22. The effect of the intake pressure on the power needs is much

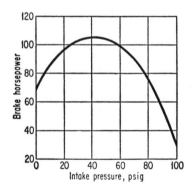

FIG. 13-22.   Effect of intake pressure on brake horsepower needed.

greater with a multistage compressor than with a single-stage unit. Most single-stage machines with up to 5-psi intake pressure might not increase the power needed or the frame loading. So it might be necessary to reduce the cylinder sizes. A vacuum pump operating against the atmospheric or some other fixed discharge pressure, but with varying degrees of vacuum at its intake, has a horsepower curve of about the same shape as that shown for a single-stage machine. A pump operating against the atmospheric discharge requires maximum horsepower when the vacuum is about 14 to 18 in. Hg, which is known as peak intake. Less power is needed at lower or higher degrees of vacuum or at absolute intake pressure.

Q Why do most compressor cylinders seem to be too hot?

A Some operators think a compressor is running too hot because they can't keep their hands on the discharge side of the cylinder. Since water at 125°F is too hot for comfort, no one would hold his hand on a cylinder at 225°F to 400°F. Most air cylinders are water-jacketed around the cylinder bore. Hot compressed air flows through a passage formed by the outside wall of the water jacket and the outside wall of the cylinder. The latter wall runs hot, but the heads will be cool except around the discharge-valve pockets.

Q What are some air-compressor pipeline troubles?

A Moisture in the line causes water hammer, reduces the carrying capacity of the line, and causes power loss by accumulating at low points. Freezing and bursting may also occur. If air is passed directly from the compressor to the piping, the heat will lengthen the lines.

RESULT: Air loss from leaky joints. Oil from the compressor is deposited in the system, causing corrosive action on the gaskets, air hose, etc.

Q How would you find leaks in an air compressor system?

A Leaks in valves and joints are very wasteful. Even tiny leaks, if there are many, waste a tremendous volume of air and power. For example, Table 13-1 shows that, in 1 year, if a $\frac{1}{32}$-in. opening at a given pressure will cost $6.50 per month in waste, then a $\frac{3}{8}$-in. opening in the same system will waste $975 per month. Air lines and equipment must be airtight. Costs of air leaks at today's increased fuel prices can be similarly calculated.

One way to find leaks is to place a lighted candle at all connections.

TABLE 13-1 Cost of Leaks through Typical Orifices at 100 psig
(Based on orifice coefficient of 0.65 and cost of 30 cents per 1000 ft³)

Leak size, in.	Loss, ft³/min	Approx. hp loss	Ft³ lost per 30-day month	Cost per month of lost air
1/32	1	1/5	43,000	$ 13
1/16	4¼	7/8	180,000	54
1/8	17	3½	730,000	119
1/4	70	14	3,000,000	900
3/8	150	30	6,500,000	1,950
1/2	270	54	11,700,000	3,510

Adapted from Parker Hannifin Corporation.

Another method is to swab soapy water around the joints; leaks will blow bubbles. Essence of peppermint placed into the air intake will reveal leaks by odor. Be careful and use tiny quantities; remember that alcohol is a fuel.

Q How would you start a large reciprocating air compressor?

A To start a large reciprocating air compressor, turn it over a few times by hand to make sure that it is free to start. The direction of rotation is usually with the top of the flywheel traveling toward the horizontal cylinder. This is known as "engine runs under." Open the valve in the air line so that the compressor can run without building up air pressure in the receiver, or open the two indicator cocks in the side of the air cylinder. Turn on the circulating water in the air-cylinder jacket.

On steam-driven compressors, open the drain cocks on the steam cylinder and drain the steam line above the throttle valve until it warms up. Then, open the throttle a little and let steam blow through the steam cylinder until it is heated. Turn the engine over so that steam blows from both of the cocks. When warmed up, give the engine a little more steam and run it slowly, bringing it gradually up to speed. Watch the governing devices to be sure they work OK. Always examine the oil level in the system, and make sure that all bearings are in good condition and receiving oil.

Q How would you clean an air-piping system?

A Inspect your air-piping system periodically and clean it mechanically if there are troublesome deposits.

REMEMBER: Even the best lube oils deposit some carbon. Mechanical removal is best. Never use kerosene, gasoline, or other light petroleum products in an air system. They are volatile and will explode when heated.

Q How are water jackets cleaned on air compressors?

A Water jackets can be washed out with water or cleaned chemically. If they are not cleaned of deposits, the machine will overheat. One way is to play a water nozzle into the jacket by hand and wash out the mud. For acid cleaning, circulate a 10 percent solution of muriatic acid and inhibitor through the jackets with a small circulating pump. But, you must have a hookup that adds acid in order to keep the solution up to 10 or even 15 percent. If the scale is high in sulfate, you may have to circulate a warm acid solution. Be sure to drain the solution thoroughly and flush out the systems with soda ash and clean water until no trace of acid is left. This is best done by a specialist. Provide sufficient ventilation at all times in order to avoid any accumulation of explosive gas, such as hydrogen.

Q What should all operators know about lubricating compressors?

A Cylinders must be lubricated to reduce friction and to eliminate the carbonization of oil. The oil chosen should have enough body to sustain the weight of the moving parts and to form a seal between the piston rings and cylinder walls. Faulty lube oil causes carbon to form in the cylinder valves, cylinder passages, piping, and receiver.

Sticking or partially closing valves, which leads to eventual failure, is one of the biggest problems with poor lube oil. If there is no intake strainer, the lube oil will contaminate, causing wear and carbonization. Then, the carbon particles torn loose become incandescent. If these incandescent carbon particles come in contact with the oil vapor given off by the lube oil, a fire or explosion can result, wrecking the machine and even killing the attendants. When the lube oil reaches a certain temperature (its flash point), it gives off an oil vapor, just as steam forms from water at a certain temperature.

Q How often should crankcase oil, whether or not it also feeds the cylinders, be changed before it loses its effectiveness?

A Often air compressors can run safely for 3 months or more between oil changes. But be sure to inspect the oil at least monthly. And check the oil level at least weekly. Once your compressor setup is right—with sufficient capacity, adequate cooling, well-positioned intake, proper pipe size and equipment, if necessary with aftercoolers, heat exchangers, and separators—*then*, and *only* then, does this timely attention to proper lubrication assure trouble-free, low-cost air for your plant.

Q How do you check inlet valves?

A Inlet valves can be checked while the machine is running. If they leak in one end of the high-pressure cylinder or if they don't operate, you can find which end is causing the trouble by watching the intercooler pressure at different loads. If the intercooler pressure drops to normal, say at half load, then the trouble is in the unloaded valves. To find the leaky inlet valve, compare the temperature of the inlet-valve covers. The cover on the leaky valve will be warmer than the others if the machine has been loaded for some time. But this check is of no value if the inlet valves have been unloaded long enough for all the covers to warm up. If nothing is wrong with the valves, check the piston rings and the cylinder.

Q What causes low intercooler pressure?

A If intercooler pressure is below normal, the trouble is in the low-pressure cylinder. Follow the same procedure that you follow in checking a high-pressure cylinder, except when shutting down the unit, hold the intercooler pressure until the leakage through the low-pressure discharge valves is checked.

Q How do you inspect compressor valves?

A When inspecting compressor valves, check the valve seats in the cylinder or in the head. Damaged seats are usually caused by valve covers that do not hold the valves securely on their seats. Valve pounding while operating damages the seat. When the seats are badly damaged and a lot of metal has to be removed, you may have to install a ring or false seat between the valve and the seat. This keeps the valve from extending past the cylinder-bore line. In case of trouble in the inlet valve, inspect the covers on the unloading valve and the valves themselves. The trouble can be caused by a valve-unloading mechanism that is not working.

Q If an air tool rated at 90 psig had difficulty operating because of low pressure, what could be the reason?
A If pressure is low, look for (1) an undersized compressor, (2) inadequate piping, (3) air leaks in the system, (4) a partially opened valve, (5) an obstruction in the piping, or (6) too many tools.

Q Explain how pressure drop varies.
A Pressure drop varies approximately as the square of the velocity of the air going through the lines. So, if the flow is doubled, the pressure drop is $2 \times 2 = 4$ times as great. This also works the other way; by enlarging the line you can reduce the velocity and reduce the pressure drop to a great extent. For example, a 3-in. line, 1000 ft long, will handle 500 ft^3/min with a 2.5-psi pressure loss, while a 4-in. line of the same length will pass about 1000 ft^3/min with the same pressure drop.

Q Where are air leaks most likely to occur in the system?
A Air leaks often occur around the valve stems and in the hose connections, unions, drains, homemade guns, and lines leading to tools that are not operating.

Q List some common compressor troubles and some possible causes.
A See Fig. 13-23.

Q What important inspections would you give your air compressors?
A Check the oil in your air compressor at set periods. Inspect the compressor at least once a month for necessary adjustment, condition of shaft packing, etc. If possible, take up all the lost motion in the pins and bearings. Air valves should have an oily surface and be free of carbon. If carbon forms, remove the deposits immediately. Make sure that all ports and passages are free from obstruction. When reassembling the air valve and its seat, do not interchange parts.

Q What does high intercooler pressure indicate?
A It means trouble in the high-pressure cylinder resulting from leaky intake or discharge valves, leakage caused by rings in poor condition, or a badly worn cylinder bore. Most air cylinders or heads have openings

Symptom	Possible Cause
Noise or knocking	Loose or burned out bearings, loose valve or unloader, loose flywheel, motor rotor shunting back and forth from unlevel mounting or belt misalignment
Squeal	Motor or compressor bearings tight, belts slipping, lack of oil, leaking gasket or joint
Intercooler safety valve blows while running unloaded	Broken or leaking hp discharge valve, or suction unloader, defective or stuck lp unloader, blown gasket
Intercooler valve blows while running loaded	Broken or leaking hp discharge or suction valve, defective hp unloader held in unloaded position, blown gasket
Sudden capacity drop	Bad leak in air operated equipment or air lines, discharge piping clogged, suction filters blocked, broken or badly leaking valves, blown gaskets, leak in intercooler
Gradual capacity drop	Accumulation of small leaks in air lines, poorly seating valves, restricted suction filters, worn rings or cylinders
Receiver safety valve blows	Defective pop valve, defective pressure switch or pilot valve, leak in control line, inoperative suction unloaders
Unit blows fuses	Fuses too small, low voltage, pressure-switch differential setting too close, unit starting against full load, electrical trouble, motor or compressor tight
Unit will not start	Blown fuse or tripped overload relay, motor or electrical trouble, defective pressure switch, motor or compressor binding
Roughness and vibration	Base too light, improper shimming under unit, foundation bolts loose, unbalance from one cylinder not pumping
Excessive oil consumption	Oil level too high, oil viscosity too light, too high oil pressure (if force-feed lubricated), worn rings and cylinders

FIG. 13-23.   Troubleshooter's dope sheet for zeroing in on compressor problems.

for connecting an indicator. Check leakage through the discharge valves by removing the plugs from the cylinder opening. For a high-pressure cylinder, make this check when the machine is shut down and with no pressure in the intercooler. Intake valves must be in the loaded position with pressure in the discharge line. Most compressor valves have slight leakage, but if you hear a continuous blow, it indicates excessive leakage. In this case, remove the valves for inspection. If the leakage is only in one end of the cylinder, this check shows which end leaks; you only need to inspect the discharge valves from one end to find the trouble.

NEW OSHA (OCCUPATIONAL SAFETY AND HEALTH ADMINISTRATION) NOISE STANDARDS

Q What is a decibel scale?
A As Table 13-2 shows, the decibel scales indicate sound power, intensity, and pressure. Today, noise, like air pollution, is getting more attention on a community and industry level. In a broad sense, noise is simply

TABLE 13-2 Decibel Scales Indicate Sound Power, Intensity, and Pressure

Sound source	Power range, W	Decibel range, dBA
Turbojet with 7000-lb thrust	10,000.0	170
Four-propeller airliner	100.0	150
Threshold of pain for most people	10.0	140
Chipping hammer	1.0	130
Centrifugal ventilating fan at 13,000 ft³/min	0.01	110
Automobile on roadway	0.001	100
Subway car, air drill	0.0001	90
Conversational voice	0.00001	80
Street noise, average radio	0.000001	70
Very soft whisper	0.000000001	40

unwanted sound. In excess amounts, it prevents people from doing their best work. One source estimates that United States industry faces an annual $10 million compensation tab for noise-related injuries. Some types of compressors and internal-combustion engines are inherently noisy, but there are ways to keep their noise within the newer and stricter standards set by OSHA, which if not adhered to can lead to costly fines.

Q What methods of protection against noise does OSHA accept?
A Only one. The government accepts only engineering controls by mechanically keeping noise away from workplaces. It does not accept protective products like earplugs and earmuffs worn by employees to deaden the noise reaching them.

Q When did the new regulation go into effect, and what is the new acceptable noise level?
A As of January 1978 the noise level must be kept no higher than 85 dBA for an 8-hr day.

Q What is a dBA?
A A decibel (dB) indicates a relative difference in power between acoustic signals, while the A indicates a weighting of noise energy. It gives less

weight to energy at low frequencies than at high—approximates the ear's response to sound. As Table 13-2 shows, a conversational voice is about 80, a soft whisper 40 dBA.

CALCULATIONS

Q When operating at sea level against a discharge pressure of 100 psig with an atmospheric intake pressure, a compressor has an actual capacity of 120 ft³/min free air. What capacity does this air have when it leaves the compressor? Disregard the increase in temperature.

A The formula (Boyle's law) is

$$p_1 v_1 = p_2 v_2$$

where p_1 = absolute initial pressure
v_1 = initial volume
p_2 = absolute final pressure
v_2 = final volume

The equation shows that the volume varies inversely as the absolute pressure and vice versa.

$p_1 = 14.7$ psi (atmospheric pressure at sea level)
$v_1 = 120$ ft³
$p_2 = 100 + 14.7 = 114.7$ psia final pressure
$v_2 = ?$

Substituting these values, we have

$$14.7 \times 120 = 1764.0 \times v_2$$

$$v_2 = \frac{14.7 \times 120}{114.7} = 15.4 \text{ ft}^3/\text{min} \qquad Ans.$$

NOTE: Isothermal compression isn't achieved in practice because it is not practical to dissipate all the heat during compression.

Q What is adiabatic compression?
A The compression of air or gas is adiabatic when all the heat of compression is retained in the air or gas. Here, no other heat enters and none leaves the compressor cylinder. The characteristic equation for adiabatic compression is

$$pv^n = c$$

where p = absolute pressure
v = volume

n = ratio of specific heat at constant pressure to specific heat at constant volume = 1.4 for air

NOTE: Pure adiabatic compression is rarely found in practice. Some of the heat of compression usually escapes.

Q How does a change in temperature affect the pressure or volume of a gas?

A When the temperature of a gas changes, and if the pressure remains constant, the volume varies directly as the absolute temperature; or if the volume remains constant, the absolute pressure varies directly as the absolute temperature. The relationships are expressed in the following formulas:

(1) $\dfrac{v_2}{v_1} = \dfrac{t_2}{t_1}$ or   (2) $\dfrac{p_2}{p_1} = \dfrac{t_2}{t_1}$ or   (3) $\dfrac{p_2 v_2}{p_1 v_1} = \dfrac{t_2}{t_1}$

where t_1 = absolute intake temperature
t_2 = absolute discharge temperature

EXAMPLE: Let us say the capacity of compressed air is computed as 15.4 ft³/min, with temperature constant at 60°F.

If the temperature of the discharge air were increased to 340°F, what would the capacity be, assuming no change in the discharge pressure?

REMEMBER: Absolute zero is 460°F below zero where all molecular movement stops. Substituting in formula (1):

$$\frac{v_2}{15.4} = \frac{340 + 460}{60 + 460} = \frac{800°F}{520°F}$$

$$v_2 = 15.4 \text{ ft}^3/\text{min} \times \frac{800}{520} = 23.7 \text{ ft}^3/\text{min} \qquad Ans.$$

The same value would be obtained by using formula (3), above, and by filling in all the known values.

Q What is the piston displacement of a 12 × 11-in. double-acting single cylinder compressor of 300 r/min if the piston rod has a 2-in. diameter?

A Piston area = 12 × 12 × 0.7854 = 113.10 in.²
Piston-rod area = 2 × 2 × 0.7854 = 3.14 in.²
Net area of the rod side of the piston = 109.86 in.²
Total net area of both sides of the piston = 113 + 109.86 = 222.86 in.²

$$\text{Piston displacement} = \frac{222.86}{144} \times \frac{11}{12} \times 300 = 425.6 \text{ ft}^3/\text{min} \qquad Ans.$$

NOTE: The stroke must be expressed in feet and the piston area in square feet when computing displacement (144 in.^{2} = 1 ft^2).

Q A two-stage compressor, at 100-psi discharge pressure, 14.7-psia intake pressure, and having an actual capacity of 1066 ft^3/min, requires 192 bhp, with a mechanical efficiency of 95.5 percent. What is the compressor efficiency?

A Since the two-stage adiabatic horsepower per cubic foot for the pressures involved is 0.153 (the *Compressed Air Handbook* figure), the total adiabatic horsepower is 1066 × 0.153 = 163. The ihp in the air cylinders is 192 × 94.5 percent, or 181.4. Therefore, the compression efficiency of the machine is 163 divided by 181.4 = 89.9 percent. *Ans.*

Q How is the piston speed computed?
A To compute piston speed, multiply the length of the stroke in feet by the number of strokes per minute, or twice the revolutions per minute. Piston speed is always expressed in feet per minute.

Q Does altitude affect compressor performance?
A Yes. If a compressor at sea level has an actual capacity of 100 ft^3/min of free air compressed to 100 psi (or 114.7 psia), the capacity of the compressed air (at constant temperature) will be

$$100 \times \frac{14.7}{114.7} \quad \text{or} \quad 12.8 \text{ ft}^3/\text{min} \quad \textit{Ans.}$$

If this same compressor is at a 5000-ft altitude and delivers 100 ft^3/min of free air, compressed to 100 psi (or 112.1 psia), the capacity of compressed air will be

$$100 \times \frac{12.1}{112.1} \quad \text{or} \quad 10.79 \text{ ft}^3/\text{min} \quad \textit{Ans.}$$

The reduction in the capacity of compressed air from 12.8 to 10.79, starting with the same capacity of free air, is from the lower density of the atmosphere at the high altitude. Compressor makers guarantee capacity not in compressed air but in *free air* or in air that is at normal atmospheric conditions at place of use. So in either of these problems, the maker would offer a compressor having a capacity of 100 ft^3/min of free air. Reduction of the volume of the compressed air delivered at altitudes must be compensated for by increasing the required volume of free air at the compressor intake. See Fig. 5-2 for atmospheric pressure at various altitudes.

SUGGESTED READING

Moore, Arthur H., and Stephen M. Elonka: *Electrical Systems and Equipment for Industry*, Robert E. Krieger Publishing Company, Inc., Melbourne, Fla., 1977 (has detailed information on motor drives for compressors).

Elonka, Stephen M., and Alonzo R. Parsons: *Standard Instrumentation Questions and Answers*, Robert E. Krieger Publishing Company, Inc., Melbourne, Fla., 1979 (has detailed well-illustrated information on instrumentation for air compressors).

Compressed Air and Gas Institute, *Compressed Air Handbook*, 3d ed., McGraw-Hill Book Company, New York, 1961.

14

HEAT EXCHANGERS

Unlike rotating and reciprocating machines that transform one kind of energy into another through motion, heat exchangers do so quietly, usually through tube walls (see Fig. 17-2). Here, we cover not the specialized forms such as boilers, air heaters, and economizers but such familiar types as feed-water heaters, steam condensers, evaporators, and deaerators. A knowledge of these is especially vital for the efficient operation of power plants.

BASICS

Q What is the function of heat exchangers?

A They transfer heat from one substance to another. Three basic ways of moving heat are (1) conduction, (2) radiation, and (3) convection. All three usually take place in heat exchangers. Heat is caused by molecular motion. At absolute zero, about −459°F, molecules stand still. The faster they start moving, the more heat they generate.

Q What is forced convection?

A Moving the liquid or gas by a pump, fan, or other device, instead of depending on natural currents resulting from heating and cooling, results in forced convection. Forcing fluid to flow over the heat source at a higher speed raises the rate of heat transfer, within limits. And the faster we force the flow of fluid the greater the rate at which it is possible to carry heat to where it's wanted.

Q What two big jobs do surface condensers perform?

A The most important job of a surface condenser is to reduce the back-pressure on the turbines so that maximum heat energy can be extracted from the steam.

REASON: The power produced in the expanding steam from atmospheric pressure to 29 in. vacuum is about the same as if the steam were expanded from 200 psig, 600°F to atmospheric.

The second function of the condenser is to recover the low-oxygen-content condensate for the boiler feed water at full temperature.

Q Explain how vacuum is created in a steam condenser.

A In a condenser the steam is reduced in volume to that which it occupied as water, from which it was generated. Thus condensing steam in a closed vessel produces a partial vacuum by reducing the volume of vapor.

EXAMPLE: 1 lb of dry steam at 14.7 psia (absolute pressure) has a volume of 26.8 ft³. In a tight vessel, if this steam of 26.8-ft³ volume at 14.7 psia were condensed into water at 142°F, its volume would shrink to only 0.0163 ft³, and thus it would occupy only $\frac{1}{1644}$ of the space. Theoretically, the absolute pressure would fall from 14.7 to about 3 psi, but in practice, the pressure of air and other noncondensable gases inside the condenser would raise this pressure just a little.

CONDENSERS

Q Name three common types of condensers.

A Jet, barometric, and surface condensers are commonly used today. However, the two broadest groups are: (1) jet condensers, where the cooling water comes into direct contact with the exhaust steam, and (2) surface condensers, where the cooling water and exhaust steam do not mix (Fig. 14-1). In the latter, steam is on one side of the tube and water is on the other side. The condenser, shown in Fig. 14-1, is usually for auxiliary service and is common in older plants and aboard older ships. Here the circulating-water pump and the condensate pump are part of the overall condenser unit.

Q Describe a modern surface condenser and its main auxiliaries.

A Figure 14-2 shows a vacuum-tight, shell-and-tube heat exchanger. Here, cooling water flows through the tubes and the prime mover exhausts

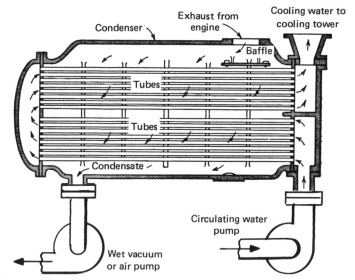

FIG. 14-1.   A surface condenser converts exhaust steam back to water again.

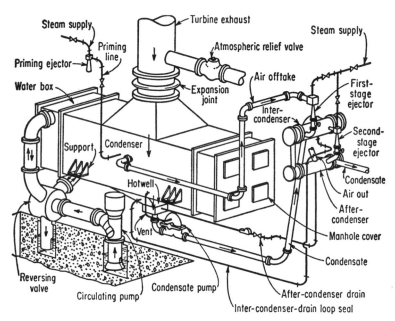

FIG. 14-2.   Auxiliaries shown are needed to keep a modern surface condenser working at top efficiency.

the steam which surrounds the tubes. The relatively cold tube surfaces condense the steam, reducing the volume of the steam and creating a vacuum. The cooling water carries away the latent heat created by condensation. Steam enters the top of the shell, is condensed as it comes into contact with the various cool tubes, and drops to the hotwell in the bottom of the shell as condensate. The purpose of the lanes leading to the hotwell is to economize on heat by heating the condensate to the highest temperature allowed by the vacuum. Subcooling the condensate is wasteful (condensate depression). A pump sends the condensate to an air ejector where the vapors and air are condensed and the pressure is raised so that the noncondensable gases can be ejected to the atmosphere. The condensate returns to the feed system for reuse. This condenser has a valve for backwashing to remove objects that tend to clog the tubes.

Q How do two-stage air ejectors work?

A See Fig. 14-3. An air ejector is a steam nozzle that discharges a high-

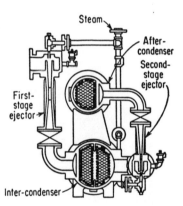

FIG. 14-3. A two-stage air ejector with both intercondensers and after-condensers.

velocity jet of steam at about 3500 ft/sec. The steam flows across a suction chamber and through a venturi-shaped compression tube. The air or gases to be evacuated enter the ejector suction where they are entrained by a jet of steam and then discharged through the throat of the ejector. The velocity of the kinetic energy is converted into pressure in the throat of the ejector and compresses the mixture to a lower vacuum or a higher absolute pressure. Two-stage ejectors have a compression ratio of about 8:1 (the ratio between the discharge pressure and the suction pressure). The ejector discharges to either a small condenser or a feed-water heater where the steam is condensed, and the air and gases are vented to the atmosphere. The two jets, shown in Fig. 14-3, are in series with intercondensers between the stages. These intercondensers condense the steam and cool the air-vapor mixture. Aftercondensers are used for the same purpose. (See injectors in Chap. 5, "Pumps.")

Q Describe a barometric condenser.

A There are many types of barometric condensers of which the ejector-jet, parallel-flow-contact type, shown in Fig. 14-4, is one. These exchangers

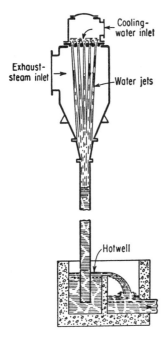

FIG. 14-4. Ejector-jet parallel-flow-contact barometric condenser.

condense the exhaust steam by bringing it into direct contact with the cooling water. They are simple and compact, but condensate mixes with the raw water. You can use them where loss of condensate isn't important or where raw water is cheap and easily treated and makeup needs are no problem. As the sketch shows, the shell is above the discharge-water level so that the water leg in the tailpipe has enough head to drain the mixed cooling water and condensate from the evacuated shell. This type of condenser needs no pump to remove the entrained, noncondensable gases.

Q Describe a countercurrent barometric condenser.

A See Fig. 14-5. A countercurrent barometric condenser uses disks to break up the flow of water. It has a two-stage air ejector with an intercondenser. The condensables must be removed by a pump. Steam, with its

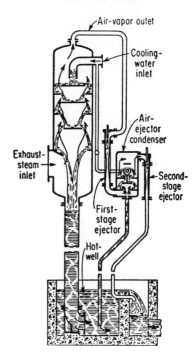

Air-vapor outlet

Cooling-
water
inlet

Air-
ejector
condenser

Exhaust-
steam
inlet

Second-
stage
ejector

First-
stage
ejector

Hot-
well

FIG. 14-5. Countercurrent barometric condenser breaks up water flow.

noncondensable gases, flows in the opposite direction to the cooling water.
Also, the cooling water breaks up into a spray to present the largest possible
surface for steam absorption.

Q How are condenser tubes fastened into tube sheets?
A To fasten condenser tubes into sheets, the tube ends are either rolled
(expanded), welded, or packed. Today, the tubes are usually expanded
and flared at the inlet end or expanded and packed at the outlet end.
Serrations or ferrules are often used at the inlets, either with or without
packing. By belling the inlets, the flow at the tube entrances is improved.

Q What materials are used in condensers?
A Condenser shells are usually made of copper-bearing steel plate, with
cast-iron or fabricated-steel water boxes and manhole plates. Tube sheets
are usually rolled muntz metal, and supports are copper-bearing steel.
Tubes of inhibited admiralty metal or arsenical copper work well with
circulating water. Admiralty metal (about 70 percent copper, 1 percent
tin, and 29 percent zinc) is inhibited with arsenic, antimony, or phosphorus.
Arsenical copper has about 9.5 percent arsenic. Aluminum brass (about
76 percent copper, 2 percent aluminum, 22 percent zinc, and with small

amounts of lead and iron) is also inhibited with arsenic. It shows a high resistance to erosion by high-velocity, aerated seawater. Copper nickel (70–30) is considered standard by the United States Navy. Today, low-nickel, high-iron copper nickel is found to have properties similar to 70–30 copper nickel.

OTHER TYPES OF HEAT EXCHANGERS

Q Name a common type of heat exchanger and give a few of its uses.
A Shell-and-tube heat exchangers are among today's most popular designs. They are used for (1) feed-water heating, (2) lube-oil cooling, (3) fuel-oil heating, (4) service-water heating, (5) compressed-gas cooling, (6) heat reclaiming from blowdown and other wastes, (7) engine cooling, (8) transformer-oil cooling, (9) refrigeration condensers, and (10) refrigeration evaporators or chillers and many others.

Q What types of tube bundles are used in shell-and-tube heat exchangers?
A See Fig. 14-6. Figure 14-6a shows the straight-tube bundle that is often used in shell-and-tube heat exchangers. The advantage of this type is that it is easy to clean mechanically. The entire bundle can be removed for cleaning.

Figure 14-6b shows a U-tube bundle. Because these tubes are rolled into the tube sheet on one end only, the expansion problem is solved. Also, there are only one-half as many tube joints. But this tube bundle is harder to clean mechanically.

Figure 14-6c illustrates a bowed-tube bundle. It is bolted solidly to the shell at each end. As the bundle heats, it bows, causing scale to crack off.

Figure 14-6d is the coil-tube bundle, which is used for very high pressures. It does away with gasketed joints in the high-pressure circuit.

Figure 14-6e is the single-pass tube bundle. It can be fitted with an expansion joint, as shown in the sketch.

Q Describe a modern shell-and-tube feed-water heater for high-pressure plants.
A Modern feed-water cycles have up to eight heaters. In such a system, the steam pressure in the lowest heater may be a vacuum, but it increases in the succeeding heaters to as high as 600 psi or more. Water pressure in the tubes being heated may run above 3000 psi. These heaters usually use steam bled from a turbine as the energy supply. Some heaters have drain-cooling and desuperheating sections. In the drain-cooling setup, the entering feed water first contacts the leaving drains (condensate) before flashing to the lower-pressure heater where the heat is released to a lower

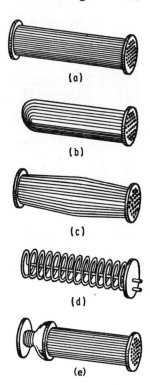

FIG. 14-6. Five typical tube bundles used in modern heat exchangers.

temperature. In the desuperheating section, the feed water leaving the heater contacts the incoming superheated steam. This raises the water temperature higher than is possible with saturated steam.

Feed-water heaters are installed in either a horizontal or a vertical position. U tubes are used to leave one end of the tube bundle free to expand. See Fig. 14-7. For high temperatures to 900°F, a 30–70 annealed copper-nickel (Monel) tube is used. These tubes are covered by impingement baffles opposite the inlets in order to avoid tube erosion at the steam and flashed-condensate inlets. The baffles fit snugly around the tubes and the shell interior to prevent short cycling. Relief valves are placed on both the tube side and the shell side of the heater.

Q Why is proper venting important in feed-water heaters?
A As steam condenses in the feed-water heaters, condensate falls to the bottom of the shell and forms a seal against the steam blowing through the shell. This prevents noncondensable gases from leaving the heater. Thus, an air blanket forms and puts the heater out of action. This condition

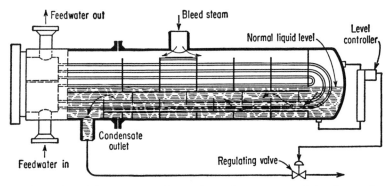

FIG. 14-7.   High-pressure feed-water heater has an automatic level control.

is most pronounced in low-pressure heaters operating below atmospheric pressure. The only protection against the forming of an air blanket is to vent the heaters properly. Make sure a vent is placed in each end of the steam space. Besides removing gases, the vents help to distribute steam throughout the shell, thus making better use of the heat-transfer surface.

EVAPORATORS

Q Why are evaporators used in power plants?
A Evaporators produce makeup water for boilers from raw water having a high solids content. Modern boilers need evaporated water to prevent scaling. Aboard ships and in areas where fresh water is scarce, evaporators are used to distill potable water (drinking water) from sea water.

Q Give five primary reasons for deaerating.
A Deaerators (1) remove oxygen, (2) remove carbon dioxide, (3) raise feed-water temperature, (4) improve heat-transfer efficiency, and (5) improve overall boiler operation.

Q Why must oxygen be removed from feed water?
A Oxygen is extremely corrosive to boilers. The maximum safe oxygen content for most boilers is about 0.005 cc/L (7 parts per billion). As steam condenses, any oxygen carried over with the steam will be highly corrosive to the condensate lines and the process equipment. Carbon dioxide may also be present in the steam and condensate; it is extremely corrosive when it condenses and combines with water.

Q Why must carbon dioxide be removed?

A Most raw waters contain free carbon dioxide, which is corrosive when combined with water to form carbonic acid. In steam, carbon dioxide is not corrosive, but when the steam condenses, the carbon dioxide combines with water and forms very corrosive carbonic acid, which will dissolve return lines and process equipment rapidly.

Q How does deaeration improve heat-transfer efficiency?
A Air or noncondensable gases in steam cause losses as high as four times in thermal efficiency. They cause an insulating thermal blanket which reduces the heat transfer across the tube wall.

Q Describe the single-effect submerged-tube high-pressure evaporator.
A See Fig. 14-8. The single effect of this unit evaporates water in one

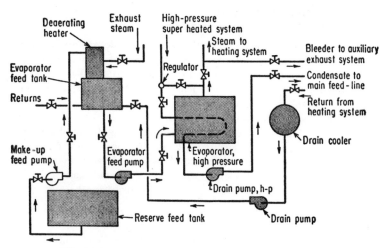

FIG. 14-8. High-pressure evaporator used aboard ships.

stage. Steam of up to 200 psi is fed into the submerged-tube bundle. Vapor thus generated can go to the distiller or into a heating system. It eventually returns as condensate for the boiler feed. Solids stay in the shell and must be removed periodically. Figure 14-8 shows a typical marine installation.

Q What are the advantages of a multiple-effect evaporator?
A See Fig. 14-9. Multiple-effect plants may be double-effect, triple-effect, etc. The advantage of a multiple-effect unit is that less steam is needed to produce fresh water. The purity of the water isn't affected by the number of effects. Single-effect plants produce about 1 lb of water per pound of

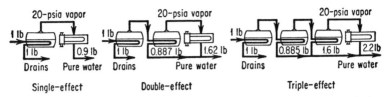

FIG. 14-9. Efficiencies of three types of evaporators favor the triple-effect design.

steam used. Double-effect plants produce about 1.6 lb of water per pound of steam, and triple-effect plants produce about 2.2 lb of water per pound of steam used.

OPERATION AND MAINTENANCE

Q What are some common troubles in surface-condenser operation?

A The greatest headache to the operator is loss of vacuum caused by air leaking into the surface condenser through the joints or packing glands. Another trouble spot is cooling water leaking into the steam space through the ends of the tubes or through tiny holes in the tubes. The tubes may also become plugged with mud, shells, debris, slime, or algae, thus cutting down on the cooling-water supply; or the tubes may get coated with lube oil from the reciprocating machinery. Corrosion and dezincification of the tube metal are common surface-condenser troubles. Corrosion may be uniform or it may occur in small holes or pits. Dezincification changes the nature of the metal and causes it to become brittle and weak.

Q Where would you look for a fault if the air ejector didn't raise enough vacuum?

A In this case, the trouble is usually in the nozzle. You will probably find that (1) the nozzle is eroded, (2) the strainer protecting the nozzle is clogged, or (3) the steam pressure to the nozzle is too low.

Q How would you stop air from leaking into a condenser?

A First, find the leak by passing a flame over the suspected part while the condenser is under vacuum. Leaks in the flange joints or porous castings can be stopped with asphalt paint or shellac. Tallow or heavy grease will stop leaks around the valve stems. Small leaks around the porous castings, flange nuts, or valve stems can't always be found by the flame test. So, you might have to put the condenser under a few pounds of air pressure and apply soapsuds to the suspected trouble parts.

Q Do you stop cooling-water flow through a steam condenser as soon as the turbine is stopped?

A You should keep the cooling water circulating for about 15 or more min so that the condenser has a chance to cool down gradually and evenly. Be sure to have cooling water flowing through the condenser before starting up in order to prevent live steam from entering the condenser unless it is cooled. Overheating can cause severe leaks and other headaches.

Q How would you stop a leaky tube that was contaminating the feed water? Discuss.

A To stop a leaky tube from contaminating the feed water, shut down, remove the water-box covers, and fill the steam space with water. By observing the tube ends, you can find the leaky tube. An alternate method is to put a few pounds of air pressure in the steam space, flood the water boxes to the top inspection plate, and observe any air bubbles. Once you have found the leaky tube, drive a tapered bronze plug (well-coated with white lead) into each end of the tube to cut it out of service. This allows you to use the condenser since the tubes need not be renewed until abut 10 percent of the tubes are plugged. See Fig. 14-10.

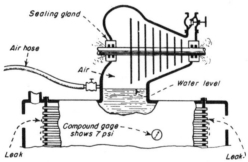

FIG. 14-10. One method of finding condenser leaks is filling steam space with water at 7 psi.

Q Why must condensate be subjected to salinity tests where brackish cooling water is used?

A Condensate may leak from the cooling-water side to the steam side of the condenser and contaminate the feed water, thus causing scale to form in the boilers. Or, brackish cooling water may leak into the steam space from cracked or porous tubes or from around the joints at the end of the tube ends, etc. By taking salinity readings of the condensate, leaks may be found before they can do any harm.

Q How is scale removed from the evaporator coils or tubes?

A In high-temperature evaporators, some solids form a hard scale on the outside of the coils. Because the scale slows down heat transfer, it must be removed. One way to get rid of it is to drain the shell at set periods and to spray the tube bundle with cold water while the tubes are still hot. This creates a thermal shock that often cracks the scale and spray-washes it off the tubes. Bowed tubes in some designs help to crack this scale. Chemicals are also used to prevent scale.

SUGGESTED READING

Elonka, Stephen M.: *Standard Plant Operators' Manual*, 3d ed., McGraw-Hill Book Company, New York, 1980 (has questions and answers on license examinations and heat-transfer calculations).

15

GAS TURBINES

Even if you have not operated a gas turbine, you have seen the largest passenger and military aircraft, which are powered by prop-jet and jet engines. The versatility of these engines is shown by their wide use in stationary energy systems for processing, power generation, and mechanical drives, base-load generation, and peaking services. They are the heart of on-site generating systems.

Here are the latest methods of utilizing waste heat from gas turbines and also the latest information on operation and maintenance. Today's units vary from tiny 25-hp capacity to giants of over 100,000 kW.

BASICS

Q How does the gas turbine use thermal energy?

A To know how gas turbines behave, we must understand the basic steps in a simple cycle (Fig. 15-1). Heat energy of the fuel is converted into mechanical energy. The compressor and the combustion chamber produce a high-energy working fluid that can be expanded in the turbine. This develops mechanical energy similar to expanding steam in a steam turbine (see Chap. 4, "Steam Turbines").

The volume of the working fluid is smallest at the compressor outlet, though its temperature is higher than at the compressor inlet. High excess-air ratio in the combustor keeps air and gas temperatures below a maximum

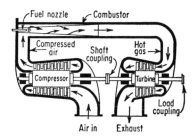

FIG. 15-1. The simple gas turbine has a compressor and combustor.

limit. At the turbine outlet, gas volume is at maximum. The main elements of the gas-turbine plant must be proportional to handle the flow of working fluid with minimum pressure loss through the system.

Q   What is the air rate of a gas turbine?
A   The air rate is the amount of air, in pounds, that enters the inlet of the compressor per unit of cycle net output.

Q   What is compression efficiency?
A   Compression efficiency is the ratio of the work needed for ideal adiabatic compression through a given pressure range to the work actually needed by the compressor.

Q   What is engine efficiency?
A   Engine efficiency is the ratio of the work actually developed by expanding hot gas in the turbine through a given pressure range to the work that would be yielded for ideal adiabatic expansion.

Q   What is machine efficiency?
A   For gas turbines, machine efficiency is the combined efficiencies of the compressor and the turbine.

Q   What is pressure ratio?
A   It is the ratio of the highest pressure in a cycle to the lowest pressure. It is usually the ratio of the highest pressure in the compressor discharge to the lowest pressure in the compressor inlet.

Q   What is thermal efficiency?
A   Thermal efficiency is the percentage of the total fuel energy input that appears as the net work output of the cycle.

Q   What is work ratio?
A   It is the ratio of the net work output of the cycle to the total work developed in the turbine or turbines.

Q   What are the basic components of a simple gas-turbine system?
A   In Fig. 15-2 the basic equipment for a simple gas-turbine system in-

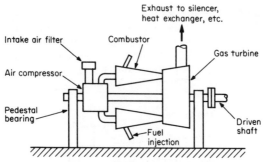

FIG. 15-2.   Basic components of simple gas turbine.

cludes a compressor, combustor, and turbine. A rotating compressor draws in air from the atmosphere, pressurizes it, and forces it into the combustor (the furnace) in a steady flow.

Fuel forced into the air burns, raising the temperature of the mixture of air and combustion products. This high-energy mixture then flows through the turbine, dropping in pressure and temperature as it does work on the moving blades. The spent gases then leave at atmospheric pressure but at high temperature. The turbine drives the compressor rotor through a shaft and also an external load through the load coupling.

TYPES OF GAS TURBINES

Q Describe a simple gas turbine.
A Going back to Fig. 15-1, a simple gas turbine has a compressor, combustion chamber, and turbine. The turbine and the compressor are on the same shaft. The compressor raises the pressure of atmospheric air and sends this air to the combustion chamber. Here, a fuel (oil, gas, or pulverized coal) burns, raising the temperature and increasing the heat energy. The hot gas in the turbine expands to develop mechanical energy, as expanding steam does in a steam turbine. This simple unit has a thermal efficiency of about 20 percent.

An open-cycle gas turbine also takes air from the atmosphere and discharges exhaust to the atmosphere. Open-cycle hookups differ in many ways, but the compressor inlet is atmospheric and there is a relatively narrow range of best pressure ratios. This puts a limit on the top-cycle pressure. These units can have a regenerator, intercooler, and other refinements and can still be open-cycle gas turbines.

Q Explain a closed-cycle gas turbine.

A See Fig. 15-3. Since any desired inlet pressure can be used in a closed-cycle gas turbine for the same pressure ratio, it operates at much higher pressure levels. This means that it has higher air density, smaller volume flows, and better heat transfer, thus allowing for smaller rotating machinery and a smaller heat exchanger. Since only clean air circulates, fouling prob-

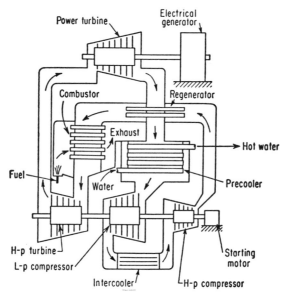

FIG. 15-3. A closed-cycle gas turbine operates at higher pressures.

lems are eliminated. A closed-cycle gas turbine gains these advantages at the cost of adding a recooler and an air heater in place of a simple combustor.

Q Sketch a single-stage-heated closed-cycle gas turbine and give the temperatures and pressures it needs for full-load operation.

A Figure 15-4 shows an Escher-Wyss system. Hot gases of 1268°F and 343 psi go into the high-pressure turbine from the combustor, and exhaust goes from the low-pressure turbine at 829°F and 96 psi. Air enters the low-pressure compressor at 61°F and 92 psi and leaves at 137°F and 347 psi.

Q How is the efficiency of a modern gas turbine increased?

A Gas-turbine efficiency is increased by converting more heat energy to mechanical energy. One way to do this is to raise the turbine inlet-

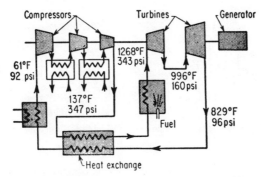

FIG. 15-4. A single-stage-heated closed-cycle gas-turbine system.

gas temperature, which, in turn, raises thermal efficiency. At higher temperatures, the best efficiency occurs at the higher pressure ratios. Increasing the temperature of the gas also betters both the air rate and the work ratio.

The next step is to add a regenerator (Fig. 15-5) to transfer heat from the exhaust to compressed air. The hotter air temperature recovered from waste heat cuts the fuel needed to bring the air up to the turbine inlet temperature. Next, add an intercooler (Fig. 15-6). Divide the compression

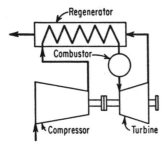

FIG. 15-5. Regenerator transfers heat from exhaust to compressed air.

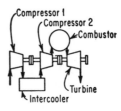

FIG. 15-6. Intercooler divides compressor into two parts.

into two parts so that the cooler air can be kept between them. Two intercoolers can be placed between three compressors, giving still more efficiency.

The next step is to split the turbine in two (Fig. 15-7) and to place a combustor before each turbine. The first combustor discharges high-temperature gas into the high-pressure turbine. As the gas does work on the turbine rotor, both its pressure and temperature drop. Partly expanded

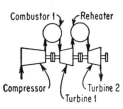

FIG. 15-7.   A combustor is placed before each turbine.

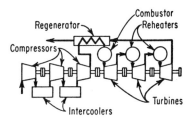

FIG. 15-8.   Turbine split into many
units.

gas then enters the second combustor and is reheated to its original temperature before going to the low-pressure turbine. Here it expands to
atmospheric pressure, while doing mechanical work. The turbine can be
split into many units for still more efficiency. Figure 15-8 shows how a
regenerator, intercoolers, and reheaters raise the efficiency of a turbine.
There are many variations to this design.

Q   Explain the intercooled, reheated-cycle two-shaft unit shown in Fig.
15-9.

A   This peak-load-carrying system generates 25 MW at 25°F air inlet.
When ambient temperature rises to 70°F, the capacity of the unit drops

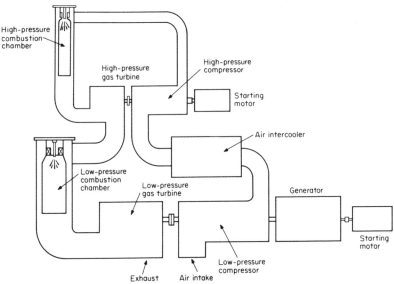

FIG. 15-9.   Intercooled, reheated-cycle two-shaft unit is ideal for peak loads.

to 21.6 MW. The maximum turbine inlet temperatures are held to 1200°F. This seven-stage low-pressure gas turbine drives both the low-pressure compressor and the generator at 3600 r/min.

The five-stage high-pressure turbine driving only the high-pressure compressor varies its speed from 3600 to 4500 r/min. Combustors burn either natural gas or heavy fuel oil. The overall pressure ratio of the cycle at full load is 15.5, one of the highest used.

Combustion chambers stand at the side of each set in the cycle. Each shaft has its own starting motor. The unit can carry full load from a cold start in only 20 min, making it ideal for peak loads.

Q Some aircraft jet engines are modified to take on jobs in stationary plants. Give the characteristics of one such unit.

A One jet engine is modified to produce shaft power and works as a gas generator. It has a 20-stage high-pressure turbine driving a 10-stage axial compressor at an overall compression ratio of 8. The high-pressure turbine exhausts into a single-stage low-pressure turbine turning at 19,500 r/min (some high-speed units go as high as 45,000 r/min) and developing full load at 1000 hp. Thermal efficiency with 1500°F in the annular combustor outlet is 21.4 percent.

Q Considering today's costly fuels, explain how gas turbines are combined with steam plants to utilize more Btu from fuel.

A High-temperature energy of the gas turbine's exhaust gas (which usually has an oxygen content of about 17 percent) is used for generating steam, instead of wasting it to the atmosphere (Fig. 15-10). In some installations, the gas turbine exhausts into a waste-heat boiler used for space heating. Or it is used to power a conventional steam turbine or engine

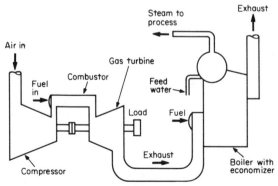

FIG. 15-10. Hot exhaust from gas turbine is used to generate steam in waste-heat boiler.

to generate additional shaft output. By using burners on the waste-heat boiler for supplementary firing, any desired amounts of steam can be thus generated.

COMPRESSORS AND COMBUSTORS

Q What types of compressors are used for gas turbines?
A Axial, centrifugal, and combined axial-centrifugal compressors are used for gas turbines.

The axial type, with various blading arrangements (Fig. 15-11), is the

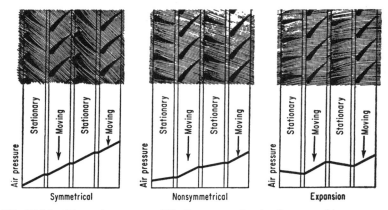

FIG. 15-11.   These three types of blading are used today for gas turbines.

most common. Symmetrical blading raises the air pressure uniformly, while nonsymmetrical blading causes a higher pressure rise in the moving blading. Expansion blading has fixed blades that expand the air as the moving blades do the compressing. For gas turbines, compressors must handle large volumes of air at high efficiencies and suitable pressure ratios.

Q Explain the construction of the various types of combustors.
A Combustors for open-cycle gas turbines are in effect direct-fired air heaters. After the air is compressed, the fuel is burned in the cycle air, raising the temperature before expansion takes place in the turbine. Inlet temperatures are limited to about 1500°F. The differences between combustors and fuel-burning equipment that affect power engineers are: (1) in a combustor, the desired product is hot flue gas and no heat is taken out in the chamber; (2) combustion takes place at 50 to 100 psi or more;

and (3) excess air is extremely high, around 500 percent. Most open-cycle combustors are all metal but operate at heat-release rates hundreds of times higher than boiler furnaces. Film cooling with an excess of air in the flame zone makes high heat loading practical.

Q Explain the construction of a single combustor.

A See Fig. 15-12. In a single combustor, air enters at the discharge end

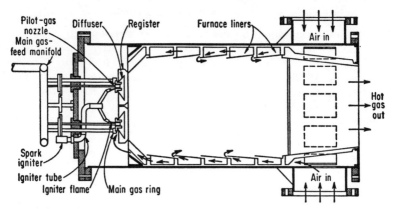

FIG. 15-12.   This single combustor receives air at the discharge end.

and moves counterflow to the travel of the flame. The air flows over ribbed liners that form the inner wall of the chamber. These liners are constructed of high-temperature alloys and are segmented for free expansion. Airflow between the liner segments forms an air film on the inner wall. Three parallel gas burners fire the combustor. The reason for having three burners instead of one is to reduce the burner-pressure loss; a wider flame front than could be had with one burner gives good temperature distribution at the outlet of the combustor.

Q How does the combustor power the gas-turbine cycle?

A Combustors burn fuel in the pressurized air after it leaves the compressor. Today's metallurgy limits the exit temperatures to about 1550°F for base loading of the turbine. Since fuels burn with a flame at about 3000°F, careful design is needed to ensure complete combustion.

Only about 25 to 30 percent of the air takes part in oxidizing the fuel. The remainder acts as a film coolant to preserve the combustor basket and as a diluent to cool the gas going to the turbine nozzles and buckets.

Q What kinds of fuels are used to power gas turbines?

A Fuels for combustors range from natural gas to distillate and residual oils. Just as with diesel engines, powdered coal has been experimented with, but disposal of the ash and its effect on blading are problems. Gas-turbine builders specify fuel characteristics to ensure trouble-free operation. For example, solid materials in a fuel gas should not exceed 30 ppm (parts per million) by weight. Size and density distribution of the dust must fall within certain limits. Water in the gas, above saturation, should not exceed ¼ percent by weight. Fuel flammability limits must also be known to ensure operating safety. The limits of flammability of a fuel indicate how well the fuel will burn in a combustor.

Q Have oil specifications for gas turbines been developed?
A Yes. Chemical properties become critical when turbine inlet temperatures exceed 1150°F. Sodium, sulfur, vanadium, and lead form corrosive compounds. Alkaline earths promote blade deposits in varying degrees. Ash-forming substances in the oil may be adjusted to reduce corrosion and to allow deposits that will shed after a few hours' shutdown of the turbine. Most residual oils must be treated.

Q How are gas turbines controlled?
A One way to control a gas turbine is to use a centrifugal governing system that raises the discharge to release air into a low-pressure accumulator. When the load increases, it slows down the turbine speed. The governor responds by admitting air to the system from a high-pressure accumulator. Small load reductions are handled by controlling the output without making use of the accumulators or changing the air pressure in the system. This is done by operating an air bypass from the high-pressure side to the low-pressure side of the circuit. The useful output of the plant is reduced when there is a slight variation in the load. Fuel consumption is also reduced when the load decreases.

OPERATION AND MAINTENANCE

Q What procedure would you follow if a unit was difficult to start?
A Check the low voltage if it is an electric motor starter. Low voltage might result from heavy loads on the electric system at other sources in the plant at starting time. If it is a pneumatic starting system, check for low air pressure. The starting motor, either electric or pneumatic, might be underpowered for the load. If the turbine does not turn freely, especially after overhaul, look for insufficient bearing clearances, misalignment of the coupling between the turbine and its compressor, or misalignment of the power takeoff coupling.

If the starting trouble is an excessive period of delay before the turbine becomes self-operating, the fuel-air mixture may be too lean or too rich.

Examine the igniters for fouling by corrosion, burning, or other deterioration. (First, compare the time delay with that set by the turbine manufacturer.) Normally, full ignition may be from 2 to 3 min, and full load by turbine in about 10 to 12 min after the first turnover.

Q What might cause the turbine to smoke and deposit excessive soot on rotor blades and in the heat exchanger?

A An overrich mixture of fuel feed, or fuel not suitable for the unit because of a high percentage of carbon residue and high viscosity. Both these characteristics are harmful for gas turbines.

Q What might cause power delivered at the power takeoff coupling to keep steadily decreasing?

A Not enough air from the compressor to achieve full power combustion, dirty intake air filter, or fuel carrying impurities into the combustor. Backpressure too high in the heat exchanger, regenerator, waste-heat boiler, or silencer. Insufficient fuel feed caused by fouled nozzles or obstruction in the oil line. Turbine blades may be fouled or corroded.

NOTE: With gas fuel, check the gas pressure.

Q Noise can be a problem, depending on local pollution laws. Explain how to correct a high-pitched and disturbing whine in gas turbines.

A A high-pitched whine is characteristic of a high-speed machine; some models rotate as high as 45,000 r/min. Whether or not such units are installed in areas having strict decibel-level ordinances, the machine must have a properly designed and installed silencer. If one is installed, the problem might be leakage from corroded areas, loosened baffling, or other silencer faults.

SUGGESTED READING

Elonka, Stephen M.: *Standard Plant Operators' Manual*, 3d ed., McGraw-Hill Book Company, New York, 1980 (has detailed "how to" illustrations of repairs, also information on heat transfer and fuels).

Elonka, Stephen M.: *Standard Basic Math and Applied Plant Calculations*, McGraw-Hill Book Company, New York, 1978 (has calculations on combustion, heat transfer, and efficiency).

16

COOLING TOWERS

Growth of population and industry places such demands on water supply that some form of conservation is necessary. This applies especially to water used for cooling. Because cooling-tower recirculation systems remove heat with minimum water loss, they are increasingly "musts" where water supply is limited, costs are high, or conservation is enforced by local codes. Air-cooled heat exchangers are used where water is scarce or is not available.

In performing their primary functions, power, process, and refrigeration systems all develop waste heat. This must be rejected from the primary system to a secondary system that physically removes it to a heat sink, either air or water, where the heat is dissipated. This secondary circuit is usually called a cooling system, but there are many types. The operating engineer must know the fundamentals of cooling by evaporation, major tower types, and maintenance, all of which we cover here.

BASICS

Q What is evaporation cooling?

A Perspiration helps to keep human beings cool by evaporation; it maintains their normal temperature of 98.5°F even though the atmospheric temperature is much warmer. Latent heat of evaporation is the primary cooling effect produced by blowing air over wet surfaces or through sheets of falling water in a cooling tower. Cooling-tower engineers refer to sensible heat (heat you can feel) as temperature; the higher the temperature of a substance, the greater is its sensible heat. When the atmospheric temperature is cooler than the water temperature, there is a tendency (discounting evaporation) for the air to cool the water; that is, for the air to get hotter (gain sensible heat), while the water gets cooler (loses sensible heat). An average of about 75 percent of the total heat removed is by evaporation (latent heat).

Q   Why is cooling water reused instead of wasted?

A   A big problem in operating refrigeration plants or condensing turbines is the removal and dissipation of the heat from the compressed refrigerant or from the exhaust steam. Heat is usually removed by transferring it to the water in a heat exchanger. From there, it may be dissipated in various ways. If the plant is near the ocean, a river, or a lake, the intake and discharge can be piped to prevent mixing the heated discharge water with the cooler inlet water. If the cooling-water source is a well or city water supply, the discharge may be piped back into the ground, a sewer, or an open waterway. But this waste of heated water is costly and, in some localities, illegal. The major reason for reusing cooling water is that few plants have a limitless water supply. Another consideration is the cost of using city water for cooling.

Since most water contains dissolved salts, the use of a continuous supply of raw water quickly coats the heat exchanger with scale. To lick this problem, a cooling tower is used. Here, water is cooled by exposing it to the air after each passage or cycle, and it can be reused a number of times.

Q   What is atmospheric water cooling?

A   By transferring the waste-heat load of the water to the atmosphere, you can reuse the same water in a continuous cycle. The heat is transferred by bringing water and air together indirectly (noncontact), as is done in an automobile radiator. Another method uses evaporative-cooling equipment, such as an atmospheric spray pond or a cooling tower. When water is cooled by evaporation losses, about 1000 Btu (heat units) is lost for each pound of water evaporated. The heat taken away in the water vapor is called the latent heat of vaporization. When air removes the heat (in vapor) from the water in this way, it can cool the water below the atmospheric temperature. This allows the water that is cooled by evaporation to serve plants having a great variety of temperature needs. It also permits a small quantity of water to cool a much greater heat load than if it were not cooled below the atmospheric temperature.

Q   Can a cooling tower cool water to a point below the wet-bulb temperature of the inlet air?

A   No. The final temperature of the cooling-tower water is always a few degrees above the wet-bulb temperature of the inlet air. (See Chap. 9, "Refrigeration," and Chap. 11, "Air Conditioning" for information on wet- and dry-bulb temperatures.) Water droplets splashing in the cooling tower wet the wood laths and expose a large surface of water to the upmoving air.

Q How can the cooling effect be speeded in a cooling tower?

A The cooling effect can be speeded by (1) increasing the air velocity over the wet surfaces, (2) increasing the exposed wet surface, (3) lowering the barometric pressure, (4) increasing the water temperature to the tower, and (5) reducing the humidity of the air.

Q What properties of air must cooling-tower designers consider?

A Cooling-tower designers must consider wet-bulb temperature, dry-bulb temperature, humidity, total heat in Btu, and air pressure, weight, and velocity.

Q What is meant by the cooling range?

A See Fig. 16-1. The cooling range is the degrees Fahrenheit that the

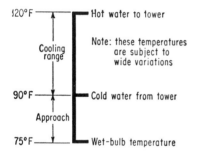

FIG. 16-1.   Cooling-range diagram.

water is cooled by the water-cooling equipment. It is the difference in the temperature between the hot water entering the cooling tower and the temperature of the cold water leaving the cooling tower.

Q What is meant by the approach?

A The approach is the difference in degrees Fahrenheit between the temperature of the cold water leaving the cooling tower and the wet-bulb temperature of the surrounding air.

Q What is meant by the heat load?

A The heat load is the amount of heat thrown away by the cooling tower in Btu per hour (or in Btu per minute). It is equal to the number of pounds of circulated water times the cooling range.

Q What is meant by drift?

A   The drift is the small amount of unevaporated water that is lost from the atmospheric water-cooling equipment in the form of mist or fine droplets. It is the water that is entrained by the circulating air. Stated another way, drift is the water loss, independent of the water lost by evaporation. Drift loss, unlike evaporation loss, can be reduced by good cooling-tower design.

Q   What is meant by water makeup?

A   The water needed to replace water that is lost by evaporation, drift, blowdown, and small leaks is known as water makeup. Evaporation losses average 0.80 percent of the water circulated for each 10°F range. The drift loss is the water carried away as droplets or mist by the air. In a well-designed induced-draft tower, the drift loss is about 0.10 percent. Most makers guarantee a drift loss of not over 0.20 percent. The amount of blowdown water wasted depends on the hardness of the circulating water, the type of water softening used, and the drift loss. Blowdown is controlled to keep the concentration of soluble and scale-forming solids below the point where scale forms or causes corrosion.

Q   What are some of the limitations of cooling towers?

A   Water that is cooled by spraying in the air cannot be cooled below the wet-bulb temperature of the air. So the condensing temperature at which the system will operate must be kept slightly above the wet-bulb temperature of the air. High-efficiency, forced- or induced-draft cooling towers will cool the condenser water to a point within 5 to 8°F of the prevailing wet-bulb temperature. Natural-draft towers seldom approach closer than 10 or 12°F of the wet-bulb temperature of the air. So, when selecting a cooling tower, it is best to increase the usual "design" wet-bulb temperature by 5 percent.

Q   What are some disadvantages of cooling towers when compared with evaporative condensers?

A   Natural-draft cooling towers depend upon the natural movement of the air, which is often unreliable. The adjacent structures or natural obstacles may deflect the breeze away from the tower. Or, a stiff breeze may cause an unusually large amount of water to be carried away from the natural-draft tower in the form of drift or air-entrained spray. This drift is often a nuisance to adjoining property. Because forced- or induced-draft towers depend on fans, they avoid these troubles. But, in freezing weather, the air must be reduced to a point where the spray water won't freeze in the sump, on the packing, or in the discharge of the tower. Furthermore, you must protect the overflow and makeup-water piping. In severe weather, you may need an auxiliary tank in the heated part of the building to accumulate the reserve water instead of using the sump in the tower. This extra tank allows the spray water to drain from the tower immediately.

COOLING SYSTEMS

Q What is a spray pond?
A See Fig. 16-2. A spray pond is made up of a number of spray nozzles that spray water droplets, not mist, into a water-collection basin. Louver

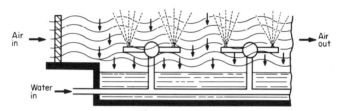

FIG. 16-2. Spray pond requires large land area, many sprinklers.

fences on the leeward side of the pond prevent the water droplets from being carried away. These enclosures are a must in restricted areas and on roof installations. Spray ponds are best suited for large-capacity service where top efficiency isn't too important and where moisture drift isn't objectionable. Spray ponds are cheaper than other cooling-tower installations, but basin costs and pumping needs are high.

Q What kinds of nozzles are used in spray ponds?
A Special nonclogging nozzles or spray heads are used in spray ponds. They operate at 3 to 15 psi (usually at 6 psi) and are spaced at 8- to 15-ft intervals on rows of pipe from 15 to 20 ft apart.

Q Describe an atmospheric cooling tower.
A See Fig. 16-3. Spray-filled atmospheric cooling towers (Fig. 16-3*a*) and packed atmospheric cooling towers (Fig. 16-3*b*) are designed for water-cooling needs of 30,000 to 40,000 Btu/min. Ranging from 6 to 15 ft high, these towers have a narrow spray pond with nozzles above it and a high louver fence. The nozzles spray downward.

Capacities range from 0.6 to 1.5 gal/(min)(ft²) of cooling-tower cross-sectional area. This is about one-fourth of the area needed by an equivalent spray pond. The louvers are always wet; hence, they add to the water surface exposed to the cooling air. Use these towers where (1) your equipment served can stand a few degrees rise in cold-water temperature at

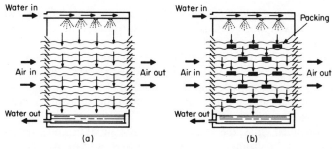

FIG. 16-3. Atmospheric towers are unpacked or spray-filled (a) or packed (b).

low or zero wind velocities, (2) drift from the cooling tower isn't objectionable, and (3) the tower can be placed so that the wind isn't cut off by other buildings, trees, etc.

Q Describe a mechanical-draft cooling tower.

A See Fig. 16-4. A mechanical-draft cooling tower is a vertical shell of

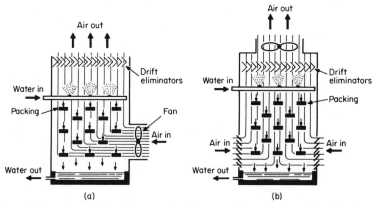

FIG. 16-4. Mechanical-draft towers have either forced-draft (a) or induced-draft (b) fans.

wood, metal, Transite, or masonry. Water is distributed near the top of the shell and falls to a collecting basin. As it falls, it passes through air that is circulated from the bottom to the top of the shell by either forced- or induced-draft fans. The air contacts the hottest water just before it leaves the tower. Because it passes against the flow of water, a given quantity of air picks up more heat than does an equal quantity of air on natural-draft equipment. So less air is needed to cool the same amount of water. Since the air is supplied by fans, the air quantity must be held to a minimum for low operating cost.

A mechanical-draft cooling tower may be filled with water droplets sprayed from nozzles, or it may be packed with a wood filling on which the water cascades from the top to the bottom of the tower. Other cooling towers combine some of the features of both the spray-filled and wood-filled designs.

In spray-filled types, the area cooled by the air is the combined surface area of the water droplets present in the tower at any one time. The net free cross-sectional area of the air spaces in a spray-filled tower is usually greater than that of a wood-filled tower for the same gross area. So there are lower air velocities and there is a longer contact time between air and water in the same sized structure for a spray-filled tower. Before discharging into the atmosphere, water-laden exhaust air passes through a drift (spray) eliminator that removes the water droplets.

In a wood-filled tower, lumber is laid through the tower both horizontally and vertically. Water, sprayed over the top layer of lumber by nozzles, troughs, or splash heads, drops from layer to layer. As the air moves upward or across the tower, it strikes a large wetted surface, repeatedly breaking up the falling water droplets and providing new droplet surfaces. The combined areas of these droplets are several times that of the wood-filled area.

The efficiency of these towers is improved by increasing the wood filling, the height or area of the tower, or the quantity of air supplied. Increasing the tower's height increases the time that the air is in contact with the water, without increasing the need for more fan power. And, increasing the tower's area while keeping the fan power constant increases the quantity of the air and the air-water contact time because of lower velocity. The water-surface area in contact with the air is increased in both cases.

Increasing the quantity of air decreases the time that the air is in contact with the water. But, since more air passes through the tower, the average difference between the water temperature and the wet-bulb temperature of the air is increased. This speeds up the heat-transfer rate.

More air means an increase in fan power. Air velocities in wood-filled towers vary from 250 to 400 ft/min. Since these towers don't depend on wind velocity, it is possible to design them for more exacting performance. They require less space and less piping than do atmospheric cooling towers. Pumping heads vary from 11 to 26 ft. The overall plant economy from the lower water temperature used by the wood-filled designs usually offsets their added operating expense and higher initial cost.

Q What is the basic principle of a forced-draft cooling tower?

A See Fig. 16-4. A forced-draft cooling tower works well with corrosive waters; since the fan can be near the ground, the parts most likely to corrode are easily serviced. However, the fan maintenance and depreciation costs of these units are high.

The main objective in these units is to have heated air leave the top of the tower at low velocity. But, at times, the air recirculates to the inlet of the fan, and with unfavorable winds, this cuts efficiency as much as 20 percent. During cold weather, recirculation can cause ice formations on nearby equipment, buildings, or in the fan ring of the tower, sometimes breaking the fan.

Because the fan size on these units is limited to a 12-ft diameter or less, more fans, motors, starters, and wiring are needed for larger towers than for the same-sized induced-draft towers. The latter can use fans with up to an 18-ft diameter. However, forced-draft cooling towers offer a neater appearance and are more adaptable to architectural surroundings. Noise is minimized by locating the fan at the top of the tower.

Q Describe a counterflow, induced-draft cooling tower.
A See Fig. 16-4. In a counterflow, induced-draft cooling tower, the fan is mounted at the top. The air movement is vertical, across the filling, and upward at a high velocity to prevent recirculation. If the unit is to handle small loads, the fan is mounted at one end to give a horizontal airflow.

Q Describe a crossflow induced-draft cooling tower.
A See Fig. 16-5. Demands for a compact design, better construction,

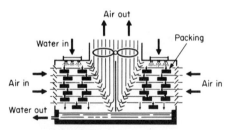

FIG. 16-5.   Crossflow (double-flow) induced-draft towers are compact.

lower cost, larger capacity, more flexible operation, and improved all-round performance produced the double-flow cooling tower. It is also called a common-flow tower. The airflow is horizontal, and fans are centered along the top. Each fan draws air through two cells that are paired to a suction chamber partitioned midway beneath the fan and fitted with drift eliminators to turn the air upward toward the fan outlet. Double-flow towers use low pumping heads, which vary from 11 to 26 ft.

The operating advantages of double-flow cooling towers are: (1) Horizontal (crossflow) air movement, as the water falls in a cascade of small drops over the filling and across the airstream, results in less resistance to airflow and, therefore, a lower draft loss. (2) Air travel is longer than in a conventional design. (3) The open water-distribution basin is accessible for cleaning during operation. (4) The close-spaced wood and diffusion deck under the water basin results in uniform water distribution to the wood filling. (5) Water loading in most cooling towers has a maximum of 6 gal/(min)(ft²) caused by a blanketing spray effect. But, a heavier loading, up to 10 gal/(min)(ft²), is possible in double-flow towers for steam-condenser service. (6) Modern double-flow units occupy less than one-twentieth of the area needed by a spray pond for the equivalent service.

Q Why are evaporative condensers often used instead of cooling towers?
A Evaporative condensers overcome some of the serious disadvantages of cooling towers. Figure 16-6 shows that the water-cooled condenser is

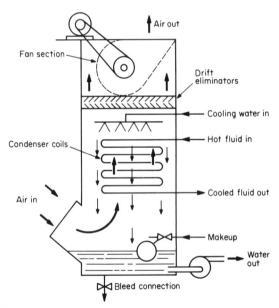

FIG. 16-6.   Evaporative condensers reduce water loss, cut pump-horsepower needs.

missing. Hot gas from the discharge of the compressor goes directly to the condensing coil inside the evaporative condenser. There, it condenses to a liquid and runs off to the receiver. Heat is removed from the condensing gas by water evaporating directly on the coil. Evaporation is speeded by an airstream induced by the fans. Then the water remaining after the evaporation drips to the sump, collects, and flows to the spray pump for recirculation. The pump horsepower of an evaporative condenser is much less than in a cooling tower. One reason for this is that there is shorter piping and less spray water to resist water flow. And water losses are much less than the water losses from a natural-draft tower. Because this condenser creates its own air movement, it can be installed either outside or indoors. But, if installed indoors, it must have a fresh-air supply and a way to discharge humid air.

Q   What is a hyperbolic cooling tower?

A   See Fig. 16-7. A hyperbolic tower is like a huge chimney—a closed

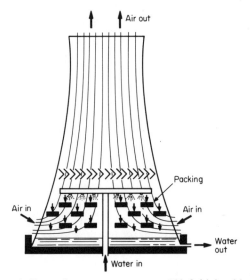

FIG. 16-7.   Hyperbolic cooling towers are up to 560 ft high, either induced- or forced-draft.

natural-draft design. Heavier outside air enters around the base of the tower and displaces lighter saturated air in the tower, forcing it up and out the top. Cooling water distributed over the packing flows countercurrent to the induced air.

Q   What are some of the outstanding advantages of hyperbolic cooling towers?

A   (1) Because of their height, ground fogging and recirculation of warm, moist vapor do not occur. (2) Atmospheric air for direct water cooling is induced through the tower by thermal power created by heating and humidifying the air. (3) Operation is assured even at zero wind conditions, which is contrary to the blow-through atmospheric tower. (4) No moving equipment is needed to create airflow. Power is used only for pumping. (5) Inspection and maintenance are cut to a minimum.

In general, the hyperbolic natural-draft tower is at its best when the difference between the desired cold-water temperature and the wet-bulb temperature is equal to or greater than the difference between the hot-water temperature and the cold-water temperature. In cooling-tower language this would be an approach equal to or greater than the range. Airflow through a natural-draft tower increases during the cooler months. This increase will offset the loss of heat transfer driving force at the lower wet-bulb temperature. This loss cannot be offset in mechanical-draft towers without increasing the air rate at the expense of using more fan horsepower.

Q Describe the operation of a hyperbolic cooling tower.

A These towers usually operate in parallel. Ths discharge pipe from the condenser delivers water to an upper culvert, which opens into the annular culverts around each tower. The amount of water diverted to any one tower can be controlled by penstocks. A simple sluice valve controls the intake to each distributor pipe within the cooling stack. After coming through the tower, the cooled water collects in a pond underneath. The walls of the pond are about 10 ft high. A wall usually divides the pond in halves so that one half can be shut off and cleaned while the other half works. All the ponds connect through penstocks to the suction culvert, and both the suction and discharge culverts can be sectionalized. Any tower can be completely isolated from its neighbor. A drain culvert usually runs along the rear of each pond for bleeding water to reduce concentration from evaporation. Penstocks control the drains.

Q Sketch a typical cooling-tower system.

A See Fig. 16-8. Here, water from the sump under the tower flows to the circulating pump by gravity. The pump forces the water through the condenser where it picks up heat from the condensing refrigerant. Warm water from the condenser goes to the sprays in the cooling tower where it is broken into drops and falls over the wood slats or packing. The drops, while traveling through the air and over the tower packing, are exposed to a blast of air induced by the cooling-tower fan. Although part of the water evaporates in this airstream, most of it is cooled. This cooled water collects in the sump and flows to the pump for reuse.

Q Describe the air-cooled heat exchanger (ACHE).

A See Fig. 16-9. Air-cooled heat exchangers are as common as the radia-

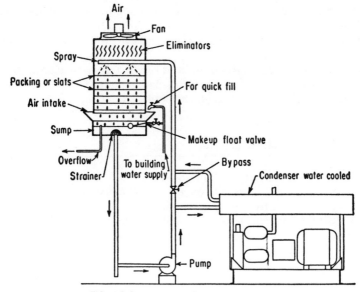

FIG. 16-8.   Basic cooling-tower system.

tor in your automobile; they are often called industrial radiators or simply
dry coolers. Basically, an ACHE consists of a bundle of finned tubes which
are rolled or welded into headers. Ambient air is moved across the tube
bundle by an induced- or forced-draft fan or by natural draft.

The warm fluid, circulating through the tubes, gives up part of its heat
to the air, which is then expelled to the atmosphere above or around

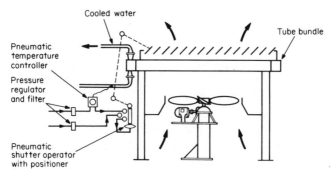

FIG. 16-9.   An air-cooled heat-exchanger fan blows cooling air through hot tube
bundle.

the unit's circumference. Different types of tubes, headers, and fans combine to form a wide variety of overall designs. The aim of each is to carry away unwanted heat as efficiently as possible, with minimum maintenance, vibration, and noise.

The main advantage of ACHE is that air is always available, while water is not. Use of air also eliminates cost and space required for cooling towers, water pumps, treating equipment, chemicals, and piping.

OPERATION AND MAINTENANCE

Q How would you start a cooling tower for the first time?

A Before starting a cooling tower for the first time, clean and inspect it. Remove any dirt from the catch basin. Check the fan for loose bolts. Make sure that the fan turns freely and that the clearance between the blade tip and the fan cylinder is OK. All the bolts on the fan driveshaft must be in place, and the flexible couplings or universal joints must be in good condition. The driveshaft guards should be secured. Check the alignment of the speed reducer, driveshaft, and motor; make sure they are lubricated. Open the vent connection at the top of the speed reducer and tighten all the bolts. Tighten the motor frame and anchor the bolts; but do not tighten too much or the wood will break when it swells. Check the nozzles, flumes, piping, and expansion joints in the walls and floor of the concrete basins. Inspect the makeup float valve and make sure that the overflow is open.

Q Why should you inspect the fans on a new cooling tower?

A Inspect the fans on a new cooling tower to make sure that they run freely and rotate in the right direction. Check the power input of the fans' motors. If the motors aren't loaded to their specified horsepower, the fan-blade pitch must be reset. New speed reducers may be noisy but will quiet down after a time. If not, excessive wear is the cause.

Q What would cause insufficient water supply?

A Insufficient water supply can be caused by (1) pump speed, pressure, or binding; (2) scale in the condenser; (3) air, dirt, or restrictions in the lines; or (4) partially closed valves.

Q How would you operate an induced-draft cooling tower in the winter?

A Shut down some cells and flow all the water over the remaining cells. Run the two-speed motors at slow speed, or shut off some of the fans. Reduce the water flow to the tower. Bypass the cooling tower with part of the water.

Q How would you deice a cooling tower?

A Ice forms on the cooling-tower louvers and fillings. To deice a tower, reverse the rotation of the fan to blow warm air out through the louvers. Stop some fans, but don't shut off the water. When the cells are thawed, start the fans and repeat this process on the other cells. If the tower operates intermittently, protect the exposed piping against freezing. This depends on the length of the shutdown and the weather.

Q How long is it safe to run a fan in reverse?
A Don't run a fan in reverse for more than 5 to 10 min. Few speed reducers supply oil to the upper fanshaft bearing when reversed, and the lube pump may not deliver oil when reversed, which would cause bearing failure. Thrust bearings and screw threads can also cause major troubles when the fan is reversed. Keep this answer in mind and proceed with caution unless you are sure of the proper operation.

Q What is algae formation in a cooling tower?
A Algae is a green, slimy growth that plugs the nozzles and prevents proper water distribution over the tower filling. It collects on equipment served by the cooling tower, reducing the heat-transfer rate. To keep algae at a minimum or to eliminate it, add a little chlorine, copper sulfate, potassium permanganate, or other chemicals to the circulating water. Some forms of plant life are difficult and build up tolerance to these chemicals. It is frequently necessary to use the services of a specialist.

Q How is scale prevented in cooling towers?
A While most water has some scale-forming materials, calcium and magnesium carbonates and sulfates cause most of the trouble in water-cooling systems. Scale reduces the heat-transfer rates. You can reduce or prevent scale by softening the makeup water with lime and soda ash, zeolite, or some of the several phosphates. Water softening or treatment requires close regulation and control by a chemist. Too high a concentration of soluble solids in the cooling-tower water raises the effective wet-bulb temperature. This, in turn, raises the temperature of the water leaving the tower and can cause sludge deposits or corrosion in the system. You can usually control the concentration of solids by either blowing down or keeping a continuous water overflow to a sewer.

Q What is delignification?
A Wood fibers contacting sodium carbonate in the circulating water dissolve the lignin that binds the fibers together. The wood surface becomes white and fibrous, eventually losing its structural strength. Trouble spots are the parts that are alternately wet and dry. Sodium carbonate, in harmful amounts, usually has a high pH value of 9 to 11. The effect of sodium carbonate may be neutralized with sulfuric acid. For the best results, carry the pH value at 7 to 7.5 (a 7.2 pH value is normal for redwood).

Q Why are two-speed fan drives used for cooling towers?
A Because of winter operation and temporary or seasonal drops in the

heat load, two-speed fan drives are used with cooling towers. At one-half speed, the fans need only about 15 percent of their full-speed power. The hot- and cold-water temperatures in a cooling tower increase 6 to 8°F for a given wet-bulb temperature at one-half fan speed. With a wet-bulb temperature of 10°F below the design temperature, the fan can run at one-half speed. Here, the same cooling range is obtained for a given amount of water. When the wet-bulb temperature and range are the same (and the hot- and cold-water temperatures are 6 to 8°F above normal), the tower needs a 60 percent more effective cooling area if the fans are run at one-half speed than if they are run at full speed. In winter, when it is not cold enough to stop the fans but when it is still cold enough to form ice at the full fan speed, you can run some or all of the fans at one-half speed.

Q   What six steps are needed in sizing the pump and pipe of any cooling-tower installation?
A   (1) Determine the amount of water in gallons per minute to be circulated to the tower. (2) Make a layout of the complete piping system. (3) Determine the static head and pressure drop through all units other than the pipe and fittings. (4) Select the pump. (5) Size the pipe. (6) Check the sizes of the pump and the pipe.

Q   How do you determine the amount of water in gallons per minute to be circulated to a cooling tower?
A   For air-conditioning and refrigeration cooling towers, the water flow required can usually be determined from the tower manufacturer's data. The average cooling-tower application requires 3 to 5 gal/(min)(ton). For cooling jobs other than air conditioning and refrigeration, the amount of water needed must be determined from the cooling load.

Q   Do cooling towers need automatic sprinklers for fire protection?
A   If induced-draft cooling towers are made of wood, have a roof over their fans, and have their supporting structure on the roof, they need automatic sprinklers. But, if they are the forced-draft type, with no roof, and if the fans are at the base to force the air up through the tower, they do not need automatic sprinklers.

Q   What mechanical maintenance does a cooling tower require?
A   Set up a preventive maintenance schedule for your cooling towers. Grease and oil the bearings and check the motor insulation yearly. Refill the speed reducers every 3000 hr. Look for oil leaks around the fan drive-shaft caused by worn oil seals. Keep the fan blades and hubs painted to avoid corrosion. Tighten the blade clamps and hub bolts and rebalance the fans when needed. Check the clearances and air gaps periodically as well as lubrication.

Q What structural maintenance does a cooling tower require?
A Replace or repair damaged cooling-tower parts immediately. Remove scale, dirt, bugs, and debris; then clean and paint the metal parts. Tighten any loose bolts, but remember that the wood swells. Drift eliminators reduce the airflow when they are dirty; so keep them clean. Wash the dirt from the wood-filling slats.

Q How do you shut down a cooling tower?
A When shutting down a cooling tower, drain it to prevent freezing and corrosion. Leave the drain open so that rain and melted snow can escape. Once a week, run the fans for 5 min in order to keep the upper fanshaft bearing oiled. Protect the metal parts from corrosion. While the tower is shut down, do any necessary maintenance and repair work so that it will be ready for the next season.

Q What is a good maintenance schedule for key tower components?
A Here is a weekly, monthly, and seasonal shutdown and start-up program provided by the Hartford Steam Boiler Inspection and Insurance Company; it should be followed:

Component	Weekly	Monthly	Seasonal shutdown	Seasonal start-up
Fan motor		Check mounting bolts	Clean and cover	Lubricate, if required; tighten mounting bolts
Speed reducer	Check oil level, visual inspection	Check oil level, check mounting bolts	Overfill with oil, clean and cover	Refill with new oil and tighten mounting bolts
Fan wheel	Visual inspection, clean foreign matter	Check bolts, check "set screws"	Clean and cover	Clean and paint hub, check blade pitch
Drive shaft	Visual inspection	Check shaft alignment	Clean and cover	Realign
Distribution system	Remove foreign matter	Remove foreign matter	Drain and clean	Inspect and clean
Cold-water basin	Remove foreign matter	Remove foreign matter	Drain and clean	Inspect and clean
Sump and screen	Remove foreign matter	Remove foreign matter	Drain line and shut off	Inspect and clean
Float valve	Visual inspection	Check valve operation	Drain line and shut off	Check operation
Overflow	Visual check	Visual check		Tighten bolts
Connections	Visual check	Tighten bolts		

Q Do the EPA and local environmental laws concern cooling towers?
A Yes, they are often strict on heat and moisture released to the atmosphere, and also on noise and chemicals used in water treatment escaping to the atmosphere.

SUGGESTED READING

Elonka, Stephen M.: *Standard Plant Operators' Manual*, 3d ed., McGraw-Hill Book Company, New York, 1980 (has information on treating cooling-tower water).

Moore, Arthur H., and Stephen M. Elonka: *Electrical Systems and Equipment for Industry*, Robert E. Krieger Publishing Company, Melbourne, Fla., 1977 (has basic data on motors for all industrial equipment).

17

BUILDING HEATING

Creating comfortable conditions in closed-in spaces is done by heating or cooling. But trying to please all the occupants gets complicated because buildings gain and lose heat. The sun's rays warm them, and the cold winds chill them. And some heat leaks out, while some cold leaks in. Too—human bodies inside are all heat engines, which require heating at times and cooling at other times.

And so conditions change from hour to hour, day to day, and season to season. The purpose of the building heating system is to adjust for these differences, supplying just enough heat to hold conditions needed for comfort. This requires various heat-transfer devices, located where needed. Here we cover the building heating systems, including today's solar systems.

BASICS

Q Explain three basic ways that heat travels.

A See Fig. 17-1. Heat travels by conduction, convection, and radiation.

Conduction results from heat flowing from one part of a body to another or from one body to another body through direct contact. Poor conductors are called insulators.

Convection currents can be set up in any fluid (gas), for example, in a moving stream of hot air rising to heat something further away. If a pump or fan, instead of natural action, moves the heated fluid, it is forced convection.

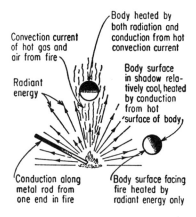

Convection current of hot gas and air from fire

Radiant energy

Body heated by both radiation and conduction from hot convection current

Body surface in shadow relatively cool, heated by conduction from hot surface of body

Conduction along metal rod from one end in fire

Body surface facing fire heated by radiant energy only

FIG. 17-1. Conduction, radiation, and convection at work.

Radiation travels in straight lines from the heat source, such as from the sun, and is unaffected by air currents. It can be focused, absorbed, or reflected. A black body absorbs radiant heat easily; polished-metal surfaces reflect radiant heat.

Q What is the coefficient of conductivity?
A See Fig. 17-2. The resistance of an object to heat flow can be predicted. Hence, heavy, dense materials transmit heat by conduction faster than do lighter, less dense materials. The heat-transfer property of a material

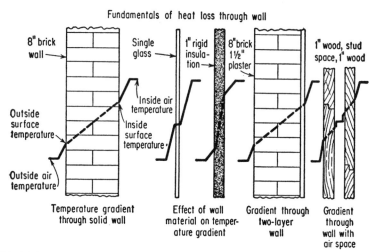

Fundamentals of heat loss through wall

8" brick wall

Single glass

1" rigid insulation

8" brick 1½" plaster

1" wood, stud space, 1" wood

Inside air temperature

Inside surface temperature

Outside surface temperature

Outside air temperature

Temperature gradient through solid wall

Effect of wall material on temperature gradient

Gradient through two-layer wall

Gradient through wall with air space

FIG. 17-2. Temperature gradient through walls depends on material and its thickness.

is measured by the letter k, which is known as the coefficient of conductivity. For example, brick has a k of 5.0. This means that 5 Btu/hr can pass through a 1-in. thick 1-ft² brick for each degree Fahrenheit difference between the outside and inside temperatures of the brick. The heat flow through a 10-in. brick is only 5.0 divided by 10, or 0.5. So, the thicker the insulation, the smaller the heat loss.

RULE: For solid, uniform materials, the rate of flow k is given for a 1-in. thickness. To get the rate of flow for any other thickness, divide k by the actual thickness (inches) of the material.

Q What is surface conductance?
A The number of Btu per hour transmitted to or from a 1-ft² surface, with a temperature difference of 1°F between the air and the surface, is called the surface conductance or f. But several factors affect the value of f. For instance, the rougher the surface or the greater the air movement past the surface, the higher f will be. For practical work, the inside coefficient is taken as 1.65 and the outside coefficient as 6.00. Figure 17.2 compares the temperature gradients through a pane of glass and a sheet of rigid insulation. Glass offers little or no resistance to heat flowing through it. So the surface resistances are the most important part of the total. By comparison, insulation resists the heat flowing through it so strongly that the surface resistances are insignificant.

Q What is the overall coefficient?
A You can save a lot of figuring by using the overall coefficients of a material. Overall coefficients have been determined for all the usual wall, floor, and ceiling constructions. It is called the U and represents the Btu per hour that flows through 1 ft² of a given wall construction for each degree Fahrenheit difference between the inside and outside temperatures. Most insulating materials have many small pores containing air. Reflective insulations, such as aluminum foil, stop heat transfer by radiation. The heat loss through glass windows is large and can be reduced by using double windows with an air space between them.

Q What are infiltration losses?
A Air leaks into and out of buildings around doors, windows, etc. The leakage into a building is known as infiltration. It brings in fresh air, but outgoing air carries away heat. Keep this leakage to a minimum by adjusting the incoming supply with positive controls, such as dampers, weather stripping, and calking.

Q What are the five basic mediums for heating?
A Steam, hot water, warm air, electricity, and solar, are the five basic heating mediums. Steam and hot water are usually generated at a central point and distributed through pipes to the heat-transfer surfaces in the

spaces to be heated. Hot air is circulated by either fans or natural means. Hot air may be heated directly from the furnace surfaces or by steam or hot-water coils. Electric heaters are light and easy to spot in most locations. Solar heating is covered at the end of this chapter.

Q What are some of the advantages of hot-water heating?
A The main claim for hot-water heating is ease of control. Because the heating medium is a liquid, the amount of heat given up depends mostly on the temperature difference between the room air and the hot water. So by varying the quantity or temperature of the water, you can get accurate control.

Q What are some of the advantages of warm-air heating?
A Warm-air heating offers positive air circulation and ventilation, and it is fairly easy to filter, humidify, or treat the air. Warm-air heating forms a natural complement to summer air conditioning and is usually the most rapid system to start.

Q What are some of the advantages of steam heating?
A Since steam gives up a large amount of heat by condensation, only a small amount needs to be circulated (1/50 by weight or 1/30 by volume), as compared with water. High heat-transfer rates allow small heating surfaces. Steam pressure assures positive circulation without pumps, making steam systems flexible and fairly cheap to install.

Q What are some advantages of electric heating systems?
A Heating with electricity has been increasingly popular in the last decade. Technically, there is no heating job that can't be done as well electrically as by any other method; some are done better, although the direct cost of heating is higher by electricity than by other means.

Q What are some advantages of infrared for comfort heating?
A It provides efficient, controllable heat; spot or limited-area heating is often best served by this method. For example, large spaces may be heated by a suitably designed infrared system because these systems project from 50 to 80 percent of their total heat input to the floor, without inducing air motion. And there is the ease of relocation to meet changing needs.

HEATING SYSTEMS

Q What is a one-pipe upfeed steam system?
A See Fig. 17-3. This is the simplest type of steam system. Steam enters and condensate leaves the radiator, or convector, through a single pipe connection. The steam supply cannot be throttled. When the supply main

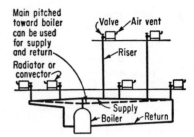

FIG. 17-3. A one-pipe hookup is simple.

(the dotted line in the sketch) pitches toward the boiler, it also serves as a return, with condensate and steam flowing in opposite directions. The use of a separate return (full line) to carry the condensate from the risers to the boiler reduces the interference between the steam and the condensate. When the supply mains run above the waterline in the boiler, they are called dry returns; when they run below the waterline, they are referred to as wet returns. Vents on the radiators relieve the air from these units but close when the steam reaches the vent. If the radiator is designed so that the vent can be adjusted, these valves may be used for balancing the system.

Q Explain the two-pipe steam system.
A See Fig. 17-4. In a two-pipe steam system, the separate flow of the

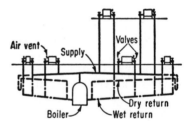

FIG. 17-4. A two-pipe system has either a wet or dry return to the boiler.

steam and condensate permits the handling of larger quantities without excessive pipe sizes. But two connections are needed at the radiator, with a valve in each. Air is removed by the vent valve on the radiator, and the supply valves can be throttled. A two-pipe system is better for large buildings; it can be piped for downfeed as well as for upfeed. In a wet-return scheme (the dot-dash lines in the sketch), the return header runs below the boiler-water level. Here, the water seal is at the lower end of each connection in order to prevent the steam from flowing into the radiators through the return connections. This can happen in a dry-return system (the dash lines in the sketch) unless the seals are added as shown.

Q Explain a one-pipe downfeed steam system.
A See Fig. 17-5. A one-pipe downfeed steam system is used in buildings of four stories or more. Smaller piping can be used because, while the steam and condensate flow in the same pipe, they move in the same direction. Therefore, resistance is less than in an upfeed system.

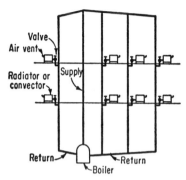

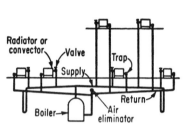

FIG.   17-5. Downfeed   one-pipe steam-heating system for large building.

FIG. 17-6. Vapor system works at lower pressure than a steam-heating system.

Q Explain the vapor heating system.
A See Fig. 17-6. The performance and control of a vapor heating system depend a great deal on how the air is removed and how the condensate is returned to the boiler. If the vent valve on the radiator is replaced by a thermostatic trap at the outlet, the air can be vented through a larger opening and its return prevented. Air is removed from the system at central points by air eliminators, usually float-and-thermostatic traps. Since this system operates at low pressure, it is called a vapor system. The throttling supply valve partly fills the radiator, giving a simple means of controlling the heat output. Other advantages claimed for vapor systems are better air removal with faster heat-up, more uniform heating, and economy of operation.

Q Explain the vacuum heating system.
A See Fig. 17-7. In a vacuum heating system, a pump pulls the air and condensate through the return lines. Return risers connect to a common main that slopes downward toward the vacuum pump. The pump withdraws both air and water from the system, expels the air, and pumps the water back to the boiler. By keeping a vacuum on the return side, there is greater differential throughout the system, which speeds the filling of the radiators. The connection from the supply to the return side should

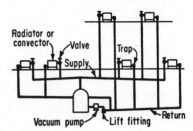

FIG. 17-7. Vacuum system with pump for returning condensate to boiler.

always be through a trap. If the return must drop below the inlet level of the vacuum pump, a lift fitting in the return is used to raise the condensate. You can use a float-controlled accumulator or receiver tank at the low point of the return, near the pump.

Q How does a one-pipe hot-water system work?

A See Fig. 17-8. The supply and return lines of a one-pipe hot-water system that go to each radiator have separate risers; both are connected to one supply main, which makes a loop back to the boiler. Special fittings, connecting the risers to the supply main, divert a portion of the water flow through the radiator. Successive radiators receive slightly cooler water because of the partial mixing of the returns from the preceding radiators with the supply water. A circulating pump moves the water through the system. A one-pipe system is used mostly in small buildings.

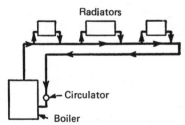

FIG. 17-8. Pump circulates heated water through one-pipe hot-water system.

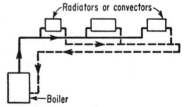

FIG. 17-9. Separate return piping is used in this two-pipe hot-water heating system.

Q Explain a two-pipe hot-water system.

A See Fig. 17-9. In a two-pipe hot-water system, the water flows from the supply main to a radiator or convector and then back to a separate return main that leads to the boilers.

Q What is a separately fired unit heater?

A See Fig. 17-10. It is an oil- or gas-fired, hot-air furnace, usually placed

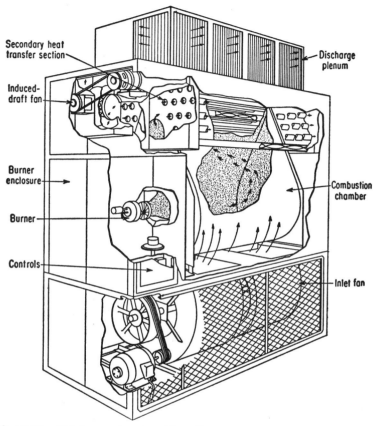

Secondary heat
transfer section

Discharge
plenum

Induced-
draft fan

Burner
enclosure

Combustion
chamber

Burner

Controls

Inlet fan

FIG. 17-10. Unit heater, burning either oil or gas, is placed in the space to be heated.

directly in the space to be heated. It is used when steam or hot water isn't available or when piping would be costly. These units range from small gas-fired propeller-fan types to large centrifugal-blower designs. Some have outputs of 400,000 Btu/hr or more. They discharge directly to the space to be heated or into a duct-distribution system. Some very large units fire coal or oil. The advantage of an oil- or gas-fired unit is that either fuel can be burned, depending on which is the most economical or the most readily available.

Q   What is the reversed-return hot-water system?
A   See Fig. 17-11. Here, the direction of the water flow in the return main is reversed to equalize the length of the circuits and, hence, to lower

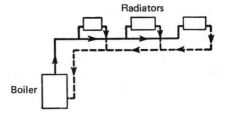

FIG. 17-11. Reversed-return hot-water heating system has lower resistance.

the piping resistances. Downfeed is customary in larger buildings, with either natural or forced circulation.

Q How does the central warm-air system work?
A There are different types of central warm-air systems. One arrangement has radiators or convectors that take care of the heat losses. Air that is warmed to room temperature is circulated for ventilation. Another scheme uses both radiators and heated air which divide the heat needs. Where ventilation is important, all the air may be drawn in from the outside, heated, and circulated. The wasted air is then sent back to the atmosphere.

Q Describe a high-pressure steam-vapor (HPSV) heating unit.
A Figure 17-12 shows a floor-mounted unit of this type. Air is pulled in close to the floor level, passes over an extended heating surface, and is discharged from the directing nozzles at the top of the unit. The positions

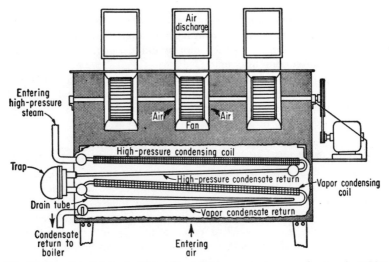

FIG. 17-12. Special dual coil handles high-pressure steam and vapor in HPSV unit.

of the heating coils, fans, and outlets are usually arranged as in the sketch. Here, high-pressure steam heats the incoming air that is drawn around the finned coils. There are many other types of steam-heating units.

Q Describe an electric heating system using resistance units.

A In Fig. 17-13 a unit ventilator which introduces outdoor air for room

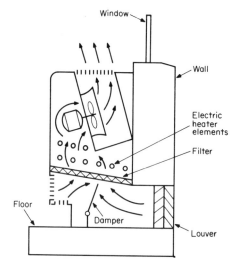

FIG. 17-13. Unit ventilator mixes inside and outside air, heats with resistance elements.

ventilation and provides heat when needed is shown. Resistance heating elements are used in conjunction with a fan, a damper, and an optional filter in a metal cabinet. Usually floor-mounted under a window, they resemble an air-conditioning unit.

The temperature of the air discharged by an electric unit ventilator is automatically adjusted to maintain desired room comfort. If heat is needed, the heaters are turned on. If cooling is needed, the heaters are turned off and outside air is introduced, up to 100 percent if necessary.

Q Describe an electric heating system using infrared units.

A In Fig. 17-14 line voltage controls the infrared heaters. This system is usually used for specialized applications where conventional thermostats are impractical. The heating rate of an individual infrared unit may be varied by an input controller or by a percentage timer.

High-intensity infrared units for comfort heating are used in three ways: (1) total space heating in which an entire plant is heated, (2) area heating in which only a small area within a plant is occupied and must be heated, and (3) spot heating in which each work station is treated as a separate heating problem.

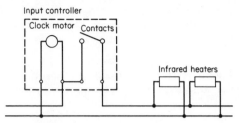

FIG. 17-14. Line-voltage control of infrared heaters uses motor-operated input controller capable of handling heater current.

The infrared sources most commonly used today are the quartz tube and quartz lamp. The quartz-tube heater has a coiled nichrome element supported by a tube. A quartz lamp heater is similar to an incandescent lamp but operates at a lower temperature, around 4000°F.

SYSTEM COMPONENTS

Q Why is an expansion tank needed in a hot-water system?
A See Fig. 17-15. An expansion tank takes care of changes in the water volume. If the expansion tank is set high enough to put enough pressure on the highest radiator, it keeps the water from boiling at the top temperature. In a forced system, the tank is connected close to the pump on the suction side. In gravity systems, it connects to the flow riser. A closed

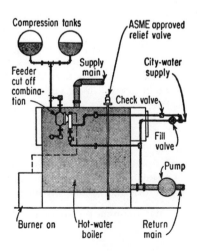

FIG. 17-15. Expansion tanks take care of changes in the heated water's volume.

expansion tank permits higher pressures. An automatic-feed valve and a relief valve, connected in series between the outside water supply and the heater, automatically keep the system full, as shown in the sketch.

Q What is a Hartford loop or Underwriters loop?

A A Hartford loop is confined usually to heating boilers. See Fig. 17-16. Where the condensate returns go directly to the boiler, as in the

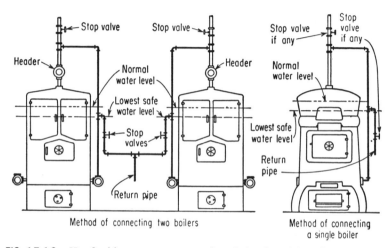

FIG. 17-16. Hartford loop prevents water from being forced into the return line.

sketch, a great pressure difference between the boiler and the returns may cause damage to the boiler. This can be due to water that is forced out of the boiler into a leaking return line, which, in turn, lowers the boiler-water level and uncovers parts of the boiler's heating surface. To prevent this, some boilers have a check valve in the returns. But the checks sometimes stick open and often leak badly.

The Hartford loop is simple and reliable. The supply line runs from the boiler steam space to a point near the bottom of the water space. The return line runs from the heating system to the supply line at a point above the highest level of the boiler heating surface but below the usual boiler-water level. If the boiler-water level drops below this point (because of a leaking return or cracked fitting), the steam from the boiler will enter the return and reduce any further loss of water from the boiler.

Q What common systems are used to supply heat from radiators?

A (1) Direct radiation, which places the radiators in the rooms to be heated. (2) Indirect radiation, where the radiators are placed outside the spaces to be heated. The heat is conveyed to the areas to be heated by forcing air through the radiators with fans. (3) Semi-indirect radiation, where radiators are installed in the spaces to be heated. Outside air is blown into the areas to be heated through the radiators.

Q Where should radiators and hot-air registers be placed to give the best results?

A Radiators and hot-air registers should be located as near as possible to the area of greatest heat loss, which is usually beneath the windows.

REASONS: (1) The heat radiated counteracts the effects of the heat lost through the windows. (2) Cold air that comes in through the window is warmed before it reaches the interior of the room. (3) Air currents from the heaters pass upward, mingling with the cold air that leaks in. This forms a screen of warm air that protects against window drafts. (4) Radiators placed under the windows save walls from becoming discolored. While direct radiation can be beneath windows, builders find it easier to place heat registers on the inside walls, even though this sacrifices heating efficiency.

Q Describe various ways to feed condensate back to the boiler in a steam-heating system.

A Condensate in a steam system can be fed back to the boiler by: (1) Gravity, where the piping is arranged so all the condensate can drain back to the boiler. (2) Return traps, where the boiler pressure forces the condensate back to the boiler. (3) Receivers and pumps, where the water drains to a receiver tank. A float in the tank actuates a steam valve (or a switch does the job if electric pumps are used) and starts the feed pump. (4) A vacuum pump, which operates effectively to return the condensate to the boiler and to maintain a slight vacuum in the system.

Q Explain how a special fitting in a one-pipe hot-water system causes circulation through a radiator.

A See Fig. 17-17. These fittings are installed at either or both of the riser connections to the supply main, depending on the diversion capacity needed. The fitting provides positive diversion to a fraction of a gallon by varying the water velocity through the main. The resistance created does not limit the number of fittings installed. Downfed radiation needs two fittings. The principle of these fittings is to have enough resistance to flow so that part of the water is diverted through the radiator. If too much resistance is built in, a larger circulating pump is needed.

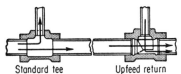

Standard tee   Upfeed return
For radiators above the main-normal resistance

For most installations where radiators are above the main, only one Monoflo Fitting (either Supply or Return) need be used for each radiator.

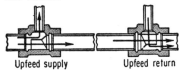

Upfeed supply   Upfeed return
For radiators above the main-high resistance

Where characteristics of the installation are such that resistance to circulation is high, two Fittings will provide the diversion capacity necessary.

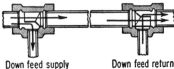

Down feed supply   Down feed return
For radiators below the main

Radiators below the main require the use of both a Supply and Return Monoflo Fitting. The increased diversion capacity provided by two Fittings overcomes the difficulty of circulating a radiator below the main.

FIG. 17-17. These fittings, installed properly, cause circulation in one-pipe system.

SOLAR HEATING

Q How is energy from the sun converted into heat for buildings?

A The most popular method is capturing sunlight in thermal collectors for heating and also for cooling buildings. Thermal collectors are also used to heat liquids for domestic and process use. A liquid (either water or antifreeze) or air is circulated through the solar collector, and its heat is transferred to tanks containing water or rocks which absorb and store the heat and through which water or air is circulated for use in the spaces to be heated.

Q What four basic components must every solar system have, whether for liquid or hot-air systems?

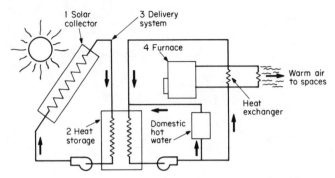

FIG. 17-18.   Solar building heating system uses backup conventional furnace when sun doesn't shine.

A   See Fig. 17-18. (1) A collector device to gather heat from the sun, (2) a storage system for storing heat, (3) a delivery system for delivering heat from solar collectors, and (4) a backup system (conventional energy) to take over when the solar system cannot handle the load.

Q   Name some types of solar collectors in use today.

A   Of the several types of collectors, the most popular is the flat-plate collector (Fig. 17-19). Other types are the evacuated-tubular and the concentrating types, used mostly for high-temperature systems of at least 180°F, in which higher temperatures are needed to drive absorption chillers used for solar-powered air conditioning.

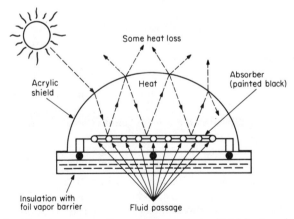

FIG. 17-19.   Flat-plate solar collector has transparent shield for trapping infrared reradiation inside.

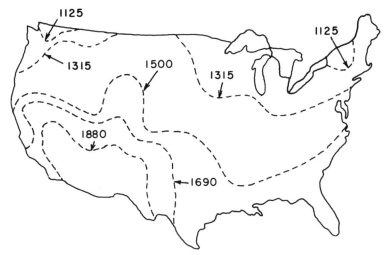

FIG. 17-20. Average solar energy available in Btu per day per square foot for different areas of the United States.

The flat-plate type consists of a casing into which insulation, a metallic absorber plate, and a transparent cover are sandwiched. The absorber plate is coated with nonreflecting black paint to absorb as much radiant heat as possible. Tubes are bonded to the absorber plate so that liquid circulating through them can carry away the absorbed heat through manifolds or headers, to the working system.

The absorbed surface facing the sun is covered with a sheet of transparent plastic or glass, which allows solar radiation to pass through but traps the infrared reradiation inside the collector, much like a greenhouse. The underside of the absorber is insulated, usually with fiberglass, to minimize heat loss.

Q Is it economical to utilize solar energy for space heating in every part of the world?

A No. Figure 17-20 shows the average amount of solar energy available, in Btu per day per square foot, for different areas of the United States. Energy collected depends on the efficiency of the solar panel and also the storage and end-use systems (Fig. 17-21). Tables available from the National Weather Service and charts published by the American Society of Heating, Refrigerating and Air Conditioning Engineers (ASHRAE) provide the monthly solar-radiation impact for different locations.

From these data, the amount of solar radiation likely to reach the surface of a collector during a year can be estimated. On a clear sunny day, direct

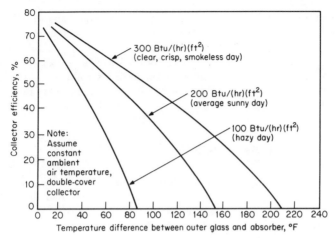

FIG. 17-21. Collector efficiency vs. temperature difference between ambient air and working fluid for three types of solar days.

radiation may be as high as 90 percent, while on a cloudy day, radiation may be too low to power the solar system.

Q What are the building-system water temperatures required?
A For domestic hot water, about 140°F. For space heating, up to 170°F. For space cooling (absorption), from 200 to 240°F.

Rule of thumb is that 1 ft² of solar collector area is needed to heat 1 gal of water a day, depending on the region and collector design. For space heating, up to 4 ft² of collectors is needed to heat each 500 ft² of floor where ceiling height is average.

Q What is the solar index?
A Look for more local radio and TV stations and newspapers to carry a solar index number in weekday weather reports.

The number, between 0 and 100, represents the percentage of heat that could be supplied on a given day by a solar domestic water-heating system.

For example, a solar index of 75 in your area means on that day the sun could have provided 75 percent of the heat needed to supply the 80 gal of hot water required by an average household.

The solar index began as a pilot program of the Department of Energy (DOE) in 1978 on 12 TV stations. It rapidly expanded across the country and is expected to be carried in 200 cities soon.

Solar data are collected daily by National Weather Service offices and fed into a computer in Colorado which calculates the index figure. The information can help families and builders with solar units to determine the efficiency of their systems and also to compute fuel savings daily to check against utility bills, says the DOE.

To find out more about solar energy or the solar index, call the National Solar Heating and Cooling Information Center's toll-free hotline: 800-523-2929 (in Pennsylvania, 800-462-4983); or write P.O. Box 1607, Rockville, Md. 20850.

OPERATION AND MAINTENANCE

Q How would you start a steam-heating system on a new job?
A Before starting a steam-heating system, make sure that the boiler is clean, both inside and out. See that the fittings and dampers are in working order. Check the pipeline for leaks, damaged fittings, broken valve wheels, and broken pipe hangers that might cause the pipe to sag. Make sure that all the important valves are working. Inspect the radiators, traps, air valves, etc. If the system is in good order, fill the boiler to the halfway mark on the water-gage glass, and start the fire. When the gage begins to show a few pounds of pressure, inspect the system again for leaks, and see that the vents blow air freely. When the air vents cease blowing, the system is filled with steam and should be hot. Any cold parts in the system are cold from being airbound. The cause may be a broken valve, a closed valve, or a defective trap or air valve. Find the trouble and correct it. Make sure that the returns are coming back to the boiler, receiver, or vacuum pump. If the returns are not coming back, the water level in the boiler will drop quickly. This can be caused by a malfunctioning return trap or pump. Test the safety valve by raising the steam pressure to the blowing-off point. Try the bottom-blow valve to make sure it works, and blow down the water-gage glass to test the water level. Check for leaks on oil heaters by watching condensate drain. Test the low-water fuel cutoff.

Q How do you control temperatures in a zoned building heated by a hot-water system?
A Intermittent control of heat is from the operation of the burner or, in forced-circulation systems, by starting and stopping the circulation (pump). With a continuous flow, the water temperature may be adjusted by controlling the firing or by blending the heated water from the boiler with cooled return water. Balancing fittings may also be used to regulate the water supply to individual radiators and convectors. Hot-water systems may be zoned to take care of changing sun and wind conditions, just as with steam. They may also be zoned vertically, because in tall buildings the pressure needed to pump water to the upper stories becomes excessive.

Q Why is zoning important in a heating system?

A As the sun shifts and the wind direction changes during the day, the heat needs in any one part of a building vary. Occupancy conditions also vary in different parts of the building. By dividing the building space into several zones, each can be supplied with heat and controlled independently.

Q How are warm-air systems controlled?
A The air quantity in warm-air systems can be regulated by fan speed, dampers, or intermittent operation. When the air temperature is varied in systems using fresh air, the supply of steam to the heating surfaces must be regulated. When fresh and recirculated air are mixed, the steam supply can be controlled by varying the proportions of the fresh air, return air, or both. Dampers and adjustable outlet grills regulate the heat supply to the individual spaces. Warm-air systems are zoned either horizontally or vertically.

Q What standard temperatures are required in various buildings? Assume that the relative humidity is normal.
A Operating rooms in hospitals require 86°F; swimming pools, 80°F; homes, offices, and theaters, 70°F; schoolrooms and hospital wards, 68°F; stores, light manufacturing plants, and machine shops, 65°F; and gymnasiums and foundries, 55°F. Consult local codes and rules.

Q What is the function of a vacuum pump in a heating system?
A See Fig. 17-22. A vacuum pump pulls the air and condensate through

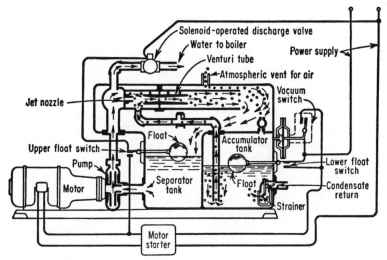

FIG. 17-22.   Vacuum pump draws water from the separator tank, forces it into the boiler.

the return lines of the vacuum and the subatmospheric system, thus maintaining a vacuum on the return side. Vacuum pumps are usually packaged units, with all the components on one base. They withdraw air-vapor moisture, discharge air to the atmosphere, and force the water and condensate returns to the boiler. Anything below 5½ in. of vacuum is called low; above that is high. A vacuum regulator controls the pump by cutting in when the vacuum drops to the lowest desired point and cutting out when the highest desired point is reached. A separate float controller operates the pump when the condensate builds to a preset point in the receiver. In some subatmospheric systems, the vacuum pump may be controlled to hold a fixed narrow pressure difference between the supply and return side. Figure 17-23 shows a special return unit. Here, hot condensate and air enter the low-pressure chamber at the nozzle and mix with the water circulated by a centrifugal pump drawing from the loop.

Q Both steam and hot-water unit heaters are popular for plant areas. Explain some of the important features of steam and return piping hookups.

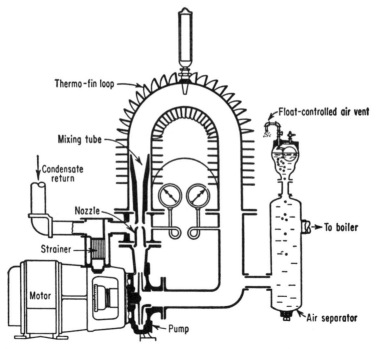

FIG. 17-23. Special return unit discharges an equal volume of water to the boiler.

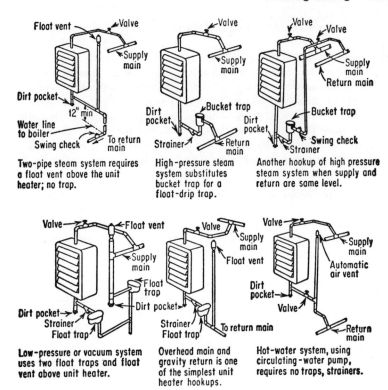

Two-pipe steam system requires a float vent above the unit heater; no trap.

High-pressure steam system substitutes bucket trap for a float-drip trap.

Another hookup of high pressure steam system when supply and return are same level.

Low-pressure or vacuum system uses two float traps and float vent above unit heater.

Overhead main and gravity return is one of the simplest unit heater hookups.

Hot-water system, using circulating-water pump, requires no traps, strainers.

FIG. 17-24.   Unit heater must be hooked up correctly to give best results.

A See Fig. 17-24. Locate your unit heaters to blow toward or along the exposed walls so that the heated air strikes the wall with a wiping effect. Do not allow air to blow directly on your workers. Avoid dripping through the unit. If you must drip, keep a close check on the return piping and trap. Use thermostatic drip traps only on units of 100 ft² or less. Be sure to install a cooling leg, at least 5 ft long, between the heater and the trap. Mount the float vents at least as high as the top of the unit heater. Use a quick vent, closing against air only, at the end of the steam main for venting the air. For high-pressure work, use a bucket trap instead of a float-drip trap. These suggestions and sketches are given by courtesy of the Trane Corporation.

Q How is heat distributed into areas to be warmed?
A Heat is distributed by radiators, convectors, baseboard units, panels, blast coils, unit ventilators, and unit heaters.

Q What steps would you take in designing and installing a steam heating system?

A When designing and installing a steam heating system, first calculate the heating requirements for each space to be heated. Then decide where radiators or room heaters are to be placed. After determining the heating load, select the boiler and its location. Lay out the piping system, with radiators, return lines, vents, traps, pumps, etc. Next, install the system, making sure that the joints are tight and that the piping is pitched so that the condensate can drain back to the boiler. Test the system and inspect the connections for signs of leakage. Insulate the piping, boilers, etc.

Q What provisions would you make for draining the piping of your heating system?

A Be sure to pitch all the mains and branches so that they drain back to the boiler or receiver. Low spots form pockets and collect water that may freeze when the plant is shut down. Pockets also cause water hammer when the plant is operating. Place water seals and small drain valves at the bottom of all loops. Use only gate valves on the mains and branches; globe valves retard drainage and form pockets. Make all reductions in pipe sizes with eccentric reducing fittings in order to avoid pocket formations.

Q How would you lay up a heating plant?

A When laying up a heating plant, guard against freezing by draining the system thoroughly. Clean the water and the fireside of the boiler, removing all ashes, soot, and scale. Leave the bottom-blow valve open and remove all the washout plugs. Check the system for needed repairs and make them at this time so that the plant will be ready for the next heating season. Or, make a list of all the needed repairs and schedule them before the start of the next heating season. Oil or grease all the parts in the fireside that might become rusty. See Chap. 2, "Boilers and Boiler-Room Auxiliaries," for the method of laying up a boiler either wet or dry.

Q What is a primary job of the entire staff in their daily chores regarding heating systems?

A To be vigilant and alert to leaks, unauthorized persons tampering with thermostats and controls, obstructed radiation, wrongfully open windows, inoperative or removed radiator vent valves (some occupants remove them to speed up heating of vacuum systems), and whatever the requirements are for proper operation. The use of personal electric heaters is troublesome for operators and often difficult to deal with.

Q What bearing does humidity have on heating requirements?

A There is a definite relationship between comfort and humidity. With proper humidity, less heat is required.

Q What problems occur during cold weather weekends and holidays?
A Parts of the heating system (and the plumbing) may freeze and burst. Upon thawing, great damage can occur to the building and its contents. Also, careless occupants and unobservant building staff allow windows to remain open.

Q Is it cheaper to shut down all heat overnight than to reduce to a lower temperature, such as 50°F?
A This decision depends on factors such as labor costs, wear and tear on starting up with intensive heating to be ready for occupancy, and freezing risks. Comparative studies of your plant will furnish some answers. Night temperature requirements are also dictated by municipal health department rules when human occupancy is involved, and these regulations should be followed in your jurisdiction.

Q What are the greatest causes of heat losses?
A Probably infiltration through loose windows and doors, and radiation loss through poor insulation, especially in attics and roofs.

SUGGESTED READING

Elonka, Stephen M.: *Standard Plant Operators' Manual*, 3d ed., McGraw-Hill Book Company, New York, 1980 (has pages of information on heating systems and their operation and maintenance).

Elonka, Stephen M.: *Standard Basic Math and Applied Plant Calculations*, McGraw-Hill Book Company, New York, 1978 (has chapter on heat transfer and efficiency calculations).

Elonka, Stephen M., and Quaid Minich: *Standard Refrigeration and Air Conditioning Questions and Answers*, 2d ed., McGraw-Hill Book Company, New York, 1973 (has latest information on the subject).

18

LUBRICATION AND BEARINGS

Reducing friction and wear between moving surfaces is especially vital today because of faster revolutions per minute, under greater loads and at higher temperatures. Example: Temperatures in a few sophisticated kinds of equipment range from cryogenic (−300°F to absolute zero of −459.8°F) to the dangerous heat of 1000°F, while speeds have reached an astronomical 360,000 r/min.

And similar to a chain and its weakest link, a machine is no better than its bearings and lubrication. Here, in addition to basics, we cover additives for solids and liquids, synthetics, the newer fire-resistant fluids, modern plastics, and ball bearings, which today last three times longer, carry 40 percent more load, and are 50 percent quieter.

BASICS

Q How are petroleum lubricants classified?

A Petroleum lubricants are classified according to the broad services for which they are widely used: (1) circulating oils, (2) gear oils, (3) machine or engine oils, (4) refrigeration-grade oils, (5) spindle oils, (6) steam-cylinder oils, (7) wire-rope lubricants, (8) greases of calcium, sodium, aluminum, lithium, or barium base, and (9) solid and synthetic lubricants.

Q Explain the meaning of hydrodynamic lubrication.

A In hydrodynamic lubrication, as the bearing slides, some oil sticks to

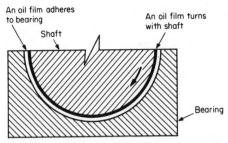

FIG. 18-1.   Film of oil sticks to turning shaft and to stationary bearing.

both the moving and stationary areas (Fig. 18-1), breaking into layers. This backs the fluid into a wedge-shaped area. But, if the oil cannot be jammed into a smaller volume, only its pressure can build up. Figure 18-2 shows how a spinning shaft drags the oil into a wedge-shaped layer between the journal and the bearing, lifting the shaft. The wedge builds up during starting, lifts the journal off the bearing surface, and keeps the journal and bearing apart during running. The last two sketches show how the supporting pressure is distributed. Oil pressure drops suddenly when the oil leaves the wedge-shaped area and enters the area where the journal and bearing surfaces diverge. In some cases this pressure may fall below atmospheric pressure.

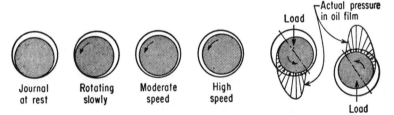

FIG. 18-2.   Pressure pattern depends on where the load is applied, as shown above.

Q   What is friction?
A   Friction is the force that resists a sliding motion or the force that acts through a plane at right angles to the main load. Lubricants are used to reduce friction.

Q   What is the coefficient of friction?
A   The friction force divided by the main load gives you the coefficient of friction.

Q   What is sliding friction?

A Sliding friction, the most common type, is caused by one solid body moving across the surface of another body. Here, adhesion, shearing, and plowing come into play. This sliding action occurs when the shaft revolves in a bearing or when a piston moves in a cylinder with no lubrication.

Q What is rolling friction?

A Friction is reduced by the rolling action of an object, such as a ball bearing. For example, compare the result of moving a load on a wheel base to moving a load without wheels by dragging it over the same surface. However, materials deform and the rolling elements slip under the load.

Q How does lubrication reduce friction?

A Lubrication reduces friction by forcing an oily film between the surfaces in order to separate them completely. Then the only friction is from the motion within the oily fluid, which causes the fluid to split into two layers. The top layer sticks to the top surface, and the bottom layer adheres to the lower surface. Each layer travels at a lower speed, shearing the layers on either side of it.

Q What are lubricating oils tested for?

A Lubricating oils are tested for (1) viscosity, (2) flash and fire points, (3) pour point, (4) carbon-residue content, (5) emulsification and demulsibility, and (6) acidity or neutralization number.

Q What are greases tested for?

A The most important tests for grease are to determine its (1) base, (2) penetration, and (3) dropping or melting point.

Q What is the viscosity of a lubricating oil?

A Viscosity is an indication of the relative fluidity of any lubricating oil, regardless of the service for which it is used. Viscosity shows how well the oil will flow at the temperatures for which it is intended. Since viscosity changes with temperature, the rate of change is denoted by a viscosity index; the higher the viscosity index, the less effect the temperature change has on the fluidity of the lubricating oil.

Q What are the flash and fire points of a lubricating oil?

A The flash point of a lubricating oil is the degree Fahrenheit at which vapors given off by heating ignite momentarily from a flame. The fire point is the temperature at which the vapors support combustion. These ratings are important on compressor oils or where the oil is to be used at high temperatures. The flash point of most good lube oils is around 300°F.

Q Why is the pour point of a lubricating oil important to plant operators?

A The pour point shows how fluid a lubricating oil can be at very low temperatures; the lower the viscosity of an oil, the lower its pour point. The pour point is important in selecting a refrigeration-grade oil. In small-diameter piping, oil having too high a pour point could congeal during an overnight shutdown in cold weather.

RESULT: Starved bearings when starting up the next morning.

Q What is the carbon-residue content of a lubricating oil?
A The carbon-residue content of an oil indicates both the amount of residual matter in the oil and the lubricating ability of the oil. For clean engine performance, the carbon-residue content should be as low as possible. This is especially important for internal-combustion engines and compressors.

Q What is the emulsification and demulsibility of a lubricating oil?
A The emulsification indicates the tendency of an oil to mix intimately with water to form a more or less stable emulsion. The demulsibility tells how easily water can be separated from the oil.

Q Why is the neutralization number of a lubricating oil important?
A The neutralization number of an oil is related to acidity. The main thing to watch is that this number does not keep rising in use. An abnormal rise usually indicates oil oxidation. Have regular laboratory tests taken to determine the neutralization number of the oil in service. Then, plot charts to show the rate of rise for the hours of oil service. In a well-refined oil, this number is usually less than 0.10. If this number is abnormal in your system, drain, flush, and install new oil. Consult your oil company.

Q What is meant by the term "base" when referring to grease?
A The base in a lubricating grease denotes the type of soap used in its manufacture; sodium, calcium, and lithium are such types. Consult a chart that will give you specific information about your greases.

Q What does the penetration of a grease mean?
A The penetration is an indication of both the consistency and the texture of a grease. Operators must know the consistency of a grease because too heavy or inert a grease in roller bearings can channel in the housing and can develop poor lube film that forms on the rollers. In pressure systems serving a number of bearings, poor penetration means trouble.

Q What is the dropping or melting point of a grease?
A The dropping or melting point of a grease is the degree Fahrenheit at which the grease softens or melts. The percentage and type of soap used in the manufacture of the grease, the viscosity of the mineral oil, and the type of alkali affect the dropping point of the grease.

TYPES OF LUBRICANTS

Q What are solid lubricants?
A Graphite is the most common solid lubricant; it is used as a dry powder or mixed in oil. As powder, it tends to fill in and smooth out irregularities in the bearing surface. When mixed with oil, it often separates out as sludge; so don't use it in forced-lubrication systems. Mica, talc, and soapstone are other forms of solid lubricants having actions similar to graphite. While inferior to graphite, they are more resistant to oxidation at high temperatures. Today, molybdenum and tungsten sulfides are more effective than graphite or mica. They have a better resistance to temperatures up to 750°F and to pressures up to 100,000 psi.

Q What are organic oils?
A Organic oils are extracted from animals, vegetables, and fish. They are decomposed easily by heat and tend to oxidize to gums at low temperatures. Since all organic oils have alochols and fatty acids, they are likely to contain free acid. Castor oil, having long molecules, has some advantages as a lubricant. It is often mixed with mineral oils to provide added protection for heavy loads. Such mixed oils are known as compounded oils. Organic oils also form stable emulsions with water, having good lubricating qualities. Never use organic oils with ammonia because soap is formed by fatty acid and an alkali.

Q What are mineral oils?
A Mineral oils are extracted from petroleum wells; they are either paraffinic or naphthenic oils.

Q Explain paraffinic oils.
A Paraffinic oils are fairly stable at high temperatures. They contain a large proportion of dissolved wax, which causes them to solidify at higher temperatures than naphthenic oils.

Q Explain naphthenic oils.
A Naphthenic oils usually contain a high percentage of asphalt. They tend to be less stable at high temperatures than paraffins but contain little or no wax. Therefore, they remain liquid at low temperatures. The viscosity of naphthenic oils varies more with temperature change than do paraffinic oils. They are usually inferior to paraffinic lubricants when used at temperatures over 150°F. Asphalt oils may be considered in the same category as naphthenic oils for lubrication.

Q Why are additives used in oils?
A Chemicals added to selected-base mineral oils give the lube oil properties it doesn't already have. Such typical additives are as follows: (1) Antioxidants that deter the reaction of oxygen with the oil. (2) Detergents that

help to keep internal-combustion-engine oils clean. (3) Viscosity-index improvers that help the oil to work at higher temperatures. (4) Oiliness agents that reduce the coefficient of friction in thin-film regions. (5) Extreme-pressure compounds that give oils the body they need to hold up under high pressure. (6) Pour-point depressants that lower the temperature at which the oil wax crystallizes. (7) Rust inhibitors that help to prevent moisture from reaching the metal they lubricate.

Q What are synthetics? Why are they used?
A Synthetic lubricants are available in the following six general types: (1) polyalkylene glycols, (2) silicones, (3) diesters, (4) organic chlorine compounds, (5) polymer oils, and (6) voltol oils.

Polyalkylene glycols come in both a water-soluble and insoluble form, each having a wide viscosity range. They resist sludge and varnish formation and have a low solvent and swelling effect on some synthetic rubbers. A low pour point and good viscosity make them popular for use in rubber and rubber-metal combinations, asbestos packings, internal-combustion engines, gears, compressors, vacuum pumps, small electric motors, etc.

Silicones have the basic elements of silicon and oxygen. Type A silicone, a colorless or light-straw-colored fluid, is heat-stable. Practical operating temperatures ranges from −40 to 300°F. It is used for light and moderate loads. Type B silicone has a freezing point of −8°F and a flash point of 575°F. It is heat-stable and can be heated in contact with the air at 500°F for over 1200 hr without jelling. It resists weathering and oxidation.

Q Why are fire-resistant turbine oils coming into use?
A Today's higher steam temperatures at the turbine throttle keep the bearing temperatures dangerously high unless a fire-resistant oil is used. Fire-resistant oils also cut the high cost of the fire-protection equipment needed when mineral oils of 700 to 800°F are used in power stations. Escaping oil spraying onto 1000°F steam lines has caused fires. Double-pipe oil systems are used so that, if oil escapes, it cannot strike 1000°F steam lines. Some insurance companies require sprinklers over oil sumps or reservoirs containing significant amounts of lubricant.

Q What are some of the fire-resistant turbine oils?
A Phosphate esters, hydrolubes, and silicone fluids in combination with other materials are common fire-resistant oils. Phosphate esters have passed a flammability drip test to 1400°F. At higher temperatures they glow but won't burst into flame.

BEARINGS AND MATERIALS

Q How do clearances between the shaft and the bearing affect operation?

A Small clearances between the shaft and the bearing cause more heat but greater load capacity. Large clearances cause less heat but mechanical troubles. So, the clearance must be kept at a happy medium. Most operators go by the rule that allows a 0.001-in. clearance to each inch of shaft diameter up to a 6-in shaft. Too much clearance allows the oil to leak out, so that hydraulic action does little good and won't support the shaft. Too little clearance causes heat because of the confined space in which the lubricating oil has to form into layers.

Q What five tests must bearing materials meet?

A Bearing materials must: (1) Resist fatigue caused by variable loading and heat stresses. (2) Have a quality of embeddability in order to allow dirt entering the clearance space to embed in the lining and not cut a groove in the shaft or bearing. (3) Have conformability in order to yield or deform slightly to allow for distortions of the machine structure while under load. (4) Resist seizure on metal-to-metal contact. (5) Resist corrosion from the lubricant and products formed in it while in service. When used as a lining, the bearing material must have bondability to give it a strong bond with the backing material.

Q Explain the Kingsbury and Michell thrust bearing.

A See Fig. 18-3. A Kingsbury and Michell thrust bearing has one part, usually the moving part, that forms a continuous collar or disk. All other bearing parts are pads that form a sector of the collar or disk. Each pad is pivoted near the center of the back of the shaft, which is the area of the greatest film pressure. The pads tilt when the shaft rotates, producing a hydrodynamic oil film between the pad and the runner. This, in turn, produces a full fluid film, separating the pad from the runner. Load capacities, which increase with speed, run up to 750 psi, with rubbing velocities up to 9000 ft/min.

Q What is a pivoted-pad journal bearing?

A See Fig. 18-4. A pivoted-pad journal bearing operates on the same principle as a pivoted-pad thrust bearing. They allow an oil wedge to

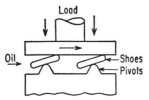

FIG. 18-3. Kingsbury and Michell thrust bearings have tilting shoes.

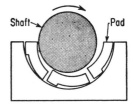

FIG. 18-4. Pivoted-pad journal bearing in action.

form with a minimum of disturbance to the journal position. They also allow an almost perfect fluid wedge to form in the small and large bearings at loads up to 500 psi.

Q   Are bearings water-lubricated today?

A   Yes, the most widely used water-lubricated bearing material, since earliest times, has been wood. The woods are usually lignum vitae and oil-impregnated maple and oak, still used for relatively low speeds. But today we have a water-lubricated plastic bearing operating at 29,500 r/min. The lining of the bearing is a laminated phenolic plastic, mounted on stainless-steel backing. Water is the lubricant, since the presence of organic and inorganic particulate matter (including oil, grease, and dust) in or about an oxygen compressor can pose a serious fire or explosion hazard.

Q   Where are hydrostatic gas bearings used?

A   For a process gas–lubricated expander, which revolves at 360,000 r/min. The process gas to be expanded and cooled enters the turbine housing and is directed around the complete periphery of the turbine wheel, which rotates. Hydrostatic gas bearings show no wear. But more important, there is no contamination of the process stream, which is one reason why process fluid–lubricated bearings are gaining in importance.

Q   Why do modern roller-contact bearings last three times longer?

A   In part, because of improvements in metallurgy, manufacturing techniques, and design. Take a tough application like main-shaft thrust bearings for gas turbines. Early bearings were made of air-melted SAE 52100 steel, which had impurities and varied in quality. Today these bearings are made of induction vacuum-melted M-50 tool steel, which has superior performance.

Q   What are some of the newer bearing materials in wide use?

A   Aluminum alloy bearings with pressure lubrication carry loads up to 10,000 psi. High resistance to corrosive agents in oil makes aluminum well suited for diesel engines, in which combustion of heavy fuels introduces corrosive elements. Sintered self-lubricated porous metal bearings are widely used for bushings. But plastic has probably made the greatest headway, especially for nonlubricated bearings. Combinations of plastic and lead are also used. And ceramics are used where high temperatures are a problem, as for sliding components in atomic reactors.

OPERATION AND MAINTENANCE

Q   Explain some of the common methods of lubrication.

A   See Fig. 18-5. A hand oil can is the most common method of lubricating,

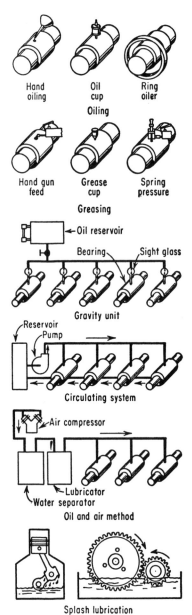

Hand
oiling

Oil
cup

Ring
oiler

Oiling

Hand gun
feed

Grease
cup

Spring
pressure

Greasing

Oil reservoir

Bearing   Sight glass

Gravity unit

Reservoir
Pump

Circulating system

Air compressor

Lubricator
Water separator

Oil and air method

Splash lubrication

FIG. 18-5. Some of the many common methods of lubrication in use today.

but it is not reliable; next is the oil cup or wick oiler, both of which provide constant gravity feed. A ring revolving on the shaft picks up oil and leaves some of it on the shaft. Grease is fed by a forced hand lubricator, grease cup, or grease applicator. When many bearings must be lubricated, a gravity system is common. The tank must be refilled often. This method saves hand oiling the individual bearings.

A circulating system furnishes oil for both lubrication and cooling. This scheme cuts oil consumption and removes dirt by a flushing action. It is used widely on steam turbines and other equipment. Aerosol lubricators atomize the oil and then distribute an oil-in-air mixture through the tubing to the bearing surfaces. The shaft knocks the oil out of the airstream, depositing it as a film between the shaft and the bearings. Oil separates from the mixture only when it hits the moving surfaces. The advantages of this are continuous feeding and uniform volume to each bearing, which does away with the feast-or-famine methods of oiling. Air also cools the bearings.

The splash method of oiling is practical for gears, enclosed reciprocating engines, etc. It is very reliable but cannot be used where a definite bearing pressure is needed to lubricate critical parts.

Q Since circulating oils is a broad term, what are some of the applications?
A Circulating oils, the most widely used of all oils, find application as steam-turbine grade oils, hydraulic oils, steel-mill circulating oils, and heavy-duty internal-combustion-engine oils.

Q Name five causes of ball bearing failure.
A (1) Carelessly allowing dirt or other foreign matter to enter the bearings. (2) Overloading from running with an excessive belt tension or with bearings misaligned. This causes the ball bearings to flake or crack. (3) Use of improper lubricants. (4) Overlubrication from forcing the ball bearings full of grease. At high speeds, overlubrication causes a churning action that results in overheating since the grease has no place to expand. (5) Lack of lubrication, resulting in wear and corrosion that quickly ruins the bearing.

Q What is the proper way to grease a ball bearing?
A When greasing a ball bearing, fill it only about three-quarters full; or, if it is filled completely, leave out the relief plug until the motor is brought up to speed. As the bearing heats, the grease expands and oozes out of the relief hole. When no more grease comes out, screw in the relief plug.

Q Describe a typical circulation oiling system for a steam turbine.
A See Fig. 18-6. In this system, the main oil pump is driven by the turbine shaft. The pump draws oil from the oil reservoir and discharges it through

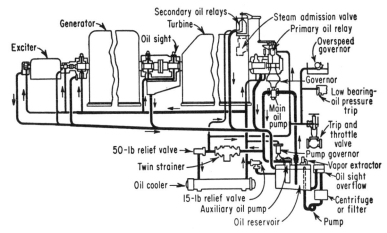

FIG. 18-6.   Circulating lube-oil system for a steam-turbine electric-generator installation.

a strainer to (1) the primary and secondary governor relays, (2) the power cylinders, (3) the oil-operated trip, (4) the throttle valve, (5) the overspeed governor, and (6) the low-bearing-oil-pressure trip. A relief valve maintains the oil-pump discharge at 50 psi and discharges the oil through an oil cooler to all bearings and gears needing lubrication. The bearing-oil pressure is kept at 15 psi by a relief valve which discharges to the oil reservoir. Oil from the bearings and power cylinders is returned to the oil reservoir. An auxiliary oil pump, used during starting and stopping, discharges oil through a check valve into the main-oil-pump-discharge piping. An overflow line from the bottom of the oil reservoir discharges to a centrifuge or filter. The clean oil is returned for reuse by a separate pump. A vapor extractor is provided in order to ventilate the oil reservoir.

Q   How would you cool a large oil-lubricated bearing that runs hot?
A   To cool a hot oil-lubricated bearing, first flood it with a clean oil. If the bearing has wicks, remove them and pour oil into the bearing. Feel the shaft near the bearing, and check for mechanical faults. Examine the oil that is washed out of the bearing for foreign particles. If the bearing is water-cooled, increase the water flow through the bearing. Keep feeding clean oil until the bearing cools. On some bearings you may have to slacken the bearing caps.

Q   Would you ever pour cold water on a hot bearing?
A   No. A suddenly cooled bearing will contract and seize the shaft, often causing the shaft to crack.

Q How are foreign particles and water removed from used lube oil?
A Settling tanks allow heavier particles and water in the lube oil to settle. Heating the oil to 180°F speeds up the settling process. Filters or screens (on the intake of the engine crankcase, for example) help to keep impurities out of the oil. A centrifuge is used to throw out water and dirt and to run the cleaned oil back into the storage tank. When the oil is constantly circulated, as in turbines, it is often centrifuged continuously.

Q Explain some of the ways that oil changes while in use.
A The oil gets contaminated with dust, metal particles, etc. Exposure to oxygen, heat, and other operating conditions causes the oil itself to change. The effect of the exposure to oxygen and heat depends on whether or not the oil has additives to help resist decomposition.

Q How is used oil reconditioned?
A Contamination and decomposition products are removed from oil in various ways. Three common methods are batch handling, continuous-total or full-flow handling, and continuous-bypass treatment.
   In the batch-handling method, the entire oil charge is withdrawn and treated at one time. The most common method is to bypass a portion of the circulating oil flow to the treating equipment. This keeps the total impurities below the danger level and avoids large treatment facilities.

Q What materials are used for cleaning the inside of lube-oil equipment?
A Use rags—never waste—to wipe the inside of tanks, bearings, or the other parts of a lube-oil system.

Q What precaution would you take with an opened lube-oil system?
A When a lube-oil system is opened, cover the openings with canvas, cloth, or plugs in order to keep out foreign matter. Fire is always a hazard.

Q What would you do if the oil pressure suddenly failed on a lube-oil system?
A If the pressure on a lube-oil system fails, stop the machinery involved immediately. Start it only after the oil pressure is brought back to normal.

Q What would you do if the oil pressure suddenly increased on a lube-oil system?
A If the pressure on a lube-oil system suddenly increases, inspect the oil flow to the bearings immediately. The trouble is usually caused by clogged strainers.

Q What would you do if the oil temperature started to rise on a lube-oil system?
A If the oil temperature starts to rise, increase the speed of the oil-service pumps and the oil-cooler circulating pump. If the temperature rise is

caused by a hot bearing, slow down the machinery, if possible, until the cause is found.

Q When would you cut in the oil coolers?
A Cut in the oil coolers when the temperature of the hottest bearing in the system reaches 100°F.

Q Would you use graphite, tallow, or organic lubricants to oil the valve stems, piston rods, or internal parts of either steam cylinders or valve chests?
A Don't use any of these lubricants, since they will be carried back to the boiler and will adhere to the heating surfaces. Eventually, they will cause blistering and rupture of the tubes, crown sheets, etc. Animal and vegetable lubricants also form soap in the boiler and cause foaming.

Q How would you inspect the lube-oil system of a turbine plant while on watch?
A To inspect the lube-oil system of a turbine plant, check the sight feed, pressures, temperatures, drain-tank discharge, and float gage on the drain tank for the presence of water. Clean the strainers once every watch, and inspect the residue for metal and rust. Open the test cocks on the water side of the oil cooler at least once every watch to see that no oil is in the water. In order to avoid water leaking into the oil from a tube or a coil failing in the cooler, always keep the oil pressure in the cooler higher than the water pressure. Check the system for oil leakage, and test the low-pressure alarm at least once every watch.

Q When is a bearing running too hot?
A Feel the bearing cautiously. If it is comfortable to your hand, it's not running hot. But the touch-test method has limitations. Bearings that are running at 160 to 170°F and are painfully hot to touch may be OK. Always check the temperature at which a new bearing runs. If later the temperature rises slightly but remains within proper limits, assume it is not overheating.

If the normal temperature of a bearing is too hot to touch, use a thermometer placed in an oil reservoir (if there is one) or a bolt hole close to the bearings or a surface thermometer to check the machine's housing temperature. If a recheck shows that the bearing is running above normal, promptly check these five areas: (1) Too much or too little lubricant. Oil-lubricated roller-contact bearings should have only enough oil to cover one-half of the bottom roller or ball; greased bearings should be only about one-third full of grease. (2) Check the oil filter for dirt-clogging. (3) Changed conditions may require use of a different lubricant. (4) Revolutions per minute or ambient (room) temperature or cooling may have been changed. (5) The wrong lubricant is being used.

Many causes of excess heat are not from lubricants, for example, misalignment of bearings, tight seals, improper functioning of cooling systems, or worn conditions of bearings.

REMEMBER: Bearings are the Achilles heel of any machine. Check temperatures regularly.

Q   What does "lifetime" lubricated mean?
A   For the predicted life of the bearing in the stipulated service. It does *not* mean *your* lifetime or even the lifetime of the machine.

NOTE: Always read the literature handed out by the major bearing manufacturers. There is much to know about care, replacement, and operation of ball, needle, and roller bearings.

Q   Give three reasons why outside storage of lube oil is unwise.
A   (1) Rainwater collects on top of drums, and then is gradually drawn past the bung by the drum's breathing during alternate hot and cold periods. (2) Brand markings and labels are washed off the drum. (3) Temperature changes from season to season produce expansion and contraction stresses, causing leaks in container seams. Always protect oil drums from weather and extreme temperatures while in storage.

SUGGESTED READING

Elonka, Stephen M.: *Standard Plant Operators' Manual,* 3d ed., McGraw-Hill Book Company, New York, 1980 (has chapter covering bearings, oil grooving, centrifuges, lube oil).

19

NUCLEAR POWER
GENERATION

In 1959, when the first edition of these two volumes was published, there was only *one* nuclear power plant generating electricity in the United States. Today there are 69 units, generating about 13 percent of our total power and saving about 12 billion barrels of oil per year. A year or two ago, it was predicted that one thousand nuclear units would be in full operation by the year 2000. But that was before the Three Mile Island malfunction.

Because the steam end of a nuclear plant is similar to that of a fossil-fired central station, operating engineers holding steam licenses are required in nuclear plants by some states (see Chap. 21), along with operators holding a Nuclear Regulatory Commission (NRC; formerly the Atomic Energy Commission, AEC) license for the reactor. Because steam operators now have an opportunity to take NRC license examinations while working in a nuclear plant, we touch briefly here on nuclear basics, the various types of nuclear reactors, and their operation.

BASICS

Q Explain or give examples of natural radiation and other radiation produced by human beings besides that occurring in nuclear plants.

A Radiation is energy that travels as waves, particles, or bundles of energy we call photons. Examples are radio waves for radio and television, microwaves to cook food, x-rays used in hospitals, radar for location and tracking of vehicles, and sunlight to which everyone is exposed daily.

Radioactive waves are emitted from solids, liquids, and gases. Liquids and gases contain very low levels, and most products produce small quantities of radioactive waves, or they have a very short life and decay rapidly to safe levels.

Some radioactive products do have long lives, high yields, and harmful chemical properties. But extremely strict federal regulations govern their release.

Q What are some typical radioactivity levels of nuclear waste and those found in other liquids consumed by human beings?

A As shown in Table 19-1, published by the American Nuclear Society

TABLE 19-1   Liquid Radioactivity Levels (picocu-ries/liter)*

Typical nuclear power plant radioactive waste discharge	1–10
Domestic tap water	20
River water	10–100
4% beer	130
Ocean water	350
Whiskey	1200
Milk	1400
Salad oil	4900

Source: American Nuclear Society.
* A curie is a unit used to measure radioactivity. A picocurie is a trillionth of a curie. A liter is approximately 1 quart.

several years ago, the exposure of persons to discharged liquids is much less than the radioactivity levels of many common liquids consumed daily by human beings.

Q Will not nuclear reactors explode like an atomic bomb if they get out of control?

A No, reactors are basically different; they do not have the mechanisms to force materials together, even under accident conditions. Yes, reactors and bombs both use uranium, but fissionable materials in power reactors are so diluted that a nuclear explosion is impossible. Nuclear reactors have an in-depth defense against any type of steam explosion, starting with the reactor vessel itself, and including the containment vessel plus anticipatory instrument control. The chief hazard is considered to be a "low-water" type of failure causing core melt-down, with no explosion occurring in the usual sense.

Q How does radiation from nuclear power plants compare with common life-shortening effects of various factors on human beings?

A As Table 19-2 shows, estimated radiation from nuclear power plants in 1970 decreased the average lifetime of humans exposed to the radiation

TABLE 19-2   Life-Shortening Effects of Various Factors in Human Experience

Factors tending to decrease average lifetime	Decrease of average lifetime
Overweight by 25%	3.6 years
Male rather than female	3.0 years
Smoking:	
1 pack per day	7.0 years
2 packs per day	10.0 years
City rather than country living	5.0 years
Actual radiation from nuclear power plants in 1970	Less than 1 min
Estimate for the year 2000 assuming hundredfold increase in nuclear power production	Less than 30 min

Source: American Nuclear Society.

by less than *one* minute. Most important, it was the *least* harmful of the five life-shortening causes surveyed.

Q What is an atom?

A See Fig. 19-1. An atom is a tiny solar system (much like our universe, but in miniature), with more than 99.9 percent of its mass in a central "sun" or nucleus. The nucleus is made up of protons and neutrons. Each plus-charged proton in the nucleus is balanced by a negatively charged, rapidly revolving electron planet. So the whole atom is electrically neutral, but the nucleus is always positive. In atom-energy work, we deal only with the nucleus of the atom. Thus, the commonly used word *atom* really means *nucleus.*

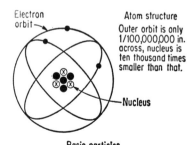

Electron orbit

Atom structure
Outer orbit is only 1/100,000,000 in. across, nucleus is ten thousand times smaller than that.

Nucleus

Basic particles

Particle	Charge	Weight (mass units)	
		Approx	Exact
Neutron	0	1	1.00893
Proton	+1	1	1.00758
Electron	−1	1/1800	

FIG. 19-1.   An atom is a tiny solar system.

Q What is the difference between combustion and fission?

A Ordinary burning involves changes in only the electrons of the elements reacting to the fire. The molecules of both the fuel and the air rearrange themselves to form other molecules that we refer to as combustion products. In this process, a tiny amount of their mass is changed into heat energy. But in a nuclear reactor, we split or fission the nuclei of certain atoms to convert about 1/1090 of their mass into heat energy. Here, the original elements that fission change into completely different elements. This does not happen in an ordinary fire.

Q How is heat produced by atoms?

A See Fig. 19-2. When a neutron hits and enters the nucleus of a uranium

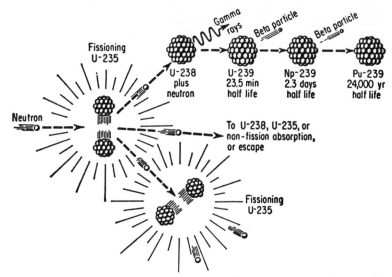

FIG. 19-2. A chain reaction is caused by neutrons that produce heat.

235 atom, it carries enough energy to upset the internal balance of the forces between the protons and the neutrons of the nucleus. This makes the excited uranium 235 atom fission into two unequal fragments; and, since the fragments become even more unbalanced than the original uranium 235 atom, they immediately eject high-speed neutrons. Each fission releases an average of 2½ neutrons. The fragments fly away from each other at high speeds and slam into their neighboring atoms, causing more vibration and, in turn, producing heat. After giving up high-speed kinetic energy, the fragments slow down to a stop and vibrate as heat somewhere in the mass of fissionable material.

Q What are some of the nuclear fuels?

A For reactors, high-speed neutrons released by fission fragments are important. They cause other atoms to fission and convert fertile materials into fissionable materials. But the only materials that can fission easily are uranium 233, uranium 235, and plutonium 239. Uranium 233 is made from thorium by the atom nuclei with neutrons. Uranium 235 is found as 0.7 percent of natural uranium; the other 99.3 percent consists of uranium 238 that can be fissioned a little by high-speed neutrons. Plutonium is made from uranium 238 by adding a neutron and letting decay take place. This decaying process transforms the excited nucleus to its final state after emitting gamma and beta radiations. Highly excited fission fragments also give off gamma, beta, and alpha radiations while decaying to a more stable state. This is why reactors must be shielded; if they are not, people in the area will receive lethal doses of radiation.

Q Explain how a chain reaction works.

A A chain reaction occurs when enough fissionable material is gathered in a reactor core to form a critical mass. There must be at least one neutron from each fission to cause another atom to fission. Holding this condition produces a steady flow of heat. But if less than one neutron per fission produces another fission, the chain action stops. By having more than one neutron per fission to cause other fissions, the heat rate steadily rises. If this happens fast, you have a bomb.

Figure 19-3 shows the conditions needed for steady heat and increasing production. The multiplication factor k tells how a chain reaction progresses. The value of k is the ratio of the number of neutrons in one genera-

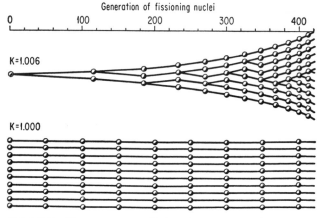

FIG. 19-3. One neutron per fission gives a constant heat output.

tion to the number of neutrons in the immediately preceding generation. The top sketch shows how one neutron in the first generation of a chain reaction has many descendants 400 generations later, when k equals 1.006. This growth occurs in a fraction of a second. The lower sketch shows how a group of neutrons produces a series of single neutrons in succeeding generations, when k equals 1.000. Here the constant chain reaction produces a constant rate of heat output. To lower the rate of neutron production, you must drop k below 1.000, so that you have fewer neutrons in the succeeding generations.

TYPES OF REACTORS

Q Describe a sodium-graphite reactor.
A See Fig. 19-4. In a sodium-graphite reactor, the graphite is used as

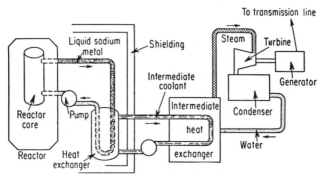

FIG. 19-4. Sodium-graphite reactor.

the moderator and liquid-metal sodium (Na) as the coolant. This permits reaching high coolant temperatures out of the reactor with moderate pressures of only about 100 psig. Because sodium becomes highly radioactive in a reactor, an intermediate heat exchanger must be used between the reactor and the boiler. The sodium gives up its heat load to another liquid metal, sodium-potassium, in the intermediate heat exchanger. The liquid metal carries the heat at high temperatures to a once-through boiler. Feed water enters at one end of the boiler and leaves as superheated steam at the other end. Each coolant loop has its own pump.

Q Describe an aqueous-homogeneous reactor.
A See Fig. 19-5. A water solution of uranium salt (uranyl sulfate) acts as the fuel, moderator, and coolant in an aqueous-homogeneous reactor.

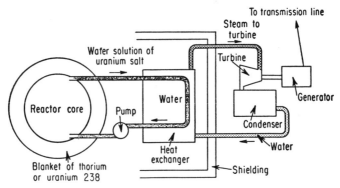

FIG. 19-5.   Aqueous-homogeneous reactor.

It circulates from the core through heat exchangers, which generate steam for the turbines. Neutrons escaping from the core may breed more fuel in a surrounding blanket. This blanket may also be a liquid and may be circulated.

Q Describe a fast-breeder reactor.
A As Fig. 19-6 shows, a fast-breeder reactor has no moderator; it uses 90 percent uranium 235 in the reactor core. Excess neutrons convert the fertile material in the blanket surrounding the core into fissionable isotopes. Like a sodium-graphite reactor, this unit also needs two coolant circuits. The control rods in one unit are made of uranium 238 instead of being neutron-absorbing "poison." They control the leakage of the neutrons out of the core.

Q What is the difference between a fast-breeder reactor and a liquid-metal-fuel reactor?

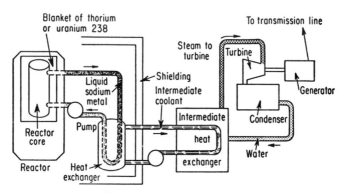

FIG. 19-6.   Fast-breeder reactor.

A A liquid-metal-fuel reactor is very similar to a fast-breeder type, except that the liquid-metal primary coolant, which removes the heat from the reactor, contains the fuel itself. An example is molten uranium dissolved in bismuth. The blanket may also be a liquid and may be circulated.

Q Describe a pressurized-water reactor (PWR).

A See Fig. 19-7. A pressurized-water reactor is designed to prevent the

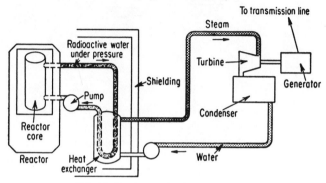

FIG. 19-7.   Pressurized-water reactor.

water coolant from boiling in the core. A pump circulates water in the coolant loop between the reactor tank and the boiler. The coolant picks up heat in the core and gives it up in the boiler. The boiler has two sections: a heat exchanger and a steam drum. Water is used under high pressure of 200 psi, both as a moderator to promote fission of uranium and to carry away the heat produced by the fission of uranium in the reactor. It passes heat through a heat exchanger to a secondary water system (not pressurized), converting the water in the secondary system to steam.

    EXAMPLES: *USS Nautilus;* Consolidated Edison, New York plant; New England Electric plants; and Duquesne's Pennsylvania plant.

Q Describe a boiling-water reactor (BWR).

A See Fig. 19-8. In a boiling-water reactor, the coolant loop of the pressurized-water type is eliminated. The coolant is also the moderator, and it picks up heat in the reactor core to form steam bubbles. These bubbles separate from the water at the water level, and steam leaves through the upper reactor-tank nozzle. Feed water enters the reactor tank below to pass up through the fuel elements in the core as both coolant and moderator. Since the steam leaving the reactor is moderately radioactive, the steam equipment must be shielded.

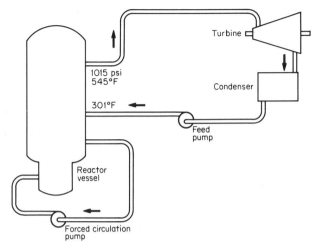

FIG. 19-8. Boiling-water reactor is simple.

EXAMPLE: Commonwealth Edison plant, Illinois.

Q Since most reactors in the United States are either BWR or PWR, show a simple line diagram of a PWR cycle.
A See Fig. 19-9. This is a pressurized boiling-water reactor at the Shippingport plant; it has a 100,000-kW rating and runs at 1800 r/min. Part way through the turbine, where the moisture builds up to 11.6 percent,

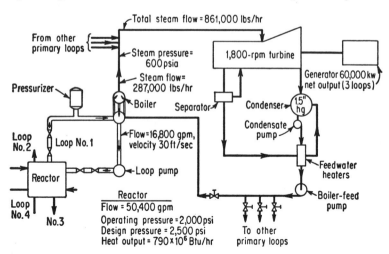

FIG. 19-9. Shippingport PWR cycle has one reactor and four coolant loops.

all the steam leaves the turbine to enter a separator. Here, all but 1 percent of the moisture drains off and the steam returns to expand through the rest of the turbine. It exhausts to the main condenser with 13.2 percent moisture. Stainless steel lines the turbine cylinder barrel between the blade rows. All blades are Stellite-faced where the steam moisture exceeds 6 percent and where the blade-tip speed is over 900 ft/sec. The gross turbine heat rate at 100,000 kW is 11,385 Btu/kWh; and at 60,000 kW it is 13,200 Btu/kWh—about 26 percent thermal efficiency at 60 percent of the station's capability. The station can be started from cold in 3½ hr. Following an overnight shutdown, it can be brought under load within 1¾ hr, which is faster than a conventional steam plant. A weekend shutdown will allow time for minor repair work within the shielding of the coolant-system components without dangerous exposure to radioactivity.

NUCLEAR REACTOR OPERATION

Q How do you control heat output in a reactor?
A When only one neutron per fission causes another fission, you have a constant heat output. There is an excess of 1½ neutrons per fission because each fission produces 2½ neutrons per fission. But this excess is absorbed by moving control rods in the reactor core (Fig. 19-10). Moving the rods up and down controls the output by soaking up more or less excess neutrons. To shut down, the rods are pushed in all the way. The rods then help soak up more than the 1½ excess neutrons per fission, and the flux and heat production quickly taper off to a low value.

Q What happens if the coolant system fails to remove heat from the reactor core?
A If this happens, the reactor core overheats and melts. As a safeguard,

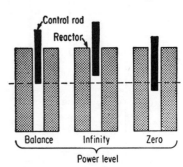

FIG. 19-10.   Heat output is regulated by moving the control rod up or down.

Control rod must hold reproduction rate at unity to keep reactor from "running away" "scram" control rods are quickly inserted to stop the chain reaction, and to shut down the reactor if the core temperature rises above a safe level.

Q What happens if the control rods fail?
A If the control rods fail, the reactor melts. After the fuel elements distort, the core breaks apart enough to stop the chain reaction. But, radioactive gases produced by the melting must be held inside the reactor tank in order to prevent contaminating the plant.

Q What happens if a reactor tank ruptures?
A A core accident or a badly leaking coolant circuit could cause a reactor tank to rupture. In this event, gases and radioactive vapor leak out under pressure. To guard against this, a containment shell is used to seal the reactor and auxiliaries completely. The shell must hold the gases under whatever pressure they have after expanding from the reactor tank.

Q Explain briefly how to operate a boiling-water reactor.
A See Fig. 19-11. The heart of this control system is an analog computer (*a* in the sketch). The reactor core model *b* responds to the control action so that you can see what you are doing. The control rods are used to manipulate the fuel elements. Indicator *c* shows the rod position in percent of travel. Water acts as both coolant and moderator. The operator can see the motion of the rod. During start-up, when neutron densities are low, activity is detected by a fission chamber. Neutron collisions are counted individually. Amplified pulses feed a log-count rate meter, whose signal operates a logarithmic recorder and indicator *d*. Higher neutron

FIG. 19-11.   Trainee can see the effect of the operation by watching this model BWR.

densities are measured by a compensated ionization chamber, feeding an amplifier. One output of the amplifier goes to a log-N recorder *e*, giving a record and indication of the neutron density. Another output of the amplifer is the rate of change of the logarithm of the power level. This goes to a period recorder *f*. The reactor period measures the rate at which the neutron density changes and is of great concern to the operator. The automatic control of the power level is by a linear servo channel. When the reactor goes critical (reaches a self-sustaining chain reaction), the neutron density or power level shows on the recorder and controller at *g*. Unlike the log-count and log-N recorders, this has a linear function. It measures neutron density by a compensated ionization chamber and special microammeter. The recorder-controller unit, in turn, feeds an amplifier and servo operating the control rod. When the desired power level is reached and the control switched to "auto," the servo holds the power level constant at any present point. It also controls changes of the power level.

To start the plant, the operator first withdraws the safety control rods. He manipulates the control handle to slowly raise the rod used for operating the control. Slowly withdrawing the control rod, he watches the log-count recorder for a measure of neutron density. He also watches the period recorder to keep the rate of increase within safe limits. If the increase is too fast, the safety controls the scram rods. During start-up, neutron density reaches the limit of the log-count scale and appears on the log-N scale. As the neutron density increases, the critical point is reached. He continues to withdraw the control rod, watching the power level on the linear scale *h* until the power level is at the desired point. Then he switches to automatic control and the power level is held constant at the set point. In order to raise the power level, the control rod is withdrawn slightly. When the desired power level is reached, the control rod goes back to its former position.

SUGGESTED READING

Elonka, Stephen M., and Anthony L. Kohan: *Standard Boiler Operators' Questions and Answers,* McGraw-Hill Book Company, New York, 1969 (has chapter on nuclear power reactors and safety).

20

PLANT SAFETY AND OSHA REQUIREMENTS

In 1970, when job-related accidents resulted in over 14,000 deaths and nearly 2½ million workers disabled, Congress passed the Occupational Safety and Health Administration ACT (OSHA). Today, the act allows an OSHA agent to visit any plant, at any time, to check on work conditions, which are outlined and enforced with stiff fines. OSHA has "tons" of literature detailing its requirements. Contact your local OSHA office and keep out of trouble.

Here we deal mostly with personal safety and equipment safety, which start with good housekeeping, clean floors around machinery, etc. Just keep Murphy's law in mind: "If an accident *can* happen, it *will* happen." Don't *you* be the cause of someone's injury.

SAFETY PROGRAM

Q How would you start a well-rounded safety program?

A Select a responsible employee who is well respected and knows something about safety; an operating engineer is a good choice.

1. Make a thorough study of safety-program methods, such as health and physical conditions of employees and safe conditions in the entire plant and powerhouse.

2. Make the plant safe according to OSHA requirements: (*a*) Properly guard all machinery. (*b*) Inspect and place in working order all safety devices. (*c*) Repair all electrical apparatus for safe operation by employees,

and guard against fire hazard. *(d)* Study material-handling problems so that you have a safe, easy flow of material through the plant. *(e)* Use good housekeeping practices. Nothing breaks down the morale of an accident-prevention program or workers' safety-consciousness faster than poor housekeeping. *(f)* Set up a system of records; then make periodic surveys of the plant to see that everything is safe. *(g)* Train employes; keep hammering away at safety. Use visual aids in the safety program. Post new posters. Use slides, sound, and motion-picture films at every gathering. Teach supervisors new ideas from safety graphs developed by NSC (National Safety Council).

Q How do industrial fires start?

A A 2-year study of fires by Factory Mutual Systems of its insured properties ranked industrial fires by class, in order of decreasing frequency:

Electrical	26.3%
Hot surfaces	11.0
Friction	9.0
Overheating	8.7
Cutting/welding	7.5
Smoking	7.3
Incendiarism	6.4
Chemical action	6.3
Open flames	5.8
Miscellaneous sparks	5.4
Molten materials	4.1
Exposure fires	2.2
	100%

These figures are valuable in learning where fire prevention should be directed. But the biggest problem is the human element.

Q How many fires are caused by people?

A While no exact figures exist, one recent analysis does indicate that 73 percent of fire losses are caused by human failures. Deficiencies were of the type that adversely affect control of fires after they have started. Shutting off sprinkler system protection valves before the fire or too soon during the fire or delaying the alarm are only a few of the causes.

FIGHTING FIRES

Q How are fires classified? How would you fight each?

A Class A fires—wood, paper, cloth, rubbish, etc.—can be extinguished by water or soda acid. Class B fires—oil, gasoline, grease, paint, etc.—

are fought with carbon dioxide (CO_2), dry-chemical, or foam extinguishers. Class C fires—electrical equipment—are controlled by CO_2, dry-chemical, or vaporizing-liquid extinguishers. Class D fires—magnesium and sodium metals—are fought with extinguishing powders.

Q How would you fight a Class A fire?

A Use a pressurized water source on Class A fires only. Start at the top of the wall and work down, wetting the surface as you go in order to knock down the flame. Then drench the surface thoroughly to prevent reflash. The range of the stream should be from 30 to 50 ft. The main extinguishing agent is water; so keep the stream away from electrical equipment.

Q How would you use a carbon dioxide (CO_2) extinguisher?

A CO_2 extinguishers are used for Class B and C fires. Direct the gas across the flaming area and sweep the fire before you. CO_2 is a nonconductor; it leaves no residue and does not affect equipment or even foodstuffs. The stream range is from 3 to 6 ft. To use a CO_2 extinguisher, unhook the hose, pull out the lock pin, squeeze the trigger or turn the handwheel, and direct the discharge at the base of the fire. Small CO_2 extinguishers may have a squeeze-grip release valve on a rupture diaphragm (Fig. 20-1).

FIG. 20-1. Carbon dioxide (CO_2) is best for Class B fires.

Q How would you use a foam extinguisher?

A Use a foam extinguisher for Class A and B fires. If possible, back the stream of foam off the opposite side of the wall in order to build up a solid blanket of foam without splashing or spreading the burning liquid. The stream range is from 30 to 40 ft. To use the extinguisher, turn it over and bump it on the ground to create pressure. Aim the foam stream at the base of a wood fire and allow it to float over the burning area. The foam forms a flowing blanket of durable bubbles filled with an inert gas.

Q How would you use a dry-chemical extinguisher?

A Dry-chemical extinguishers are used for Class B, C, and some D fires. If possible, direct the stream into the nearest corner of the fire and sweep it across the flame. The chemical releases a smothering gas on the fire, while a fog or dry chemical shields the operator from the heat. The spray range is from 8 to 12 ft. To use a dry-chemical extinguisher, remove the ring pin, free the hose, push the lever down, and squeeze the nozzle handle. Other types require you to unhook the hose, pull a lock pin, and squeeze the trigger.

Q How are Class D fires fought?

A Class D fires, involving magnesium or soda metals, are fought with approved extinguishing powders for the metal recommended by local fire departments. It is suggested that local fire departments be consulted for details.

CAUTION: The fumes are dangerous to breathe.

Q Describe a gas mask and explain how it is used.

A See Fig. 20-2. A gas mask has a facepiece with glass eyepieces and is held in place by headbands. The facepiece has a corrugated tube connecting to a canister that is held against the chest of the operator and supported by a harness about his neck and body. The headbands must be adjusted so the facepiece is held tightly against the face to prevent gas from entering the mask. Test the facepiece for tightness by holding your palm over the bottom of the canister and inhaling strongly. The facepiece should collapse against the face and remain there as long as you hold your breath and keep your hand over the canister. Air or gases enter through a check valve in the bottom of the canister, pass through the purifying chemicals

FIG. 20-2.   Proper use of a gas mask must be thoroughly understood by every operator.

contained in it, and leave the top of the canister to be inhaled through the corrugated tube. Inhaled dry air enters the facepiece through the tube and is discharged over the eyepieces to prevent fogging.

The canister should be kept dry, because moisture causes deterioration of its contents. The date when you break the seal (on the canister) and attach the canister to the mask should be recorded on the label on the canister. No canister should be continued in service for more than 1 year, regardless of its use.

The canister protects the wearer against carbon monoxide fumes for about 2 hr. A timer fitted to the canister registers the number of respirations on a dial. One complete revolution of the pointer marks about 2 hr use, after which the canister should be replaced and marked in order to prevent reuse by mistake. Never forget to reset the dial pointer of the timer to zero when a new canister is connected to the mask. Gas masks purify the air breathed through them but should not be used in an atmosphere containing less than 16 percent oxygen. There are several types of canisters; be sure that you have the correct one such as for ammonia or other gases.

CAUTION: Do not drop canisters into water because they may explode.

Q How can you tell when there isn't enough oxygen to use a gas mask?
A Test the atmosphere with a flame safety lamp if there is any doubt as to whether the air contains at least 16 percent oxygen. If the flame in the compartment of the safety lamp goes out when it is placed in the area, don't enter it wearing a gas mask. Don't use an open flame to test the air because it might cause an explosion if explosive gases are present.

Q What is an oxygen-breathing apparatus?
A An oxygen-breathing apparatus is used in places where the oxygen content of the air is dangerously low or where gas masks can't be used in areas having dangerous concentrations of poisonous or asphyxiating gases. Here, the facepiece is supplied by oxygen cylinders.

Q Is it harmful to breathe smoke?
A Smoke is very irritable to the air passages in the human body. Choking and coughing, resulting from breathing smoke-filled air, often prevents inhaled air from reaching the lungs. Since smoky air is generally poor to begin with, the victim suffocates quickly if there is no escape to open air. Smoke usually lacks oxygen but may contain carbon monoxide, which also causes suffocation. Plastic products which are exposed to fire emit toxic gases that can be fatal.

SPRINKLER SYSTEM

Q What is the purpose of a standpipe?
A A standpipe and hose system provides for first-aid fire fighting by the occupants of the building. It also helps the fire department to get water to the upper stories quickly.

Q How are standpipe systems classified?
A There are four major standpipe systems. (1) Wet systems have an open supply valve and water under pressure at all times. (2) A second arrangement uses approved devices to admit water to the system automatically by opening a hose valve. (3) Another setup admits water to the system through the manual operation of approved, remote-control devices located at each hose station. (4) Dry standpipes are provided with water through the fire-department pumper connection.

Q What governs the size of a standpipe?
A Standpipe size is determined by the size and number of fire streams needed simultaneously and by the distance from the outlets to the water supply. Standpipes for use with a 2½-in. hose should have at least 4-in. risers for buildings not exceeding six stories or 75 ft in height and 6-in. risers for taller buildings. Standpipes for small hose should have at least 2-in. risers for buildings not exceeding four stories or 50 ft in height and 2½-in. risers for taller buildings. In buildings of unusual height, standpipes are sometimes supplied by a series of fire pumps and tanks, which are usually about twenty stories apart.

Q What governs the number of standpipes?
A The number of standpipes depends on local conditions, such as occupancy, the character and construction of the building, exterior exposures, and accessibility. Standpipes supplying 2½-in. hose should be located so that all portions of each story will be within the reach of the stream from a nozzle attached to not over 100 ft of hose, and they should be placed where they are protected against mechanical and fire damages. Hose outlets should be near or in stairway enclosures or fire escapes so that they are easily accessible to firemen.

Q What is a dry-pipe system of automatic sprinklers?
A The piping in a dry-pipe sprinkler system normally contains air under pressure instead of water. When a sprinkler opens, the air escapes and water is admitted automatically by the operation of a dry-pipe valve. After the valve operates, the entire sprinkler equipment functions as a wet-pipe system.

Q Describe a nonfreezing sprinkler system.

A Where a system is subjected to below freezing temperatures, even for short periods, an ordinary wet-pipe sprinkler system cannot be used. There are several types of nonfreezing sprinkler systems. However, because of high costs and increased maintenance problems, it is usually better to heat the properties to be protected than to install nonfreezing sprinkler systems. In some cases, dry-pipe systems are not as favorable as wet-pipe designs.

Q What types of sprinkler protection are available for unheated buildings or sections subject to freezing?

A To protect unheated buildings or areas subjected to freezing temperatures, you can install (1) a standard dry-pipe system; (2) small, dry-pipe systems controlled by so-called air checks, cold-weather valves, or small, dry-pipe valves; (3) a preaction or deluge system, required for public entertainment and large industrial hazardous areas; (4) nonfreezing solutions; or (5) a manual shutoff system with drained piping.

Q What care and maintenance would you give to a sprinkler system?

A To maintain a sprinkler system, examine all the control valves at regular intervals, preferably once each week. At the same time, read all the gages showing the water and air pressures on the system to make sure that normal pressures are maintained. Provide for regular water-flow tests using the test pipes at the top of the system and at the main drain valves.

If a sprinkler valve is closed, shutting off any part of the system, notify the owner or manager of the property immediately. Keep the valves open and the sprinkler system in service to the greatest extent possible during alterations and repairs. After the alterations or repairs, make a special inspection to make sure that all the valves are open, properly secured, and in working order.

Refer any proposed changes in fire hazards or the class of work being done in the building to the inspection department having jurisdiction to determine whether changes in the sprinkler system will be needed. Added protection may also be needed because of changes in exposure from other buildings.

Check the automatic sprinklers regularly, making sure that they are in good condition, clean, free from corrosion or loading, not painted or whitewashed, and not bent or damaged. Always have extra sprinklers on hand. Keep the piping in good condition and free from mechanical injury. Maintain all pipe hangers, replacing broken ones promptly and refastening any that become loose.

Check the air pressure on each dry-pipe system at least once a week and pump up the system when it is necessary. Maintain the priming pump at its proper level above the dry-pipe valve. In cold weather, make sure that the valve closet is heated. Before and during freezing weather, make sure that all low-point drains on the dry-pipe system are kept free of water. Clean and reset each dry-pipe valve once a year during warm weather.

Always notify the central station before operating any valve or disturbing the sprinkler system. Make periodic inspections to check the water level in the gravity tank. Keep the heating devices in order and maintain the proper temperature in the gravity tank during freezing weather. Insurers or their representatives should always be notified in advance if a gravity tank is to be out of service for any reason.

Inspect the pressure tanks regularly, checking the water level, air pressure, and, during freezing weather, the heating of the tank enclosure. Start each fire pump once a week and operate all of them until water discharges freely from the relief valve. Inspect regularly, checking for ample pressure, the proper supply of lube oil, the operative condition of the relief valve, and the water level in the priming tank.

Inspect the fire-department connections regularly. Test the outside or open sprinkler equipment at least once a year. The local codes may vary; most of the above are based on the Fire Underwriters Codes. Since the codes are continually changing, consult local fire and insurance company authorities on the latest requirements for your installation.

ENTERING CLOSED SPACES

Q What is one of the great dangers of entering empty tanks?

A Tanks that have been sealed for a long period of time are usually unsafe to enter. This is true even if the tank contains no oil residue or water. Moist steel surfaces consume oxygen by rusting, and the oxygen content of empty tanks can be reduced to less than 4 percent; yet there is 21 percent oxygen in the outside air, by volume. You cannot tell from the odor that a tank is deficient of oxygen. But once inside, the victim dies almost immediately.

Q What is the danger of entering an idle boiler shell?

A Operators are often overcome when entering an idle boiler shell. If a boiler shell is washed out, left to dry, and then sealed for some time, it is unsafe to remove the manhole and enter it without first ventilating the shell. Since most iron surfaces of the shell use up oxygen, always ventilate it before entering.

Q What precautions would you take before entering a manhole?

A Before entering a manhole, free it of dangerous gases in one of the following ways:

1. Force a current of fresh air into the manhole with a blower. Place the nozzle of a hose connected to the blower near the floor of the manhole. This forces the gases up and out of the opening.

2. Remove the covers from the adjacent manholes. This should allow the gases to clear gradually through the open ducts; but this won't work if the ducts in the manhole are plugged.

3. Hang a strip of canvas, about 2 ft wide, from the top of the manhole guard within the manhole. If a good breeze is blowing, this makes a wind chute that directs air into the manhole.

Q Do organic substances deplete the oxygen in tanks?

A We have already mentioned the fact that iron or steel removes oxygen from the atmosphere in enclosed spaces. But decomposing organic matter also causes an oxygen deficiency, and foul water may generate hydrogen sulfide, which is a common constituent of so-called sewer gas. This gas contains carbon dioxide, ammonia, and other gases of organic decomposition. Some of these are explosive.

Q How would you protect workers if they must enter a tank?

A Before allowing workers to enter a tank, make sure that it is ventilated. If the gases inside the tank make it necessary to wear a gas mask, fasten a rope around each person who is to enter the tank and station another person at the manhole. Check the tank with a flame safety lamp to see if there is enough oxygen to sustain life. If there is not, equip the workers with oxygen-breathing apparatus.

Q Is breathing carbon dioxide dangerous?

A Yes. Carbon dioxide is an impure gas that, in human beings, is carried by the blood to the lungs for expulsion. One of the most common causes of dangerous atmospheres is fires, which use great quantities of oxygen and produce carbon dioxide. A concentration of more than 2 to 3 percent carbon dioxide forces a man to breathe rapidly and with much discomfort.

Q Is carbon monoxide dangerous?

A Carbon monoxide is the most dangerous of all common gases. A few seconds in air containing 2 percent carbon monoxide causes unconsciousness; death follows in 3 to 4 min. You often hear of a death caused when a garage door isn't open and an automobile engine is started. Blood absorbs carbon monoxide 300 times faster than it absorbs oxygen. So oxygen is choked out and cannot get into the bloodstream. This deadly gas gives no sign of its presence; you cannot smell it.

Q Are petroleum gases dangerous?

A The gases and vapors from petroleum products in fuel bunkers and other tanks are both toxic and explosive. Safety codes and regulations require that such spaces be tested before they are entered. The effects of petroleum vapors vary with the composition, concentration, and length of exposure. Small quantities cause mild exhilaration; they make you "slap-happy." But with increased concentration, intoxication is followed by un-consciousness and sometimes death. Some people are known to be "petro-leum sniffers," addicted to inhaling petroleum vapors because it makes then feel "high." Only trained people should test explosive gases or vapors. If you must work in such a tank, call in an expert.

Q How would you handle a victim poisoned by gas?

A If a person is poisoned by gas, move him to an area where the air is fresh and circulating. Send for a doctor or an ambulance and begin first aid immediately. If the victim has stopped breathing or is weak and gasping, start artificial respiration. Keep it up until his breathing is normal or until rigor mortis sets is (stiffening of the body that occurs at death). If an inhalator is handy, attach it to the victim's nose; *but don't stop artificial respiration.* Keep the person warm by placing blankets over and under him. Hot-water bottles or heated bricks also help, but take care not to burn him. Aid his circulation by rubbing his arms and legs toward his body, through the blankets. After the victim revives, keep him lying down. When he is fully conscious, give him hot coffee or tea but no alcohol.

Q How would you transport an injured person using the fireman's carry?

A See Fig. 20-3.

(1)   (2)   (3)   (4)   (5)

Fireman's carry

FIG. 20-3.   Fireman's carry is important for transporting an injured person.

FIRST AID FOR SHOCK

Q What are signs of severe shock?

A Symptoms of severe shock are a very pale face, covered with beads of sweat; wide, staring eyes, with enlarged pupils; cold, clammy skin; feeble breathing or breathing with long sighs; and a very weak pulse.

Q What would you do in case of severe shock?

A If a worker is stricken with severe shock, send for a doctor or an ambulance immediately. Lay the victim down comfortably, with his head lower than his feet. Don't move him or ask him questions. Keep him warm with blankets placed both under and over him. Hot-water bottles or heated bricks may be used, but take care not to burn him. Turn the victim's head to one side, in case there is vomiting. If he is conscious and there is little breathing, give him a stimulant: one-half teaspoon of aromatic spirits of ammonia in one-half glass of water every 15 min, or hot coffee or tea. Don't give him alcohol. If the victim is unconscious or if there is severe bleeding, *don't* give him any stimulants.

Q What is the first thing to do if a person's breathing has stopped because of drowning, suffocation, gas poisoning, or electrical shock?
A Get good air into his lungs—quickly. The best way is by artificial respiration, alternately compressing and releasing the victim's chest, or by the cardiopulmonary resuscitation (CPR) method, requiring a CPR-trained and certified person.

Q Explain methods of artificial respiration.
A Refer to the latest Red Cross manual on artificial respiration and resuscitation for approved methods and training.

Q How would you get a victim off a "hot line" (electric)?
A If possible, kill the circuit; but if this will take too long, remove the victim from the "hot line" by using rubber gloves, a long, dry stick; a dry board, dry clothing, or some other nonconductor. Do not touch the live circuit or the victim's body while he is still on the line.

DANGERS OF REFRIGERANTS

Q Why is it dangerous to inhale ammonia gas?
A Ammonia gas in itself is not harmful; but when ammonia comes in contact with moisture, it forms aqua ammonia (ammonium hydroxide), which is dangerous. In your haste to stop an ammonia leak, you may rush into the room without a mask. As you inhale the ammonia gas, it mixes with the moisture in your throat and lungs and forms aqua ammonia in your respiratory system. Depending on the air's ammonia saturation, your lungs get irritated. If it is bad, you might not get out of the room alive. Blindness as well as skin burns can result.

Q How would you enter a room where there is a bad ammonia leak?
A Before entering a room where there is an ammonia leak, put on an all-purpose gas mask. Then spray the room with water because it absorbs the ammonia quickly and washes it to the floor. Use leather gloves to protect your hands. Don't use an all-purpose gas mask if the air contains more than 3 percent ammonia. You will know when that point is reached because ammonia will start to penetrate the mask's filter. If your skin is irritated, wash it in vinegar.

Q What precautions should you take if ammonia gets in your eyes?

A Whether ammonia or any other refrigerant is used, keep your eyes away from the refrigerant lines, especially on the high-pressure side of the system. If a liquid refrigerant hits your eyeball, it freezes immediately. Don't rub your eyes. Use a sterile mineral oil as an eye wash and follow it with a weak solution of boric acid or a sterile salt solution (not over 2 percent table salt).

Q Is ammonia gas dangerous in contact with flame?

A Ammonia gas itself is not explosive and doesn't burn easily. But at high temperatures, it burns with a greenish-yellow flame. It decomposes at about 1800°F into its constituent parts of nitrogen and hydrogen. Hydrogen burns and, when mixed with air in the right proportions, it is explosive.

Q What should every operator know about the dangers of carbon dioxide?

A When carbon dioxide leaks, it mixes with air. There is nothing to worry about if the leak is small. But when air is mixed with more than 0.50 percent carbon dioxide, you get headaches and feel drowsy; larger doses will cause you to pass out and possibly to suffer brain damage. When the air contains about 8 percent carbon dioxide, you suffocate. So, if the leak is large, use an oxygen-breathing apparatus or an air-line mask when fixing it. Don't use an all-purpose gas mask because it relies on the atmospheric condition in the room. Human beings suffocate with less than 7 percent oxygen in the air. The flame of a safety lamp goes out when there is 16 percent oxygen in the air. If this flame won't burn, don't use an all-purpose gas mask.

Q Is Freon dangerous?

A Freon is a nonpoisonous and nonirritating gas; but a large Freon leak, causing over 20 percent concentration with air, knocks you out. Freon itself won't burn, but in the presence of a flame or hot surfaces above 1000°F, it decomposes into toxic products that are extremely irritating and poisonous. So take all precautions when welding. Unlike ammonia, Freon-12 does not form explosive mixtures when it breaks down into its constituent parts.

"CLEANING" FLUIDS CAN BE KILLERS

Q Is it safe to use carbon tetrachloride as a cleaning solvent?

A Carbon tetrachloride was often used as a cleaner, but it is a killer, and is no longer permitted by statutes. It evaporates rapidly and has a very toxic vapor. In a confined space, with no direct ventilation, the vapor quickly overcomes a worker. It can also harm the skin and body organs.

Q Why shouldn't gasoline be used as a cleaning solvent?

A Gasoline is dangerous because its vapors not only are explosive but have a toxic effect on the respiratory system. Gasoline also burns the hands and skin, causing infection or dermatitis. The chemical action of gasoline dries out the skin's natural protective oils.

The most dangerous hazard is the explosion of gasoline vapors. A hazard also exists when other low-flash-point solvents, such as naphtha or benzol, are used. Gasoline, when vaporized in air, has three times the explosive energy of TNT. To make this powerful explosive, vapor must be mixed with the air. It explodes at different mixtures; the most dangerous is a 6 percent gasoline mixture with 94 percent air, by volume. Thus, a small residual coating of gasoline, left in the crankcase after cleaning, can generate enough explosive vapor to blow up the machine. Remember that the fumes are heavier than air and sink to lower levels; this is why automobile pits are being banned.

SAFETY HINTS

Q Dry ice (solid carbon dioxide) is used around plants for making shrink fits; it has many other applications. What are some safety precautions to take when using it?

A Because the temperature of dry ice is $-109°F$, it can cause frostbite similar to a severe burn. If kept in a tight container, the pressure of dry-ice gas can cause an explosion. So take the following precautions:

Wear gloves when handling either dry ice or metal that has been in contact with it. Never put dry ice in a drink; a small piece can cause frostbite. Never place dry ice in a tight container except one that is specifically designed for it. When sawing dry ice, see that the guards are in place and use a wooden strip to push the dry ice against the saw blade. In a small, enclosed space, gas from the dry ice can cause suffocation; if breathing quickens, dizziness occurs, or your ears start to ring, get to fresh air at once. Learn to use artificial respiration.

Q Explain why low voltage is a killer.

A You cannot feel an electric current of 1 milliampere (mA) or less. From 1 to 8 mA, the shock isn't painful and muscular control is OK. From 8 to 15 mA, the shock is painful, but muscular control isn't lost and you can let go. From 15 to 20 mA, the shock is painful, control of the muscles is lost, and you cannot let go. From 20 to 50 mA, there is painful, severe muscular contraction and breathing becomes difficult. A 50- to 100-mA charge often causes ventricular fibrillation (a heart condition resulting in instant death). A 200-mA charge, or more, causes severe burns and muscular contraction. Chest muscles clamp the heart and stop it for the duration of the shock. One hundred and ten volts alternating current is a killer.

Q Name a few safety precautions that every shopman should know.
A Every shopman should develop good safety habits. (1) Never let chisels get mushroom heads; keep them ground off. (2) Don't let mushroom handles develop on spanner wrenches. (3) Never carry tools in your pockets. (4) Use eyeshields when handling strong chemicals or when chipping or grinding. (5) Don't lift heavy objects. (6) Rigging must be done properly— study the knot-tying section of a good rigging book. (7) Don't wear rubber heels around oily floor plates. (8) Keep the floors wiped clean. (9) Follow safety precautions when using ladders. (10) Don't use compressed air for blowing dust from clothes. (11) Don't be a practical joker on the job.

Q What safety rule must every maintenance and repair man know before working on machinery?
A Before starting work on any engine or motor, line shaft, or other power-transmission equipment, or a power-driven machine, make sure that it cannot be set in motion without your permission.

Q Explain four ways to prevent machinery from being set in motion.

FIG. 20-4.   Use a padlock and sign when working on vital equipment.

A See Fig. 20-4. (1) Place your own padlock on the control switch, lever, or valve, and keep the key in your pocket.

   REMEMBER: Even if someone has locked the controls before you, you are not protected unless you put your own padlock on it.

(2) Place a "Men at Work" sign at the control, and padlock or block the mechanism in some effective way. *Never* allow someone else to do this for you. (3) Be sure that in removing your padlock and sign you don't expose someone else to danger. (4) If a duplicate key to your padlock is lost, get a new padlock.

SHUTDOWN PROTECTION

Q What protection should you give a plant to be shut down for an extended period?
A Before shutdown, eliminate fire hazards. Dispose of waste material

from building and yard areas. Remove flammable liquids from idle process tanks. Shut off electricity and gas to inactive machinery; disconnect or shut off compressed gas cylinders at manifolds.

Wherever possible, shut off all electric circuits at the main switchboard, except those needed for lighting, fire pumps, and alarms. Then shut off main gas valves and deenergize transformers.

Q Should all heat be shut off in a plant being inactivated?
A No. Maintain sufficient boiler operation for heat to avoid freeze-up of sprinkler systems and gravity tanks. Also, provide steam for steam-driven fire pumps.

Boilers taken out of service for an extended period should be drained, cleaned, and left dry. However, wet layup of boilers for a brief period is usually satisfactory (see illustrations in *Standard Plant Operators' Manual* for detailed layup methods). Inspect boilers remaining in service to assure efficient condition. Where limited operations continue, remaining personnel should practice good housekeeping and maintain equipment.

If shutdown occurs when outside temperatures are expected to drop below freezing, maintain enough heat to provide at least 40°F in areas of sprinklers, fire pumps, process water piping, and cooling-water jackets. A heat tracing system (electrical heating cable) may be installed where practicable. (For complete shutdown precautions, consult Factory Mutual System, Boston, Mass.)

Q Water expands 10 percent on freezing, causing millions of dollars in damages each winter. Prepare a cold weather checklist that will prevent damage in the average plant.
A A Cold Weather Checklist prepared by the Hartford Steam Boiler Inspection and Insurance Company should be followed by every plant because every one of our 48 contiguous states, from Florida to Maine, has had record low temperatures of below zero and will have them again, without warning.

COLD WEATHER CHECKLIST

Boilers and Piping

1. Drain and blow out all idle equipment.
2. Check service water lines for possible freezing.
3. Replace damaged insulation.
4. Check tracing around control lines and transmitter boxes.
5. Check all steam traps for proper function.

Compressor Air Systems

1. Check air driers.
2. Drain air tanks.
3. Check aftercoolers and intercoolers.
4. Drain, blow out, and flush with glycol all idle compressor jackets.

Air Conditioning and Refrigerating Systems

1. Drain, blow out, and flush all seasonal equipment, condenser lines, tubing, and piping.
2. Check all outside dampers.
3. Cut back cooling tower fan speeds.

Pressure Vessel Vents

1. Correct low spots in long runs.
2. Drain loops and bends.
3. Enlarge vent diameters at point of outside discharge.
4. Protect vessel vents from ice or snow accumulation.

Relief Valves

1. Protect against snow or ice accumulation.
2. Clear relief valve body drains.
3. Protect valve disks from freezing shut.
4. Relocate relief valves to heated areas wherever possible.

Mechanical Equipment

1. Drain all idle pumps and compressors. Make sure jackets are vented.
2. Provide proper lubrication for cold weather operation.
3. Provide heated enclosures around operating equipment wherever possible.
4. Install no-flow switches and alarms in cooling water lines.

Personnel and Procedures

1. Institute a freeze-up procedure and educate all personnel in its use.
2. Appoint a "weather watcher" to monitor weather reports.
3. Instruct personnel in the proper methods of thawing out frozen equipment safely.
4. Provide cold weather gear (gloves, heavy clothing, etc.).
5. Recruit standby personnel to monitor instrumentation when needed.

6. Set up priority for steam usage in order to keep critical equipment in use and provide adequate tracing steam.

Q What practical use should everyone involved with pressure vessels make of Table 20-1?

TABLE 20-1   1978 Accident Report

Power boilers	Accidents	Injuries	Deaths
Tube rupture	322	3	0
Shell rupture	47	0	1
Furnace explosions	80	11	1
Flarebacks	11	0	0
Low water failures	490	3	0
Misc. overheating failures	139	0	0
Piping failures	111	4	1
Poor maintenance of controls	99	0	0
Unsafe practice	40	0	0
Construction code violation (welds)	20	0	0
Dry fired	22	0	0
Tube sheet crack	69	0	0
Total—power boilers	1450	21	3
Heating boilers			
Tube sheet crack	67	0	0
Dry fired	23	0	0
Gas explosion	17	2	0
Shell rupture	54	0	0
Furnace explosions	49	1	0
Furnace overheated (bagged)	39	0	0
Low water failures	358	0	0
Runaway burner	12	0	0
Inadequate safety valve	4	0	0
Construction code violation	5	0	0
Domestic water heater	41	0	0
Total—heating boilers	669	3	0
Pressure vessels			
Air aftercooler	9	10	0
Air tank cracked, legs or compressor supports	37	0	0
Heat exchanger	53	0	0
Nitrogen tank	2	0	0
PG vessels—in-service	1	0	0
PG vessels—filling and handling	0	0	0
Autoclave (quick-actuating door)	4	6	2
Air tank explosions	9	2	1

TABLE 20-1   1978 Accident Report (*Continued*)

Power boilers	Accidents	Injuries	Deaths
Acetylene tank	3	0	0
Jacketed kettle	22	7	0
Condensate tank	12	2	0
Misc. UPV failures	269	10	2
Steam-jacketed still	8	0	0
Unsafe practice	3	0	0
Construction code violation	3	0	0
Safety valve failure	3	0	0
Total—unfired pressure vessels	438	37	5
Cast-iron boilers			
Gas explosion (furnace)	55	3	0
Failure of low-water cutoff	1146	0	0
Pilot light failure	24	0	0
Malfunction of burner control	29	0	0
Operator error	12	0	0
Cracked section	1247	0	0
Total—cast-iron boilers	2513	3	0
Grand total	5070	64	8

Source: The National Board of Boiler and Pressure Vessel Inspectors.

A   The report shows that there were 5070 accidents, 64 injuries, and 8 deaths. These statistics tell us that low water in boilers was the major cause of damage and that furnace explosions were responsible for most injuries. This table should be posted where operators responsible for the equipment indicated will take every precaution to avoid similar accidents.

Q   What is a service and maintenance contract?
A   Some machinery, instrumentation, and electrical equipment manufacturers have service and maintenance contracts designed to fit any situation. Maintenance should be performed *only* by qualified personnel. It is safer, and more economical in the long run, to have such contracts.

Where staffs are not adequate, always consult the manufacturer of your equipment before letting some inexperienced employee damage expensive equipment and worse possibly injure employees.

SUGGESTED READING

Elonka, Stephen M.: *Standard Plant Operators' Manual,* 3d ed, McGraw-Hill Book Company, New York, 1980 (has chapter on fire fighting, safety).

21

LICENSE REQUIREMENTS FOR BOILER OPERATORS TO CHIEF ENGINEERS ON LAND OR SEA

Today, boilers and energy systems are installed and operated in office buildings, factories, hospitals, aboard ship, by licensed or unlicensed operators. A good example of job opportunities for licensed operators is the state of Ohio. As of June 30, 1978, Ohio had 19,907 active operator licenses, of which 11,354 were engineers, 6003 high-pressure boiler operators, and 2550 low-pressure boiler operators. Of these, 150 were women, who were operators in electric generating stations, steel mills, food processing plants, schools, etc.

Steam is also generated by nuclear reactors (see Chap. 19). Several states, as the following pages show, now require nuclear plant operators to have a steam license, in addition to the Nuclear Regulatory Commission's license. Of special interest today, many NRC (formerly AEC, Atomic Energy Commission) licensed operators received their nuclear training aboard nuclear submarines while in the United States Navy.

As of this writing (1980), nuclear power is generated by some 500 reactors worldwide in 33 countries; 69 of these reactors are in the United States, where another 144 units are under construction.

License requirements in the United States and Canada and also U.S. Coast Guard requirements for engine room personnel are detailed in the following pages. Unfortunately, instead of one national license for each job category (American merchant personnel require one national Coast Guard license/certificate), only nine of our states require licenses, along with some cities and counties. By contrast, Canada today has a national provincial license, honored by all but two provinces. Standards in the United States vary considerably. To help you get started in this promising field, we list the addresses of all examiners, complete with Zip code.

TABLE 21-1   United States License Requirements for Boiler Operators and Stationary Engineers

States and cities	Class license	Education, experience, and remarks	Plant capacity for class license
Alabama	No state license		
Mobile Board of Engineers Examiners, City Hall, Mobile, 36602	1. Fireman (special permit)	Age 21, 12 months practical experience	One boiler only, up to 50 psi
	2. Wide-open engineer	Same as above	Unlimited
Alaska Dept. of Labor, 650 West International Airport Rd, Anchorage, 99502	1. Fireman apprentice	Depends on examiner's opinion	Under supervision of licensed operator
	2. Boiler operator, third class	Same as above	Up to 3500 lb/hr
	3. Boiler operator, second class	Same as above	Up to 100,000 lb/hr
	4. Boiler operator, first class	Same as above	Unlimited
Arizona	No state license		
Arkansas Boiler Inspection Div., Capitol Hill Bldg., Little Rock, 72203	1. Boiler operator, low-pressure	6 months on-the-job training	Up to 15 psi steam, or 30 psi water for hot-water boiler
	2. Boiler operator, high-pressure	6 months on-the-job training	Unlimited

TABLE 21-1 United States License Requirements for Boiler Operators and Stationary Engineers (*Continued*)

States and cities	Class license	Education, experience, and remarks	Plant capacity for class license
California			
Los Angeles: Elevator & Pressure Vessel Div., City Hall, Los Angeles, 90012	No state license		
	1. Auxiliary engine operator	Age 19; 3 months as oiler, wiper; or 90-day training course, 60 days of which is operating, oiling, wiping engines or turbines	Work under licensed operating engineer
	2. Steam engineer	Age 21; 1 year as steam engine operator; or 3 years as oiler, wiper, or auxiliary engine operator	50 hp or more
	3. Steam engineer	Age 21, 3 years as fireman, water tender, or assistant engineer	500 hp and up
	4. Steam engineer, unlimited	Age 21, 3 years as fireman, water tender, or assistant engineer; or 1 year in charge of steam plant	Unlimited
	5. Boiler operator	Age 21, no experience necessary	Up to 35 boiler hp
San Jose: Bureau of Fire Prevention, 476 Park Ave., San Jose, 95110	1. Special boiler operator	Age 18, sufficient experience to operate a specific boiler	Up to 30 boiler hp, but at only one station
	2. Fireman	Age 18, same as above	Work under licensed engineer
	3. Second-grade steam engineer	Age 21, 3 years operating and maintaining boilers, 2 years of which with high-pressure type	Up to 500 boiler hp unless under first-grade engineer
	4. First-grade steam engineer	Age 25, 5 years in charge of boilers, of which 3 years are with high-pressure type	Unlimited steam power plant

Location	License	Requirements	Scope
Colorado	No state license		
Denver: Bldg. Inspection Dept., 1445 Cleveland Pl., Denver, 80202	1. Boiler operator, class B	Age 21, 3 years boiler operation or equivalent, 2 years high school	15 to 100 psi and 10 to 100 boiler hp
	2. Boiler operator, class A	Age 21, 3 years boiler operation or equivalent, high school graduate	Over 15 psi and 10 boiler hp for steam boiler, 250°F in entire system for hot-water boiler
	3. Stationary engineer, class A	Age 21, 4 years operating, maintaining boilers, refrigeration machinery; high school graduate	Unlimited steam plant, including refrigeration
Pueblo: City Engineer, Division of Inspection, 211 East D St., Pueblo, 80103	1. Boiler tender, class D	Age 21, experience not specified	Under supervision of licensed engineer
	2. Boiler operator, class C	Age 21, experience not specified	Low-pressure boiler over 300 ft² heating surface
	3. Operating engineer, class B	Age 21, 2 years of operation	Any boiler or steam engine except automatically fired boilers
	4. Chief engineer, class A	Age 21, 5 years operation of boilers and associated machinery	Unlimited steam plant
Connecticut	No state license		
Bridgeport: Power Engineers Board of Examiners, City Hall, Bridgeport, 06115	1. Low-pressure boiler operator	Age 21; 6 months as boiler or water tender, or assistant to licensed engineer, boiler or water tender; or 6 months at technical school; or 1 year operating low-pressure boilers	Up to 15 psi

TABLE 21-1 United States License Requirements for Boiler Operators and Stationary Engineers (Continued)

States and cities	Class license	Education, experience, and remarks	Plant capacity for class license
	2. Boiler operator or water tender	Age 21; 1 year as boiler or water tender, oiler, or assistant to licensed operator or boiler or water tender of plants over 15 psi or 25 boiler hp; or 1 year of technical school and 6 months operating steam boilers	Over 25 boiler hp and 15 psi
	3. Power engineer	Age 21; 4 years as boilermaker or machinist and 1 year in steam boiler plants; or 2 years engineering school and 1 year in steam power plant; or holder of state or U.S. operating engineer license; or 3 years boiler or water tending and work with boilers and steam engines	Unlimited capacity
Delaware	No state license		
Wilmington: Board of Examining Engineers, Public Bldg., Wilmington, 19801	1. Fireman, Red Seal	Age 18, 6 months assisting fireman or engineer with boilers over 15 psi	Boilers of over 15 psi
	2. Engineer, third-class, Red Seal	Age 21, 1 year operating, maintaining steam power plants	Unlimited
	3. Engineer second-class, Blue Seal	2 years experience operating and maintaining steam power plants	Unlimited
	4. Engineer first-class, Gold Seal	5 years experience operating and maintaining steam power plants	Unlimited
	5. Hoisting engineer ID card	Age 21, 1 year operating hoisting engines (steam)	Unlimited

District of Columbia Occupational & Professional Licensing Division, 614 H St., N.W., Washington, 20001	1. Steam and hot water boiler heating boiler engineer, class 6	Age 21, 1 year of low-pressure boiler operating experience other than a miniature boiler	Up to 15 psi steam but not over 200 hp steam or hot water
	2. Steam engineer, class 5, high-pressure boilers	Age 21, 6 months experience in operation of high-pressure steam boilers	Up to 25 hp but not over 125 psi
	3. Steam engineer, class 4, high-pressure boilers	Age 21, 6 months experience in operation of high-pressure steam boilers	Up to 75 hp but not over 125 psi
	4. Steam engineer, class 3, high-pressure and low-pressure steam and hot water heating boilers	Age 21, 2 years high-pressure boiler operating experience, or 4 years of low-pressure boiler operating experience (1 year allowed for mechanical engineer degree)	Up to 400 hp
	5. Steam engineer, class 2	Age 21, in addition to third-class experience, 1 additional year of high-pressure boiler operating experience, or 3 years of high-pressure boiler operating experience if unlicensed	Up to 750 hp
	6. Steam engineer, class 1	Age 21, in addition to third-class experience, 2 additional years of high-pressure boiler operating experience if unlicensed	Unlimited horsepower

TABLE 21-1 United States License Requirements for Boiler Operators and Stationary Engineers (*Continued*)

States and cities	Class license	Education, experience, and remarks	Plant capacity for class license
Florida	No state license		
Tampa: Boiler Bureau, 301 N Florida Ave., Tampa, 33602	1. Fireman, low-pressure	Age 21, no experience required if can pass examination	Take charge, operate up to 15 psi boiler
	2. Fireman, high-pressure	Age 21, 6 months firing or assisting first- or second-class engineer	Take charge, operate 10- to 50-hp plant
	3. Engineer, third-class, hoisting and portable	Age 21, at least 6 months operation of hoisting and portable equipment	Take charge, operate portable boilers with engines and machinery other than boiler feed pump in operation and internal-combustion engines
	4. Engineer, second- class steam	Not specified	Take charge, operate steam plants up to 175 hp
	5. Engineer, second- class steam/refrigeration	Age 21, at least 2 years as oiler, fireman, or assistant under licensed first-class engineer; or graduate of approved technology school with 1 year experience as oiler, fireman, or assistant under licensed first-class engineer	Take charge, operate steam plants up to 175 hp, refrigeration and internal-combustion engines
	6. Engineer, first-class steam	Not specified	Take charge of any steam plant of any capacity or pressure
	7. Engineer, first-class unlimited	Age 21; (*a*) 3 years as oiler or assistant to licensed first-class engineer; or (*b*) 3 years firing or assistant engineer of steamboat or steam locomotive with 1 year as assistant to first-class engineer;	Take charge, operate any type of steam plant, all refrigerating or generating machinery driven by steam, diesel engines, internal combustion, or electricity

or (*c*) 2 years machinist or boilermaker plus apprentice time and 2 years as assistant to first-class engineer; or (*d*) mechanical engineer degree and 1 year under licensed first-class engineer; or (*e*) 2 years as second-class engineer while holding second-class engineer's license; or (*f*) holder of first- or second-grade license issued by U.S. government or U.S. Coast Guard

Georgia	No state license		
Guam	No license		
Hawaii	No state license		
Idaho	No state license		
Illinois	No state license		
Chicago: Boiler & Pressure Vessel Inspection, 121 North LaSalle St., Chicago, 60602	1. Boiler tender	Age 21; proof of familiarity with boiler operation and construction	All boilers over 10 psi
	2. Water tender	Same as above	Same as above
	3. Engineer	Age 21; 2 years as machinist or engineer related to boilers, steam engines	Same as above
Decatur: Board of Examiners, Steam Engineers, Decatur, 62521	1. Second-grade engineer	Age 21, 6 months with boilers, steam equipment	Boilers over 15 psi, up to 75 boiler hp
	2. First-grade engineer	Age 21, 2 years in charge of steam boilers, engines	Unlimited

TABLE 21-1 United States License Requirements for Boiler Operators and Stationary Engineers (*Continued*)

States and cities	Class license	Education, experience, and remarks	Plant capacity for class license
East St. Louis: Boiler & Elevator Inspector, City Hall, East St. Louis, 66201	1. Engineer	3 years under licensed engineer in charge of power plant	All boilers over 10 boiler hp and 15 psi
Elgin: City Hall, Elgin, 60120	First-class engineer	Age 21, 1 year with steam-generating equipment	All boilers over 15 psi
Evanston: Building Dept., Municipal Bldg., Evanston, 60201	1. Water tender	Age 21, must prove familiarity with steam-generating equipment	All boilers, pressure vessels above 15 psi
	2. Engineer	Age 21, engineer or machinist with 2 years of managing, operating, or constructing boilers, steam engines, or ice machines	Unlimited
Peoria: City Boiler Inspector, City Hall, Peoria, 61602	1. Boiler tender	Age 21, 3 years in boiler room	All boilers over 15 psi
	2. Second-class engineer	Same as above	Same as above
	3. First-class engineer	Same as above	Same as above
Indiana	No state license		
Hammond: Board of Examiners, City Hall, Hammond, 46320	1. Water tender	Age 21	Any steam boilers
	2. Engineer	Age 21, 2 years in charge of steam boilers and engines—1 year if 2 years as machinist in steam-engine works or 1 year in steam plant if degreed engineer	Same as above

Terre Haute: Board of Examiners, City Hall, Terra Haute, 47801	1. Third-class license	Age 21, 2 years firing steam boilers, or 1 year in charge of steam engines, turbines, boilers	Up to 50 boiler hp
	2. Second-class license	Same as above	Up to 200 boiler hp
	3. First-class license	Age 21, 5 years operating steam plants	Unlimited
Iowa	No state license		
Des Moines: Dept. Building Inspectors, City Hall, Des Moines, 50307	1. Fireman, second class	Age 18, 1 year helping fireman in boiler plant	Heating plant up to 50 boiler hp
	2. Fireman, first class	Age 18, 2 years as fireman or fireman's helper in boiler plant	Heating plant up to 75 boiler hp
	3. Third-class engineer	Same as above	Steam plant up to 125 boiler hp
	4. Second-class engineer	Age 18, 3 years in steam plant and knowledge of refrigeration, heating, ventilation and electrical apparatus	Steam plant up to 200 boiler hp
	5. First-class engineer	Age 18, 5 years in steam engineering or refrigeration plants, with experience in operating such plants	Unlimited
Sioux City: 6th and Douglas Sts., Sioux City, 51102	1. Fourth-class hydronic heating engineer	1 year operation, construction of steam engines, boilers, internal-combustion engines, turbines, etc., engineering technical school time credited	Low pressure of 51 to 100 hp, high pressure of 0 to 25 hp[a]

[a]Low pressure = not to exceed 15 psi steam, 30 psi water. High pressure = over 15 psi steam, 30 psi water. For operating steam and hot-water boilers (hydronic), horsepower of system = overall aggregate of hp of boiler(s) + all motor(s) or engine(s) connected to boiler(s). One boiler hp = firing rate of: 40 ft³ of natural gas per hr; or 0.285 gal No. 2 fuel oil per hr; or 4 lb of 10,000 Btu coal; or factory input rating on nameplate of boiler; 1 hp of refrigeration = 2546 Btu or 746 W electric output; 1 ton refrigeration = 12,000 Btu or 1 hp electric output; 1 hp on boilers = 33,475 Btu output or 42,000 Btu input; 1 hp on boiler = 13.1 hp refrigeration; 1 hp boiler = 10 kW electric energy.

States and cities	Class license	Education, experience, and remarks	Plant capacity for class license
	2. Third-class hydronic heating engineer	2 years operation, construction of steam–internal-combustion engines, boilers, turbines, etc., engineering technical school time credited	Low pressure of 101 to 200 hp, high pressure of 26 to 100 hp[a]
	3. Second-class hydronic heating engineer	3 years operation, construction of steam–internal-combustion engines, boilers, turbines, etc., engineering technical school time credited	Low pressure of 201 to 400 hp, high pressure of 101 to 200 hp[a]
	4. First-class hydronic heating engineer	5 years operation, construction of steam–internal-combustion engines, boilers, turbines, etc., engineering technical school time credited	Low pressure of 401 hp and up, high pressure of 201 hp and up[a]
Kansas	No state license		
Kentucky	No state license		
Covington: Examiner of Engineers, City Hall, Covington, 41011	1. Second-class engineer	Not specified	All boilers over 10 psi
	2. First-class engineer	Not specified	Same as above

[a]Low pressure = not to exceed 15 psi steam, 30 psi water. High pressure = over 15 psi steam, 30 psi water. For operating steam and hot-water boilers (hydronic), horsepower of system = overall aggregate of hp of boiler(s) + all motor(s) or engine(s) connected to boiler(s). One boiler hp = firing rate of: 40 ft³ of natural gas per hr; or 0.285 gal No. 2 fuel oil per hr; or 4 lb of 10,000 Btu coal; or factory input rating on nameplate of boiler; 1 hp of refrigeration = 2546 Btu or 746 W electric output; 1 ton refrigeration = 12,000 Btu or 1 hp electric output; 1 hp on boilers = 33,475 Btu output or 42,000 Btu input; 1 hp on boiler = 13.1 hp refrigeration; 1 hp boiler = 10 kW electric energy.

Louisiana	No state license		
New Orleans: Mechanical Inspection Section, City Hall, New Orleans, 70112	1. Hoisting and portable engineer	Age 18; any engineer passing tests who operates or is in charge of hoisting or portable equipment; boilers, steam or internal-combustion engines, cranes, derricks, hoists, air compressors; power-driven equipment	Unlimited portable equipment
	2. Special operator	Age 18, 2 years operating steam boilers or more than 30 gal water and up to 240 ft² heating surface, of up to 15 psi	Act as assistant under third-class engineer, or in charge of boilers of up to 30 gal of water and up to 120 ft² heating surface, of any pressure; refrigeration systems from 5 to 20 hp
	3. Third-class operating engineer	Age 18; 2 years operating steam engines or boilers from 20 to 50 boiler hp; or at least 2 years apprentice engineer with steam engines or boilers of first-, second-, or third-class hp rating; or hold mechanical engineer degree	Act as assistant under second-class engineer, or in charge of boilers up to 75 hp, steam engines up to 75 hp, internal-combustion engines up to 75 hp, refrigeration and air-conditioning systems totaling 75 hp
	4. Second-class operating engineer	Age 18, 3 years operating steam engines or boilers from 51 to 150 boiler hp, or 6 months in steam plants while holding mechanical engineer degree	Act as assistant under first-class engineer, or in charge of boilers up to 150 hp, steam engines up to 150 hp, internal-combustion engines up to 150 hp, refrigeration and air-conditioning systems totaling up to 150 to 200 hp, depending on refrigerant or system design
	5. First-class operating engineer	Age 18, 4 years as operating engineer with 150 hp boiler or over, or 1 year in steam plants while holding mechanical engineer degree	Unlimited boilers, steam engines, internal-combustion engines, refrigeration and air-conditioning systems

TABLE 21-1 United States License Requirements for Boiler Operators and Stationary Engineers (Continued)

States and cities	Class license	Education, experience, and remarks	Plant capacity for class license
Maine: Boiler Rules & Regulations, State Office Bldg. Annex, Augusta, 04330	1. Boiler operator, low-pressure, heating	Any engineer or fireman who has operated in steam plants for 1 year	Heating plant with steam boilers up to 15 psi, or hot-water boilers up to 160 psi on 250°F, or both in schools or municipally owned buildings
	2. Boiler operator	6 months experience in steam power plants	In charge of heating plant up to 20,000 lb/hr, or operate in any plant under engineer licensed for that plant
	3. Fourth-class engineer	High school graduate or equivalent and 1 year operating under licensed engineer in charge of plant	50,000 lb/hr plant, or operate in any plant under engineer licensed for plant
	4. Third-class engineer	1 year operating on fourth-class license	100,000 lb/hr, or operate in plant under engineer licensed for plant
	5. Second-class engineer	2 years operating on third-class license	200,000 lb/hr, or operate in any plant under engineer licensed for plant
	6. First-class engineer	2 years operating on second-class license	Unlimited capacity
Maryland Department of Licensing & Regulations, 203 E. Baltimore St., Baltimore, 21202	1. Fourth-grade engineer	Age 21, 2 years with steam boilers and engines	Hoisting or portable boilers
	2. Third-grade engineer	Same as above	Up to 30 boiler hp
	3. Second-grade engineer	Same as above	Up to 500 boiler hp

Massachusetts Board of Boiler Rules, 1010 Commonwealth Ave., Boston, 02215			Unlimited
	4. First-grade engineer	Same as above	
	1. Second-class fireman	Not specified	Any capacity boiler under first-class fireman or licensed engineer
	2. First-class fireman	6 months operating boilers while holding second-class fireman license, or 1 year as engineer or fireman operating boilers	Boilers with safety valves set not over 25 psi, or operate any boilers under licensed engineer or higher grade fireman
	3. Portable-class engineer	Not specified	Any portable boilers and engines
	4. Special engineer	Not specified	Up to 250 boiler hp and up to 50-hp engine in a specific plant
	5. Fourth-class engineer	Not specified	Portable boilers and steam engines
	6. Third-class engineer	Operating for 1½ years on steam engine or fireman license	In charge of up to 500 boiler hp and up to 50 hp engines or turbines
	7. Second-class engineer	Not specified	In charge of up to 150 boiler hp, engines or turbines, or operate in first-class plant under licensed engineer
	8. First-class engineer	3 years in charge of plant with one 150-hp engine, or 1½ years in second-class or first-class plant while working on second-class license	Unlimited steam plant

States and cities	Class license	Education, experience, and remarks	Plant capacity for class license
	9. Assistant nuclear power plant operator	1 year in steam plant as fireman, water tender, control room assistant to engineer in charge of 8-hr-day shift (Massachusetts is the only state thus far requiring steam license in nuclear plant)	Any nuclear plant; operate auxiliaries, control room and/or related systems under supervision of nuclear power plant operating engineer, or nuclear power plant senior supervising engineer[a]
	10. Nuclear power plant operating engineer	1½ years in steam or nuclear-steam power plant on second-class engineer license or assistant nuclear steam license; 1 year of nuclear plant engineering school equivalent to assistant nuclear operator license, but applicant must complete 6 months operating as assistant nuclear-steam power plant operator, or have B.S. in engineering and 1 year in steam plant	Any nuclear plant; shift supervisor in charge of nuclear power plant, its auxiliaries, prime movers, related control systems
	11. Nuclear power plant senior supervising engineer	2 years in steam plant on Massachusetts first-class engineer or nuclear power plant engineer license; 1 year of nuclear power plant engineering courses equivalent to nuclear power plant operating engineer experience	Any nuclear plant; in full charge of entire nuclear power plant, prime movers, auxiliaries, control systems as the designated shift supervisor
Michigan	No state license		
Dearborn: Bldg. & Safety Division, 4500 Maple, Dearborn, 48126	1. Low-pressure boiler operator	1 year experience	Low-pressure boilers, unlimited. All boilers of over 300 ft² heating surface and over 15 psi must have licensed operator on duty

[a]This license does not entitle holder to operate plant using fossil fuel as major source of heat energy.

Classification	Requirement	Scope
2. High-pressure boiler operator	2 years experience	Unlimited hp or high-pressure boiler
3. Fourth-class engineer	2 years experience	Portable equipment operator
4. Third-class engineer	3 years experience[a]	Limited to aggregate 1000 ft² boiler heating surface and prime movers to 100 hp
5. Second-class engineer	4 years operating experience or M.E. degree and 1 year on high-pressure boilers or prime movers[a]	High-pressure boiler up to 2500 hp (aggregate) and 250-hp prime movers
6. First-class engineer	5 years experience as stipulated in by-laws[a]	Unlimited boilers capacity and/or prime movers
7. Turbine and reciprocal engine operator	4 years experience with turbines and engines	Unlimited horsepower of prime movers

Detroit:
Safety Engineering, Examination Div., City-County Bldg., Detroit, 48226

Classification	Requirement	Scope
1. Miniature boiler operator	Age 18, 1 month operating high-pressure boilers	Up to 16-in. inside-diameter boiler shell, 5 ft³ gross volume of furnace and 100 psi gage
2. Low-pressure boiler operator	Age 18, 1 year with high-pressure boilers and steam prime movers	Low-pressure plants up to 5000 ft² boiler heating surface
3. High-pressure boiler operator	Age 18, 2 years with low- or high-pressure boilers, or 1 year on low-pressure license	Boiler plants of all pressures, but not over 4000 ft² heating surface, and engine turbine up to 10 hp
4. Portable steam equipment operator	Age 19, 1 year with high-pressure boilers or steam prime movers	Steam locomotives and portable boilers to 2000 ft² heating surface: portable steam equipment to 150 hp

[a]Varying credits given to mechanical engineers or registered engineers, or for approved steam apprentice programs. Experience may be waived on documentary evidence of equivalent education.

TABLE 21-1 United States License Requirements for Boiler Operators and Stationary Engineers (*Continued*)

States and cities	Class license	Education, experience, and remarks	Plant capacity for class license
	5. Third-class stationary engineer	Age 20; 1 year on high-pressure boiler operator license; or 1 year on low-pressure boiler license and 1 year with high-pressure boiler; or 1 year in high-pressure boiler plant of over 4000 ft^2 heating surface on high-pressure license; or 3 years in high-pressure boiler plant of over 4000 ft^2 heating surface; or 1 year in high-pressure boiler plant of over 4000 ft^2 plus 3 years with steam prime movers of over 10 hp; or 3 years in high-pressure plant up to 4000 ft^2 heating surface	Boilers up to 7500 ft^2 heating surface and up to 100 steam engine-turbine hp
	6. Second-class stationary engineer	Age 21; 1 year on third-class stationary engineer license; or M.E. or E.E. degree and 1 year in steam-electric power plant; or 4 years in high-pressure boiler plant of 7500 ft^2 heating surface; or 1 year in high-pressure boiler plant of over 7500 ft^2 plus 4 years with steam prime movers over 100 hp; or 1 year in high-pressure boiler plant of over 7500 ft^2 plus 4 years in high-pressure boiler plant of over 4000 ft^2 heating surface	Boiler plants up to 20,000 ft^2 heating surface and steam engine-turbine up to 200 hp
	7. First-class stationary engineer	Age 22, 6 years in high-pressure boiler plant of over 20,000 ft^2 heating surface plus 6 years with prime movers of over	Unlimited capacity

	200 hp, or 2 years with high-pressure boilers of over 20,000 ft² plus 6 years with high-pressure boilers of over 7500 ft²	
Grand Rapids: Inspection Services, City-County Bldg., Grand Rapids, 49502	1. Boiler operator	1 year with high-pressure boiler	All boilers of 10 boiler hp and 15 psi must have licensed operator[a]
	2. Boiler engineer	3 years as boiler operator under licensed boiler engineer	Same as above
Saginaw: Board of Examiners, Stationary Engineers, City Hall, Saginaw, 48602	1. Fireman, limited-horsepower	Age 21, grammar school education and 2 years firing boilers	Same as above
	2. Fireman, unlimited-horsepower	Same as above	Same as above
	3. Engineer, low-pressure	Same as above	Same as above
	4. Engineer, high-pressure	Same as above	Same as above
Minnesota Division of Boiler Inspection, 444 Lafayette Rd., St. Paul, 55101	1. Fourth-class engineer[b]	Age 18, must satisfy inspector that applicant can safely operate low-pressure boiler of up to 30 boiler hp	All boilers require licensed operators except those in private residence or apartment houses under five families
	2. Third-grade engineer	Age 18, 6 months with steam boilers up to 30 boiler hp	Up to 30 boiler hp
	3. Second-class engineer, grade C	Age 19, 1 year with low-pressure boilers of up to 100 boiler hp	Up to 100 boiler hp

[a] No plant capacity specified.
[b] Shift engineers can operate a shift up to one grade license higher than required for engineer in charge of plant.

TABLE 21-1 United States License Requirements for Boiler Operators and Stationary Engineers (Continued)

States and cities	Class license	Education, experience, and remarks	Plant capacity for class license
	4. Second-class engineer, grade B	Age 20, 1 year with steam boilers of up to 100 boiler hp	Up to 100 boiler hp
	5. Second-class engineer, grade A	Age 21, 1 year with all classes steam boilers, steam engines, or turbines	Up to 100 hp steam boiler, engine, or turbine
	6. First-class engineer, grade C	Age 21, 3 years with all classes low-pressure steam plants	Up to 300 boiler hp, low-pressure
	7. First-class engineer, grade B	Age 21, 3 years with all classes steam boiler plants	Up to 300-boiler-hp plants
	8. First-class engineer, grade A	Age 21, 3 years with all classes steam boilers, engines or turbines	Up to 300-boiler-hp plants, engines, turbines
	9. Chief engineer, grade C	Age 21, 5 years with all classes low-pressure steam plants	All classes low-pressure boilers
	10. Chief engineer, grade B	Age 21, 5 years with all classes steam boilers	All classes steam boilers
	11. Chief engineer, grade A	Age 21, 5 years with all classes steam boilers, engines or turbines	Unlimited steam plant
Mississippi	No state license		
Missouri	No state license		
Kansas City: Codes Administration Division, City Hall, Kansas City, 64106	1. Plant fireman	Age 21, Letter from employer stating ability to operate boiler plant equipment safely	Limited to designated plant or system

2. Fireman	Age 21, 1 year experience with boilers, must satisfy examiner of safe operation of boiler and fuel burning equipment	Boilers over 15 psi and up to 126 psi
3. Plant operating engineer	Age 21, 3 years with fuel-burning equipment, or 2 years with fuel-burning equipment while holding M.E. degree from school accredited by the state of Missouri	In charge of plant specified on license
4. Operating engineer	Age 21, 3 years with all kinds of power plant equipment, know ASME codes for power plant equipment, or M.E. degree from state of Missouri school and 1 year in power plants	Unlimited steam plants
St. Joseph: Dept. of Public Works, City Hall, St. Joseph, 64501		
1. Special permit	Prove to examiner competence and experience to have charge and operate power, heating, and refrigeration equipment	Only specified equipment under first-class licensed operator
2. Heating engineer	Same as above	All boilers of 15 psi or less for heating purposes only
3. Second-class engineer	1 year practical experience in boiler room or power plant or equipment	All boilers of 15 psi or more
4. First-class engineer	3 years practical experience in boiler room or power plant, or equivalent	Unlimited steam boilers, pressure vessels, refrigeration and air-conditioning units
St. Louis: Dept. of Public Safety City Hall, St Louis, 63103		
1. Boiler operator	Not specified	Boilers generating saturated steam of 15 psig minimum to 125 psig maximum, each boiler of over 100 ft² rated heating surface

TABLE 21-1 United States License Requirements for Boiler Operators and Stationary Engineers (Continued)

States and cities	Class license	Education, experience, and remarks	Plant capacity for class license
	2. Class 2 stationary engineer	Age 19, 1 year operating boilers under Class 1 or Class 2 engineer, or 1 year in maintenance work on steam boilers and/or engines or turbines or on direct-fired natural gas or manufactured gas engines of over 200 brake hp, and/or ammonia compressors of over 50 tons, or registered M.E. or engineer in training	Boilers up to 1500 ft² heating surface from 15 to 300 psig, or hot water or other liquid defined in code. Also operate associated compressor, ammonia compressors, pump and feed-water heaters, electric generators, etc.
	3. Class 1 stationary engineer	Age 21, 2 years on Class 2 license, or registered M.E. or engineer in training, and employed in engineering or research division of power plant for 12 months	Unlimited capacity
Montana Dept. of Labor & Industry, 815 Front St., Helena, 59601	1. Traction engineer	Age 18, 6 months as assisting traction engineer	Any steam traction unit
	2. Low-pressure engineer	Age 18, 3 months operating low-pressure boiler	Up to 15 psi steam, 50 psi hot-water boiler
	3. Third-class engineer	Age 18, 6 months with boilers in this classification	Up to 100 psi steam, 150 psi hot-water boiler
	4. Second-class engineer	Age 18, 2 years with boilers and steam-driven machinery in this classification under second- or first-class engineer, or hold third-class license and 1 year with steam units under second- or first-class engineer	Up to 250 psi steam, 375 psi hot-water boiler

5. First-class engineer	Age 18, 3 years with steam boilers and units under first-class engineer; or hold second-class license and 1 year with steam boilers under first-class engineer; or hold third-class license and 2 years under first-class engineer	Unlimited steam power plants
Nebraska		
Lincoln: Board of Examiners, City-County Bldg., Lincoln, 68508	No state license	
1. Fireman	Age 19, 1 year operating steam boilers	All boilers of 15 psi and over require licensed operator, but class license not specified
2. Third-grade engineer	Age 19, 1 year operating steam boilers	
3. Second-grade engineer	Age 19, 3 years operating steam boilers	
4. First-grade engineer	Age 19, 5 years operating steam boilers	
Omaha: Dept. of Public Safety, City Hall, Omaha, 68102		
1. Fireman	Age 21, 1 year with steam boilers under licensed operator	Up to 15 psi and heating surface up to 750 ft²
2. Limited stationary engineer	Age 21, 1 year with steam boilers under licensed operator of like or higher grade	Up to 100-hp steam prime movers
3. Third-grade engineer	Same as above	Any steam boiler plant but no prime mover
4. Second-grade engineer	Age 21, 3 years with steam boilers under licensed engineer of like or higher grade	Any steam power plant up to 100 boiler hp

States and cities	Class license	Education, experience, and remarks	Plant capacity for class license
	5. First-grade engineer	Age 21, 5 years with steam power and/or heating plants	Any steam-power, refrigeration, or compressor plant
Nevada	No state license		
New Hampshire	No state license		
New Jersey Trenton: Mechanical Inspection Bureau, Trenton, 08625	1. Boiler fireman, low-pressure	Age 17, 3 months fireman helper or coal passer	(*a*) Steam or hot-water boilers over 15 psi and 6 boiler hp, (*b*) steam or hot-water heating plant above 499-ft² heating surface, 1000 kW, or 4,000,000 Btu; (*c*) prime movers over 6 hp; (*d*) 6-ton system with flammable or toxic refrigerant
	2. Boiler fireman-in-charge, low pressure	Age 17, 3 months in boiler room under licensed operator	Act in any capacity in low-pressure heating plant
	3. Boiler fireman-in-charge, high pressure	Age 17, 6 weeks training by licensed operator; 6 months as low-pressure fireman reduces 6 weeks to 30 days	Act as chief of 500 boiler hp plant or assume shift under chief engineer of up to 1000 boiler hp plant
	4. Third-grade engineer (blue seal)	Age 18, 6 months while holding fireman-in-charge license in third-grade engineer plant, or as assistant in such plant	Act as chief engineer of up to 1,000 boiler hp, 100 engine hp, or 65 tons refrigeration, or operate in any plant under chief engineer
	5. Second-grade engineer (red seal)	Age 18, 1 year on third-grade license, or equivalent experience	Act as chief engineer of up to 3000 boiler hp, 500 engine hp, or 300 tons refrigeration, or operate in any plant under chief engineer

	6. First-grade engineer (gold seal)	Age 18, 1 year on second-grade license as supervising or chief engineer, or 2 years as operating engineer under first-grade engineer, or equivalent experience	Act as chief engineer of any steam generating capacity
	7. Nuclear engineer (gold, red, or blue seal)[a]	Hold certificate of U.S. Nuclear Regulatory Commission qualifying for operation of nuclear power plant equipment	
New Mexico	No state license		
New York	No state license		
Buffalo: Division Fuel Devices, City Hall, Buffalo, 14202	1. Second-class engineer	Age 21, 2 years as fireman, oiler, or helper on repairs of boilers and engines	30 to 100 boiler hp
	2. First-class engineer	Age 22, 1 year operating on second-class license	100 to 150 boiler hp
	3. Chief engineer, unlimited	Age 24, 3 years operating on first-class license	Unlimited plant capacity
Mt. Vernon: Boiler Inspector, City Hall, Mt. Vernon, 10500	1. Fireman	Age 21	Steam boiler or battery of boilers of 75 boiler hp (combined), or combined 825 ft² heating surface, 15 psi and evaporating 2586 lb of water/hr from 212°F
	2. Second-class engineer	Age 21	Same as above, except boiler hp of up to 150 instead of 75

[a]Gold seal designates a first-grade license; red seal a second-grade license; and blue seal a third-grade license. Black seal designates a boiler fireman. If "in charge," the license is so stamped on the face.

TABLE 21-1 United States License Requirements for Boiler Operators and Stationary Engineers (Continued)

States and cities	Class license	Education, experience, and remarks	Plant capacity for class license
	3. First-class engineer, unlimited	Age 21	Unlimited plant capacity
New York City: Bureau of Examinations, Civil Service Comm., Municipal Bldg., New York, 10013[a]	1. Fireman, with or without oil-burner endorsement	Age 21, 2 years as fireman, water tender, oiler, or assistant stationary or marine engineer	All boilers over 15 psi and 100 ft^2 heating surface require licensed operator, but class plant for license not specified
	2. Portable engineer	Age 21; 5 years as fireman, oiler, or assistant to licensed operating engineer in N.Y.C. within last 7 years; or 5 years as boilermaker or machinist engaged in prime mover repair or manufacturer, 1 year being under licensed engineer in N.Y.C. in last 3 years; or at least 1 year in stationary plant under N.Y.C. engineer while holding M.E. degree; or 1 year in stationary plant under recognized N.Y.C. engineer while holding any engineer's license issued by U.S. government, state, or jurisdiction	
	3. Third-grade engineer (with or without oil-burner endorsement)	Same as above	
	4. Second-grade engineer	Age 21, 2 years continuous work on third-grade N.Y.C. license	

[a] Administered by the Department of Buildings, License Division, Room 1521, 120 Wall Street, New York, NY 10005. New York City has a variety of requirements, and the Department of Buildings should be consulted for details.

Location	License	Requirements	Scope
	5. First-grade engineer	Age 21, 1 year continuous work on second-grade N.Y.C. license	All steam boilers
Niagara Falls: Board of Examiners, Stationary Engineers, City Hall, Niagara Falls, 24302	1. First-class fireman	Age 19, 6 months as helper in boiler room	Not stipulated
	2. First-class engineer	Age 20, 1 year on fireman license	Not stipulated
	3. Chief engineer	Age 21, 3 years on first-class engineer's license	Any boiler or pressure vessel up to 100 boiler hp
Rochester: City Public Safety Bldg., Rochester, 14614	1. Third-class engineer	Age 21, 1 year in steam plant	Up to 500 boiler hp
	2. Second-class engineer	Age 21, 2 years in steam stationary plant	Up to 1500 boiler hp
	3. First-class engineer	Age 21, 3 years in stationary steam plant	Unlimited steam plant
	4. Chief engineer	Age 21, first-class license and 5 years in power steam plants	
Tonawanda: Smoke Abatement Office, City Hall, Tonawanda, 14150	1. Special engineer	Age 21, must prove capability of operating a specific power plant	Limited to specific plant, up to 30 boiler hp and or engine hp, up to 100 psi
	2. Second-class engineer	Age 21; 3 years firing boilers or operating engines, etc., or building power units; or technical school graduate	Up to 100 boiler hp
	3. First-class engineer	Age 21, 2 years on second-class license	Up to 225 boiler hp
	4. Chief engineer	Age 21, 3 years on first-class license	Power plant of any capacity

TABLE 21-1 United States License Requirements for Boiler Operators and Stationary Engineers (*Continued*)

States and cities	Class license	Education, experience, and remarks	Plant capacity for class license
White Plains: Fire Dept., Municipal Bldg., White Plains, 10601	1. Second-class engineer	Age 21, 2 years under second-class engineer, or equivalent	High-pressure plant of 30 to 100 hp
	2. First-class engineer	Age 21, 3 years under first-class engineer, 1 year holding second-class license	High-pressure steam plant of 100 to 500 hp
	3. Chief engineer	Age 21, 4 years under chief engineer in high-pressure plant, and 1 year holding first-class license	Any high-pressure steam plant
Yonkers: Board of Examiners, City Hall, Yonkers 10700	1. Fireman	Age 21	All boilers require licensed operators, but class plant for license not stipulated
	2. Portable engineer	Age 21	
	3. Second-class engineer	Age 21	Up to 500 boiler hp
	4. First-class engineer	Age 21	Unlimited
North Carolina	No state license		
North Dakota	No state license		
Ohio Division of Steam Engineers 2323 West Fifth Ave., Columbus, 43216	1. Low-pressure boiler operator	Age 18, 600 hr as boiler room attendant, operating, maintaining, or erecting boilers	All boilers over 30 boiler hp, but under 15 psi must have licensed operators; class plant for license stipulated

	Requirement	Scope
2. High-pressure boiler operator	Age 18, 1200 hr as boiler room attendant, operating, maintaining, or erecting boilers	Same as above
3. Stationary steam engineer, third class	Age 18, 1800 hr as engineer, oiler, fireman, or water tender of steam boilers	Same as above
4. Stationary steam engineer second-class	Age 18, 3600 hr practical experience as operating stationary steam engineer	Same as above
5. Stationary steam engineer first-class	Age 18, 5400 hr practical experience as operating steam engineer	Unlimited capacity
Oklahoma	No state license	
Oklahoma City: Boiler Inspector, City Hall, Oklahoma City, 73102	First-class engineer — Age 21, 2 years in steam plants under practical engineer	Unlimited capacity
Tulsa: Board of Examiners, 200 Civic Center, Tulsa, 74103	1. Fireman — 1 year in steam plants	All heating boilers above 15 psi and 1,000,000 Btu, steam boilers above 15 psi and 100 ft² heating surface require licensed operator, but class plant on license not stipulated
	2. Third-class engineer — 1 year in steam and refrigeration plants	
	3. Second-class engineer — 3 years in steam and refrigeration plants	Up to 15-psi boilers and up to 75-ton refrigeration and air-conditioning plants
	4. First-class engineer — 5 years in steam and refrigeration plants	Unlimited
Oregon	No state license	

TABLE 21-1 United States License Requirements for Boiler Operators and Stationary Engineers (*Continued*)

States and cities	Class license	Education, experience, and remarks	Plant capacity for class license
Panama Canal Zone Cristobal, Canal Zone[a]	Yes, but not stipulated		
Pennsylvania	No state license		
Erie: Bureau of Licenses, Municipal Bldg., Erie, 16501	1. Class 3 water tender	Age 21, 1 year with steam-generating equipment, high school grad; tech school degree in lieu 1 year experience	Up to 100-hp steam-driven machinery, 2000 ft² heating surface boiler; any size power equipment under licensed engineer
	2. Class 2 stationary engineer	Age 21, 2 years holding water tender license	Up to 200-hp steam-driven machinery, 4000 ft² heating-surface boiler; any size power equipment under licensed chief engineer
	3. Class 1 chief stationary engineer	Age 21, 2 years holding class 2 license	Unlimited
Philadelphia: Bureau of Licenses & Inspections, Municipal Services Bldg., Philadelphia, 19107	1. Grade D fireman	Age 21, 2 years in boiler room	Over 15 psi, 30-boiler-hp steam prime movers; 25-ton refrigeration equipment
	2. Grade C portable and stationary engineer	Age 21, 2 years assistant engineer or helper	Not specified
	3. Grade A stationary engineer	Age 21, 2 years assistant engineer or helper	Unlimited

[a]The republic of Panama may have jurisdiction over licenses in the Canal Zone.

Location	License	Requirements	Scope
Pittsburgh: Bureau Bldg. & Inspections 100 Grant St., Pittsburgh, 15219	1. Fireman	Age 21, 2 years assistant engineer or helper	All boilers and pressure vessels require licensed operators, but license class for plant not specified
	2. Portable engineer	Age 21, 2 years as engineer, oiler, fireman of steam boilers	Not specified
	3. Stationary engineer	Not specified	Unlimited
Rhode Island	No state license		
Providence: Dept. Public Service, City Hall, Providence, 02903	1. Boiler operation, fireman, and water tender	Age 18, 6 months apprentice under licensed operator while holding permit	All boilers over 30 boiler hp but not over 100 hp refrigeration over 15 tons require licensed operator, but class license for plant not specified
	2. Stationary engine operator	Age 21; 5 years boiler operator; or 3 years assistant to licensed engineer; or 1 year in steam plants while holding permit if degreed engineer	Unlimited
Woonsocket: Licensing Steam Engineer, City Hall, Woonsocket, 02895	Boiler operator	Age 21, 6 months apprentice under licensed operator while holding permit	All boilers up to and including 150 boiler hp
South Carolina	No state license		
South Dakota	No state license		

TABLE 21-1 United States License Requirements for Boiler Operators and Stationary Engineers (*Continued*)

States and cities	Class license	Education, experience, and remarks	Plant capacity for class license
Tennessee	No state license		
Memphis: Safety Engineer Division, 125 N. Main St., Memphis, 38103	1. Third-grade engineer	Age 21, 3 years in steam plants	Up to 50 boiler hp, 50-hp compressor, 40-ton refrigeration, or assist second- or first-grade engineer
	2. Second-grade engineer	Same as above	Up to 100 boiler hp, 100-hp internal-combustion engine, 100-hp compressor, 75-ton refrigeration, or assist first-grade engineer
	3. First-grade engineer	Age 21, hold third- and second-grade licenses	Unlimited
Texas	No state license		
Houston: Public Works Department Bldg., Inspection Division, Air Condition & Boiler Section, Houston, 77001	1. Boiler operator	No prerequisite	Low-pressure hot-water-heating boilers, high-pressure steam boilers up to 1,004,000 Btu
	2. Third-grade engineer	2 years licensed engineer, oil, water tender, boiler repairman, fireman, or 6 months of above if degreed engineer	Up to 1,674,000 Btu boiler, or act as shift engineer of up to 6,696,000 Btu under second-grade engineer
	3. Second-grade engineer	3 years stationary engineer, oiler, water tender, fireman, if 1 of 3 years as licensed engineer, or of degreed engineer and 1 year of above	Up to 6,696,000 Btu boiler, or unlimited capacity under licensed operator

State/City	License	Experience	Capacity
	4. First-grade engineer	5 years stationary engineer, oiler, water tender, fireman if 3 of 5 years as licensed engineer, or if 3-year apprentice program completed need only 2 years as licensed engineer	Unlimited
Utah	No state license		
Salt Lake City: Power and Heating Div., City & County Bldg., Salt Lake City, 84111	1. Second-class fireman	Age 18, 1 year in steam plants	Low-pressure boilers up to 50 boiler hp
	2. First-class fireman	Age 18, 2 years in steam plants	Low- or high-pressure boilers, unlimited capacity
	3. Second-class engineer	Age 20, 3 years in steam plants	Low- or high-pressure plant up to 100 hp
	4. First-class engineer	Age 20, 4 years in steam plants	Any capacity above 100 hp
Vermont	No state license		
Virginia	No state license		
Washington	No state license		
Seattle: Dept. of Bldgs., 503 Seattle Municipal Bldg., Seattle, 98104	1. Small power-boiler fireman	Same as fifth-grade fireman	Under 100 psi and 350,000 Btu/hr boilers
	2. Grade 5, boiler fireman	1 year in care of boilers; or completion of in-service training course	Up to 15 psi and up to 500 ft² heating surface, 5,000,000 Btu/hr input boilers
	3. Grade 4 boiler fireman	3 years of operation in steam power plants	Boilers of 20,000,000 Btu/hr input

TABLE 21-1 United States License Requirements for Boiler Operators and Stationary Engineers (*Continued*)

States and cities	Class license	Education, experience, and remarks	Plant capacity for class license
	4. Grade 3 steam engineer	3 years in steam plants; or 1 year in steam plant after serving 3 years in steam engine works; or 1 year in steam plants if degree from school of technology	Boiler capacity up to 50,000,000 Btu input
	5. Grade 2 steam engineer	Same as above	Boiler capacity up to 300,000,000 Btu/hr input and up to 1500 boiler hp
	6. Grade 1 steam engineer	Same as above	Unlimited
Spokane: Dept. of Buildings, City Hall, Spokane, 99201	1. Fireman	Age 18	Steam boiler up to 300 ft² heating surface or heating boiler up to 15 psi
	2. Third-class engineer	Age 21, 1 year as steam engineer	Up to 100 boiler hp, or shift engineer under second-class engineer
	3. Second-class engineer	Age 21, 1 year as steam engineer	Up to 200 boiler hp, or shift engineer under first-class engineer
	4. First-class engineer	Age 21, 2 years on steam license, or 1 year steam engineer while holding M.E. degree	Unlimited
Tacoma: Boiler Inspector, 930 Tacoma Ave. South, Tacoma, 98402	1. Provisional license (restricted)	License indicates applicant is not qualified, can be reexamined after 6 months	All restrictions noted on face of license

License	Requirements	Capacity
2. Class 5 small power boiler fireman	Produce satisfactory evidence of qualification	Boiler plant up to 440,000 Btu/hr input
3. Class 4 low-pressure boiler fireman	Same as above	Up to 5,000,000 Btu/hr input, up to 15 psi, or hot water boiler up to 160 psi of 240°F water temperature
4. Class 3 high-pressure boiler fireman	1 year as low- or high-pressure plant helper; trainee or apprentice for 2 years, or engineering/technology graduate and 3 months in boiler room	Unlimited under licensed engineer, or up to 20,000,000 Btu/hr input
5. Class 2 operating engineer	3 years operating power boilers, or engineering/technical graduate, or engineering apprentice with 2 years of power boiler operation	Unlimited under chief engineer, or up to 300,000,000 Btu/hr input
6. Class 1 chief operating engineer	5 years operating high-pressure boiler plants; or engineering graduate, or apprentice in training program with 3 years high-pressure boiler experience	Unlimited
West Virginia	No state license	
Wisconsin	No state license	
Kenosha: Board of Examiners, City Hall, Kenosha, 53140		
1. Third-class engineer	Age 21, 2 years in steam plants	Up to 50 boiler hp
2. Second-class engineer	Age 21, 2 years in steam plants	Up to 150 boiler hp
3. First-class engineer	Age 21, 2 years in steam plants	Unlimited

TABLE 21-1 United States License Requirements for Boiler Operators and Stationary Engineers (*Continued*)

States and cities	Class license	Education, experience, and remarks	Plant capacity for class license
Milwaukee: Dept. Bldg. Inspection & Safety Engineering, Municipal Bldg., Milwaukee, 53202	1. Low-pressure fireman	Age 21, 1 year in steam boiler plants	Operate up to 3 low-pressure plants (within 3-block area) of up to 10 boiler hp
	2. High-pressure fireman	Age 21, 1 year in steam boiler plants	Up to 75 boiler hp but no steam engines except boiler auxiliaries
	3. Third-class engineer	Age 21, 2 years in high-pressure steam plants	Up to 75 boiler hp and steam engines
	4. Second-class engineer	Age 21, 3 years in high-pressure steam plants	Up to 300 boiler hp
	5. First-class engineer	Age 21, 4 years in high-pressure steam plants	Unlimited
Racine: Stationary Engineer Examiner, City Hall, Racine, 53203	1. Third-class engineer	Age 19, course of instruction in steam boiler operation	Up to 75 boiler hp, or act as assistant to second-class engineer
	2. Second-class engineer	Age 21, 2 years in steam boiler plants	Up to 300 boiler hp, or act as assistant to first-class engineer
	3. First-class engineer	Age 21, 2 years in steam boiler plants	Unlimited steam-generating plant
Wyoming	No state license		

Source: Stephen M. Elonka survey of licensing agencies (1980).

TABLE 21-2. U.S. Merchant Marine QMED Ratings and Marine Engineer's Steam License Requirements

U.S. Coast Guard	Class rating or license	Education, experience for 4000-hp vessels and over[a]
Apply to: Merchant Marine Licensing, U.S. Coast Guard, any U.S. port	1. QMED (Qualified Member of Engine Department) a. Fireman b. Oiler c. Water tender d. Machinist e. Refrigerating engineer f. Electrician g. Deck engineer h. Junior engineer i. Boilermaker j. deck and engine mechanic k. Pumpman l. Engineman	QMED is any person below rating of licensed officer (engineer) and above rating of coal passer or wiper who holds certificate of service as QMED issued by Coast Guard. Must (a) speak English language, (b) present certificate of health from U.S. Public Health Service attesting that eyesight, hearing, and physical condition are adequate for performing duties required by a QMED. Medical examination is same as for an original license as an engineer. Applicant for QMED must have: (1) 6 months service at sea in a rating at least equal to that of coal passer or wiper in engine department of vessels having such certificated persons, or in engine department of tugs or towboats operating on high seas or Great Lakes, or bays or sounds directly connected with the seas; or (2) graduate from a schoolship approved by Coast Guard, or (3) courses of training approved by Coast Guard and service aboard a training vessel; or (4) graduate from U.S. Naval Academy or U.S. Coast Guard Academy. QMED applicants as *boilermaker* or *pumpman* must prove by examination they are qualified for rating. QMED applicants for deck engine mechanic or engineman must also prove by examination they are qualified for rating. An *engineman* must hold endorsements as fireman/water tender and oiler, or junior engineer—have 6 months service as junior engineer, fireman/water tender, or oiler on steam vessels of 4000 hp, or over, or proof from "partially automated" 4000-hp vessel, or over, of 2 weeks completion of training in

U.S. Coast Guard	Class rating or license	Education, experience for 4000-hp vessels and over[a]
		engine department. Any holder of a merchant mariner's document endorsed for any unlicensed rating in the engine department, QMED—any rating, or deck engine mechanic, is qualified as an engineman. Examination subjects required for QMED ratings are listed in Table 21-3
Apply to: U.S. Coast Guard, Merchant Marine Licensing, any U.S. port	1. Third assistant engineer	(1) 3 years in engine department of steam or motor ships, one-third may be on motor vessels; 2½ years must be as qualified member of engine department, 1 year 6 months must be as fireman, oiler, water tender, or junior engineer on steam ships; or (2) 3 years as machinist apprentice in building, repairing of marine, locomotive, or stationary engines, together with 1 year in engine department of steam ships as oiler, water tender, or junior engineer, one-third may be on motor vessels; or (3) engineering graduate from (*a*) U.S. Merchant Marine Academy; (*b*) nautical schoolship; (*c*) U.S. Naval Academy; or (*d*) U.S. Coast Guard Academy; or (4) graduate of U.S. government training schools acceptable as 4 months sea service if additional service obtained prior to enrollment; or (5) graduate from marine engineering or technology school with 3 months service in engine department of steam ships, one-third acceptable from motor vessels; or (6) graduate of mechanical or electrical engineering from technology school with 6 months in engine department of steam vessels; or (7) 1 year as oiler, water tender, or junior engineer on steam ships while holding license as third assistant engineer of motor vessels; or (8) completion of an approved 3-year apprentice engineering training program

TABLE 21-2 U.S. Merchant Marine QMED Ratings and Marine Engineer's Steam License Requirements (*Continued*)

U.S. Coast Guard	Class rating or license	Education, experience for 4000-hp vessels and over[a]
	2. Second assistant engineer	(1) 1 year as engineer in charge of watch, while holding license as third assistant engineer of steam vessels; or (2) 2 years service as assistant engineer to engineer in charge of watch, while holding license as third assistant engineer of steam vessels; or (3) 5 years in engine department of steam or motor vessels, 1 year of which may be on motor ships; 4 years and 6 months as qualified member of engine department, 2 years and 6 months as fireman, oiler, water tender, or junior engineer on steam vessels; or (4) while holding license as second assistant engineer of motor vessels, either (*a*) 6 months as third assistant engineer of steam ships; (*b*) 6 months as observer second assistant engineer on steam vessels; or (*c*) 1 year as oiler, water tender, or junior engineer of steam vessels
	3. First assistant engineer	(1) 1 year as second assistant engineer of steam vessels; or (2) 2 years as third assistant or junior second assistant engineer in charge of watch on steam vessels while holding license as second assistant engineer of steam ships; or (3) while holding license as first assistant engineer of motor vessels, either: (*a*) 6 months as second assistant engineer of steam vessels; (*b*) 6 months as observer first assistant engineer on steam vessels; or (*c*) 1 year as oiler, water tender, or junior engineer of steam vessels; or (4) 3 years as oiler, water tender, or fireman on steam ships for license as first assistant engineer of steam towing or ferry vessels of up to 2000 hp; or (5) while holding license as third assistant engineer of steam ships of any horsepower, 3 months as third assistant engineer or observer first assistant engineer on steam vessels for license as first assistant engineer of steam

TABLE 21-2 U.S. Merchant Marine QMED Ratings and Marine Engineer's Steam License Requirements (*Continued*)

U.S. Coast Guard	Class rating or license	Education, experience for 4000-hp vessels and over[a]
		towing or ferry vessels of not over 2000 hp; or (6) 3 years as oiler, water tender, or fireman on steam vessels for license as first assistant engineer of steam vessels of up to 1000 hp
	4. Chief engineer	(1) 1 year as first assistant engineer of steam vessels; or (2) 2 years as second assistant or junior first assistant engineer in charge of watch on steam ships while holding license as first assistant engineer of steam vessels; or (3) while holding license as chief engineer of motor vessels, either (*a*) 6 months as first assistant engineer of steam vessels; (*b*) 6 months as observer chief engineer on steam vessels; or (*c*) 1 year as oiler, water tender, or junior engineer of steam vessels

Source: U.S. Coast Guard.

[a]Limitation of horsepower on license is based on applicant's qualifying experience, but in no case is an applicant's license limited to a lower horsepower than the highest horsepower on which 25 percent or more of experience was obtained. An applicant whose qualifying service has all been on Coast Guard inspected vessels of 4000 hp or over is considered eligible for an engineer's license of *unlimited* horsepower.

Applicant for license as engineer officer of either steam or motor (diesel–internal-combustion engine) vessels shall pass written examination listed in Table 21-4.

TABLE 21-3 Examination Subjects Required for QMED Ratings

Subjects	Machinist	Refrigerating engineer	Fireman	Water tender	Oiler	Electrician	Junior engineer	Deck engineer
1. Application, maintenance, and use of hand tools and measuring instruments	X	X	X	X	X	X	X	X
2. Uses of babbitt, copper, brass, steel, and other metals	X	X		X	X	X	X	X
3. Methods of measuring pipe, pipe fittings, sheet metal, machine bolts and nuts, packing, etc.	X	X		X	X	X	X	X
4. Operation and maintenance of mechanical remote control equipment	X				X		X	
5. Precautions to be taken for the prevention of fire and the proper use of firefighting equipment	X	X	X	X	X	X	X	X
6. Principles of mechanical refrigeration; and functions, operation, and maintenance of various machines and parts of the systems		X					X	
7. Knowledge of piping systems as used in ammonia, Freon, and CO_2, including testing for leaks, operation of bypasses, and making up of joints		X					X	
8. Safety precautions to be observed in the operation of various refrigerating systems, including storage of refrigerants, and the use of gas masks and firefighting equipment		X					X	
9. Combustion of fuels, proper temperature, pressures, and atomization	X	X	X	X	X	X	X	X
10. Operation of the fuel oil system on oil burning boilers, including the transfer and storage of fuel oil			X	X	X		X	X
11. Hazards involved and the precautions taken against accumulation of oil in furnaces, bilges, floorplates, and tank tops; flarebacks, leaks in fuel oil heaters, clogged strainers and burner tips	X	X	X	X	X	X	X	
12. Precautions necessary when filling empty boilers, starting up the fuel oil burning system, and raising steam from a cold boiler			X	X	X		X	
13. The function, operation, and maintenance of the various engineroom auxiliaries	X	X		X	X		X	
14. Proper operation of the various types of lubricating systems	X	X		X	X	X	X	X
15. Safety precautions to be observed in connection with the operation of engineroom auxiliaries, electrical machinery, and switchboard equipment	X			X	X	X	X	
16. The function, operation, and maintenance of the bilge, ballast, fire, freshwater, sanitary, and lubricating systems	X	X		X	X	X	X	X
17. Proper care of spare machine parts and idle equipment	X	X		X	X		X	X
18. The procedure in preparing a turbine, reciprocating, or diesel engine for standby; also the procedure in securing	X	X		X	X	X	X	X
19. Operation and maintenance of the equipment necessary for the supply of water to boilers, the dangers of high and low water and remedial action			X	X	X		X	
20. Operation, location, and maintenance of the various boiler fittings and accessories			X	X	X		X	
21. The practical application and solution of basic electrical calculations (Ohm's law, power formula, etc.)	X					X	X	
22. Electrical wiring circuits of the various two-wire and three-wire dc systems and the various single-phase and polyphase ac systems						X	X	X
23. Application and characteristics of parallel and series circuits						X	X	X
24. Application and maintenance of electrical meters and instruments						X	X	X

TABLE 21-3 Examination Subjects Required for QMED Ratings (Continued)

Subjects	Machinist	Refrigerating engineer	Fireman	Water tender	Oiler	Electrician	Junior engineer	Deck engineer
25. The maintenance and installation of lighting and power wiring involving testing for, locating and correcting grounds, short circuits and open circuits, and making splices						X	X	X
26. The operation and maintenance of the various types of generators and motors, both ac and dc						X	X	X
27. Operation, installation, and maintenance of the various types of electrical controls and safety devices						X	X	X
28. Testing and maintenance of special electrical equipment, such as telegraphs, telephones, alarm systems, fire-detecting systems, and rudder angle indicators						X	X	
29. Rules and regulations and requirements for installation, repair, and maintenance of electrical wiring and equipment installed aboard ships						X	X	X
29a. Pollution laws and regulations, procedures for discharge containment and cleanup, and methods for disposal of sludge and waste from cargo and fueling operations	X	X	X	X	X	X	X	
30. Such further examination of a nonmathematical character as the Officer in Charge, Marine Inspection, may consider necessary to establish the applicant's proficiency	X	X	X	X	X	X	X	X

Source: U.S. Coast Guard.

TABLE 21-4 Subjects for Engineer Officers' Licenses of Steam or Motor Vessels

Subjects	Steam				Motor			
	Chief engineer		Assistant engineer		Chief engineer		Assistant engineer	
	Over 2000 hp	2000 hp and less	Over 2000 hp	2000 hp and less	Over 2000 hp	2000 hp and less	Over 2000 hp	2000 hp and less
General								
1. Pumps and compressors	X	X	X	X	X	X	X	X
2. Heat exchangers	X	X	X	X	X	X	X	X
3. Propellers and shafting	X	X	X	X	X	X	X	X
4. Steering and miscellaneous machinery	X	X	X	X	X	X	X	X
5. Valves—reducing, control, etc.	X	X	X	X	X	X	X	X
6. Condensers, air-ejectors and vacuum	X	X	X	X	—	—	—	—
7. Engineering definitions and principles	X	X	X	X	X	X	X	X
8. Instruments	X	X	X	X	X	X	X	X
9. Lubrication	X	X	X	X	X	X	X	X
10. Inspection	X	X	X	X	X	X	X	X
11. Mathematics	X	X	X	X	X	X	X	X
12. Sketch	—	X	X	X	—	X	X	X
13. Three-dimensional drawing	X	—	—	—	X	—	—	—
14. Ship construction and repair	X	X	X	X	X	X	X	X
Steam engines								
21. Reciprocating—construction, operation, maintenance	X	X	X	X	—	—	—	—
22. Turbine—construction, operation, maintenance	X	X	X	X	—	—	—	—
23. Reduction gear and miscellaneous	X	X	X	X	—	—	—	—
24. Steam governors	X	X	X	X	—	—	—	—
Motor								
31. Construction, operation, maintenance	—	—	—	—	X	X	X	X
32. Operating principles	—	—	—	—	X	X	X	X
33. Fuel injection	—	—	—	—	X	X	X	X
34. Air compressors	—	—	—	—	X	X	X	X
35. Operation and maintenance of auxiliary diesel engines	X	X	X	X	—	—	—	—
36. Air—starting, combustion	—	—	—	—	X	X	X	X
37. Governors	—	—	—	—	X	X	X	X
Boilers								
41. Watertube—construction, operation, maintenance	X	X	X	X	X	—	X	—
42. Firetube—construction, operation, maintenance	X	X	X	X	X	—	X	—
43. General—construction, operation, maintenance	X	X	X	X	X	—	X	—
44. Safety valves	X	X	X	X	X	—	X	—
45. Corrosion and feed water	X	X	X	X	X	—	X	—
46. Fuels and combustion	X	X	X	X	X	—	X	—

TABLE 21-4　Subjects for Engineer Officers' Licenses of Steam or Motor Vessels (*Continued*)

Subjects	Steam				Motor			
	Chief engineer		Assistant engineer		Chief engineer		Assistant engineer	
	Over 2000 hp	2000 hp and less	Over 2000 hp	2000 hp and less	Over 2000 hp	2000 hp and less	Over 2000 hp	2000 hp and less
Electricity								
51. Direct current - - - -	X	X	X	X	X	X	X	X
52. Alternating current - - - - - - - - - -	X	X	X	X	X	X	X	X
53. General—switchboards, controls, wiring- - - - - - - - -	X	X	X	X	X	X	X	X
54. Storage batteries - - - - - - - - - - - -	X	X	X	X	X	X	X	X
55. Electric drive - - - - -	X	X	X	X	X	X	X	X
56. Problems - - - - - - - -	X	X	X	X	X	X	X	X

Source: U.S. Coast Guard.

TABLE 21-5 Canadian Stationary Engineer's License Requirements

Province	Class of certificate	Education, experience, and remarks	Plant capacity for class of certificate
Alberta Labour, General Safety Services Division, 10339–124 Street, Edmonton, T5N 3W1	1. Fireman	6 months operating any boiler	Chief of power plant up to 50 boiler hp
	2. Fourth-class engineer	12 months assisting in operation of power plant exceeding 25 boiler hp; or 12 months as operator in a pressure plant; or holder of degree in mechanical engineering or equivalent; or completion of vocational course if satisfactory to chief inspector or as one-half above with completion of an approved course	Shift engineer of plant up to 100 boiler hp Chief of power plant up to 100 boiler hp Chief of power plant up to 500 boiler hp of pressure not exceeding 20 psi Chief of power plant of coil-type drumless boilers up to 500 boiler hp when used for underground thermal flooding in oil fields Shift engineer of power plant up to 500 hp Shift engineer of power plant of coil-type boilers up to 1000 boiler hp used for underground thermal flooding Assistant engineer in power plant up to 1000 boiler hp
	3. Third-class engineer	12 months as chief in plant exceeding 50 boiler hp while holding fourth-class certificate; or 12 months as chief in plant of coil-type boilers exceeding 100 boiler hp while holding fourth-class certificate; or 12 months	Chief of power plant up to 500 boiler hp Chief of any power plant not exceeding 20 psi Chief of any power plant of coil-type drumless boilers up to 1000 boiler

TABLE 21-5 Canadian Stationary Engineer's License Requirements *(Continued)*

Province	Class of certificate	Education, experience, and remarks	Plant capacity for class of certificate
		shift engineer in plant exceeding 100 boiler hp while holding fourth-class certificate; or 12 months shift engineer in power plant of coil-type boiler exceeding 500 boiler hp while holding fourth-class certificate; or 12 months as assistant engineer in power plant exceeding 500 boiler hp while holding fourth-class certificate; or one-half above and holder of degree in mechanical engineering or equivalent; or one-half above and 12 months maintenance; or one-half above and completion of approved course in power engineering	hp when used for underground thermal flooding in oil fields Shift engineer of power plant up to 1000 boiler hp Shift engineer of power plant of coil-type boiler up to 1500 boiler hp Assistant engineer in any power plant
	4. Second-class engineer	Hold third-class certificate and 24 months chief in power plant exceeding 100 boiler hp; or 24 months chief in power plant of coil-type boilers exceeding 500 boiler hp; or 24 months shift engineer in power plant exceeding 500 boiler hp; or 24 months shift engineer in power plant of coil-type boilers exceeding 1000 boiler hp; or 24 months assistant engineer in power plant exceeding 1000 boiler hp; or 36 months shift engineer in power plant exceeding 100 boiler hp; or one-half above and	Chief of power plant up to 1000 boiler hp Chief of power plant of coil-type boilers up to 1500 boiler hp Shift engineer in any power plant

	holder of degree in mechanical engineering or equivalent. Credit of 9 months in lieu of experience for completion of approved course in power engineering	
5. First-class engineer	Hold second-class certificate and 30 months chief of power plant exceeding 500 boiler hp; or 30 months chief of power plant of coil-type boilers exceeding 1000 boiler hp; or 30 months shift engineer in power plant exceeding 1000 boiler hp; or 30 months shift engineer in power plant of coil-type boilers exceeding 1500 boiler hp; or 45 months as assistant shift engineer in power plant exceeding 1000 boiler hp; or one-half above and holder of degree in mechanical engineering or equivalent; or 30 months as inspector of boilers and pressure vessels under Canadian Shipping Act; credit of 12 months in lieu of experience for completion of approved course in power engineering	Chief of any power plant Shift engineer of any power plant
6. Special oil well	6 months in power plant on oil rig	Chief on power plant up to 100 boiler hp on oil rig
7. Temporary certificate	Hold certificate one grade less than certificate required	Any capacity

TABLE 21-5 Canadian Stationary Engineer's License Requirements (Continued)

Province	Class of certificate	Education, experience, and remarks	Plant capacity for class of certificate
	8. Provisional stationary engineer, fourth, third, second, or first class[a]		
British Columbia Safety Engineering Services Division, 501 West 12th Ave., Vancouver V5Z 1M6		All provinces and the two territories, except Ontario and Quebec, have an *interprovincial agreement;* thus the service times and examination for power engineers in those provinces and territories are virtually the *same* as in Alberta. All plant ratings, qualifications for examinations, examinations, and marking procedures are very similar for the first-, second-, third-, and fourth-class engineers. Anything *below* fourth is a provincial item and may vary from province/territory to province	
Manitoba Mechanical & Engineering Div., 611 Norquay Bldg., Winnipeg, R3C 0P8		Same as Alberta above, except that the old fireman class has been eliminated and replaced with a fifth class. All age limitations have been dropped	
New Brunswick Dept. of Labor, P.O. Box 6000, Fredericton, E3B 5HI		Same as Alberta (also see British Columbia), except that horsepower ratings have been changed to therm hour ratings. Therm hour of a boiler other than electric boiler is horsepower of boiler shown on certificate multiplied by 2 and divided by 3. Therm hour rating of electric boiler is horsepower of boiler shown on certificate divided by 3	
Newfoundland and Labrador Engineering & Technical Services Div., Confederation Bldg., St. John's A1C 5T7		Same as Alberta (also see British Columbia)	

[a] A provisional certificate is one grade lower than the certificate of qualification that corresponds to the certificate issued by the other provinces.

Northwest Territories
Yellowknife, X0E IHQ

Same as Alberta (also see British Columbia)

Nova Scotia
Board of Examiners,
P.O. Box 697, Halifax,
B3J 2T8

Same as Alberta (also see British Columbia)

Ontario
Operating Engineers
Branch, 400 University
Ave., Toronto,
M7A 2J9

1. Stationary engineer, fourth-class

1 year operation in Ontario plants on provisional fourth-class stationary engineer certificate; or 3 months in stationary plant or low-pressure stationary power plant; or a third-class certificate of Canadian Shipping Act, or 12 months on boilers, engines, and auxiliaries of naval or merchant steam ships

(1) Act as chief operating engineer (*a*) in charge of any stationary power plant up to 50 therm hours[a] where rating of refrigeration compressors is up to 2,544, including total of not more than 5,088; or (*b*) any low-pressure stationary plant up to 134 therm hours; or (*c*) any steam-powered plant up to 7,632 therm hours, or (*d*) any compressor plant up to 10,176, or (*e*) any plant in *a* or *b* with total rating up to 3,816 therm hours, including refrigeration compressors up to 7,632 therm hours

(2) Shift engineer in (*a*) any stationary power plant up to 134 therm hours where therm hour rating of refrigeration compressors is up to 5,088 and that of compressors including refrigeration compressors is up to 10,176; or (*b*) any low-pressure stationary plant up to 400 therm hours; or (*c*) any steam-powered plant; or (*d*) any refrigeration plant up to 20,352 therm hours; or (*e*) any compressor

---

[a]Therm hour = 100,000 Btu/hr or 39.3082 brake hp.

TABLE 21-5 Canadian Stationary Engineer's License Requirements (*Continued*)

Province	Class of certificate	Education, experience, and remarks	Plant capacity for class of certificate
			plant; or (*f*) any plant in *b* or *c* above, with total therm hour rating of refrigeration compressors up to 15.264 and rating of compressors including refrigeration up to 30.528 therm hours (3) Assistant shift engineer in (*a*) any stationary power plant up to 400 therm hours; or (*b*) any low-pressure stationary plant, steam-powered plant, refrigeration plant, or compressor plant
	2. Stationary engineer, third-class	1 year operation in Ontario plants on provisional certificate as a third-class stationary engineer; or hold fourth-class certificate with 1 year in stationary low-pressure power plant	(1) Act as (*a*) chief operating engineer in charge of any power plant up to 134 therm hours with refrigeration compressors up to 5.088 and compressors including refrigeration up to 10.176 therm hours; or (*b*) any low-pressure stationary plant up to 400 therm hours; or (*c*) any steam-powered plant; or (*d*) any refrigeration plant up to 20.352 therm hours; or (*e*) any compressor plant; or (*f*) any plant of *a* or *b* where total therm hour rating includes refrigeration compressors up to 15.264 or compressors, including refrigeration compressors up to 30.528 (2) Act as shift engineer in (*a*) any sta-

Classification	Qualifications	Permitted duties
	tionary plant up to 400 therm hours including rating of refrigeration compressors up to 15.264, with combined rating up to 30.528; or (b) any low-pressure stationary plant, steam-powered, with compressor including refrigeration	Act as chief operating engineer in (a) stationary plant up to 400 therm hours including that of refrigeration compressors of not more than 15.264, or that of combined compressors up to 30.528 therm hours; or (b) chief operating engineer in any low-pressure stationary plant, steam-powered, compressor, or refrigeration plant; or (c) act as shift engineer in any plant
	(3) Act as assistant shift engineer in any plant	
3. Stationary engineer, second-class	1 year operation in Ontario on provisional certificate as second-class stationary engineer; or (1) hold certificate as stationary engineer (third-class) with experience on certificate and 18 months in stationary power plant up to 134 therm hour rating; or (2) hold certificate as first-class steam engineer (Merchant Shipping Act or Canadian Shipping Act) with 1 year in plant up to 134 therm hour rating; or (3) approved degreed engineer with 24 months experience in plant up to 12,000 therm hours in Ontario hydro plants	
4. Stationary engineer, first-class	Hold second-class certificate, with experience as second-class stationary engineer and 30 months in stationary power plant; (1) have spent not less than 6 months of the 30 in plant up to 134 therm hour rating; and (2) 24 of the 30 months in therm	Chief operating engineer in charge of any plant

TABLE 21-5 Canadian Stationary Engineer's License Requirements (*Continued*)

Province	Class of certificate	Education, experience, and remarks	Plant capacity for class of certificate
		hour rating above 300; or (3) hold approved engineering degree and 36 months operating experience in 12,000 therm hour plant	
	5. Provisional stationary engineer, fourth-, third-, second-, or first-class[a]	Not specified	
Prince Edward Island Boiler Inspection Branch, Box 2000, Charlottetown, C1A 7N8		Same as Alberta (also see British Columbia)	
Quebec Edifice La Laurenti-enne 425 St-Amable, 3ième étage Québec, G1R 4Z1	1. Fifth-class, heating–steam engines	4 months in heating or steam engine plant, or fabrication, installation, or repair of steam engines and boilers	Any heating or steam plant up to 100 hp, or fourth- or lower-class plant for one day, or any electric boilers up to 200 boiler hp
	2. Fourth-class, heating–steam engines	Hold fifth-class license and serve with such for 2 years in fifth-class plant, or 9 months in fourth-class or higher plant, or 6 months in fifth-class plant; or hold fourth- or higher-class license in marine, heating, or steam engines for past 1 year; or complete technical courses; or work under	Any heating or steam plant up to 300 hp, or third-class plant for one day, or electric boiler plant up to 400 boiler hp

[a]A provisional certificate is one grade lower than the certificate of qualification that corresponds to the certificate issued by the other provinces.

fourth-class or higher engineer for: (*a*) 1 year as helper in fourth-class plant, (*b*) 10 months as helper in fourth-class plant plus completed technical courses, (*c*) 8 months as helper in fourth-class plant and completed technical courses

3. Third-class, heating–steam engines	Hold fourth-class license and serve under third-class operator for one of the following periods: (*a*) 1 year third-class plant, (*b*) 10 months in third-class plant plus completing technical courses, (*c*) 8 months in third-class plant plus completing technical courses, (*c*) 8 months on license in marine heating or steam engines for past 1 year; or complete 3-year course in technical school	Any heating or steam plant up to 600 hp, or second-class plant for one day, or electric boiler plant up to 600 boiler hp
4. Second-class, heating–steam engines	Hold third-class license and serve under second-class operator in heating and steam engine plant for one of the following periods: (*a*) 18 months in second-class plant, (*b*) 16 months in second-class plant, plus completed technical courses, (*c*) 14 months in second-class plant plus completed technical courses; or hold second-class license for marine, heating, or steam engines for 1 year	Any heating or steam engine plant up to 1000 hp, or any electric boiler plant
5. First-class, heating–steam engines	Hold second-class license in heating and steam engines plus serving un-	Unlimited capacity

TABLE 21-5 Canadian Stationary Engineer's License Requirements (*Continued*)

Province	Class of certificate	Education, experience, and remarks	Plant capacity for class of certificate
		der first-class operator for: (*a*) 2 years in first-class plant of which 1 year in charge, (*b*) 22 months in first-class plant of which 1 year in charge plus completed technical courses, (*c*) 20 months in first-class plant of which 1 year in charge plus completed technical courses; or hold first-class license in heating and marine steam engines for 1 year	
Saskatchewan Boiler & Pressure Vessel Unit, 1150 Rose St., Regina, S4P 2YR		Same as Alberta (also see British Columbia)	
Yukon Territory Box 2703, Whitehorse, Y1A 2C6		Same as Alberta (also see British Columbia)	

Source: Stephen M. Elonka survey of licensing agencies (1980).

INDEX

This is a combined index for Volumes I and II. Volume I contains pages 1 to 319; Volume II contains pages 321 to 622.

THE AUTHORS

Stephen M. Elonka is a contributing editor to *Power* magazine (he was senior associate editor before retiring) and is the creator of the famous Marmaduke stories (technical fiction) published monthly in *Power* since 1948. He is a Licensed Chief Marine Engineer, Oceans, Unlimited Horsepower. He has worked as a machinist building diesel and airplane engines and has sailed aboard 21 merchant ships (both steam and diesel) and two U.S. Navy vessels during World War II.

A licensed regular instructor of vocational high school, New York State, as the United States entered World War II in 1942, he was assigned to the U.S. Merchant Marine Academy at King's Point, N.Y. After a year as assistant training officer, he completed the famous steam Sea Project (study assignment for cadet midshipmen at sea) and requested sea duty "because that's where the action is." An engineering officer (Lieutenant Commander, U.S. Naval Reserve) aboard the *USS Wheatland*, at war's end, he was commissioned as Lieutenant Commander, U.S. Maritime Service, by Rear Admiral Telfair Knight, and was assigned as national engineering training officer based in Washington, D.C., for organizing the peace-time training program.

Steve Elonka has written hundreds of engineering articles and is the author and coauthor of thirteen books by ten publishers around the world, some translated into foreign languages.

Joseph F. Robinson holds a B.P.S. degree from Pace University. He saw active service in the Navy during World War II (shipboard engineering duty), and was Lieutenant Commander (Engineering Duties), U.S. Naval Reserve (retired). He was the Instructor in Charge of the officers in the Naval Boiler School in Philadelphia, and has sailed with the Merchant Marine. He is a Licensed Chief Marine Engineer, Oceans, Unlimited Horsepower, Stationary Engineer, New York City, and Commissioned Inspector of Boiler and Pressure Vessels, National Board (New York, Pennsylvania, Maryland, and Washington, D.C.). Mr. Robinson has authored technical and training manuals and curricula for shipboard engineering, and has a High School/Trade School license for the teaching of stationary engineering in the New York City school system (evening trade schools). For twenty-five years, he was with the Bureau of Plant Operation and Maintenance, Board of Education, City of New York, retiring as Borough Supervisor.